Roadside Geology of Connecticut and Rhode Island

James W. Skehan

2008
Mountain Press Publishing Company
Missoula, Montana

First Printing, September 2008

Roadside Geology Series
Roadside Geology is a registered trademark
of Mountain Press Publishing Company

Library of Congress Cataloging-in-Publication Data
Skehan, James William, 1923-
    Roadside geology of Connecticut and Rhode Island / James W. Skehan.
        p. cm.— (Roadside geology series)
        Includes bibliographical references and index.
        ISBN 978-0-87842-547-1 (pbk. : alk. paper)
        1. Geology—Connecticut—Guidebooks. 2. Geology—Rhode Island—Guidebooks. 3. Connecticut—Guidebooks. 4. Rhode Island—Guidebooks. I. Title.
    QE93.S54 2008
    557.46—dc22

                                                    2008025080

PRINTED IN THE UNITED STATES OF AMERICA

Mountain Press Publishing Company
P.O. Box 2399 • Missoula, Montana 59806
(406) 728-1900

I dedicate this book to Nicholas Rast, a world-class geologist and my best friend for many years. Nick, born in 1927 in Ishfahan, Iran, was educated at University College London and received his PhD from the University of Glasgow, Scotland. In 1959 he was appointed to the faculty of geology at the University of Liverpool, where he developed an outstanding reputation for teaching, research, and administration. In 1971 he was recruited to chair the department of geology at the University of New Brunswick. I was fortunate to meet Nick, the "Jonathan of my life," on a field trip to Mount Katahdin together with his wife, Diana, and their children. He later was recruited to the Hudnall Chair of Geology at the University of Kentucky. Nick and I collaborated on research on three continents until his untimely death in 2001. He was much admired for his breadth of scholarship not only in geology but in fields beyond the sciences. He was a beloved friend who loved life fully. Nick had a great capacity for friendship and an exuberant love of the Earth. His presence and dynamism enriched all who came within his orbit.

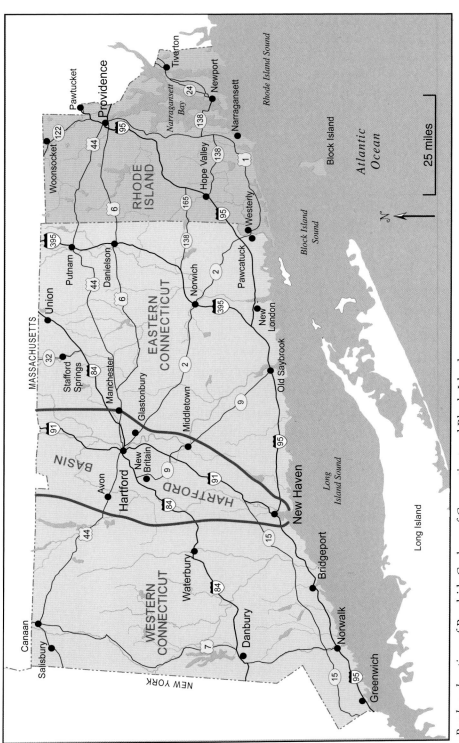

Roads and sections of Roadside Geology of Connecticut and Rhode Island.

Contents

Acknowledgments

I gratefully acknowledge the unparalleled contribution to this volume by Christine C. Bronchuk, my research assistant and interim librarian at Weston Observatory who bore most of the responsibility for library research and draft preparation of illustrations and maps. She collaborated with Frances Ahearn on the final version of the road maps. My graduate student colleagues at Harvard University, Brian Skinner of Yale University and Katherine Skinner of Yale University and Yale Medical School, along with Janet Stone and long-time friend Daniel Murray, were leading cheerleaders for my Roadside Geology projects. Leo Hickey and his wife, Judy, were helpful in providing accommodations during some aspects of field studies. Pamela Aey Adams, director of Connecticut State Parks, was most helpful on facilitating my studies.

Geologists who contributed constructive reviews of early drafts of the manuscript include Carl Koteff, Robert N. Oldale, Ralph Lewis, Daniel Murray, Leo Hickey, Brian Skinner, and Janet Stone. Several other geologists provided helpful discussions of both bedrock and glacial geology. I am especially grateful to Janet Stone and Bob Oldale of the U.S. Geological Survey for whatever success they have had in helping to educate me in glacial geology. Robert Wintsch, Bill Burton, and Bob Tracy were helpful in providing information on bedrock geology. However, I take full responsibility for any errors of fact or interpretation of either the bedrock or glacial geology.

Several people at the Peabody Museum of Natural History in New Haven provided assistance in a number of ways. Jay Ague, curator of mineralogy, provided helpful discussions on high pressure and temperature metamorphic rocks of Connecticut. Leo Hickey, former director of the museum, and Ellen Faller arranged for photography of minerals from the Peabody collection.

Daniel P. Murray of the University of Rhode Island provided photographs of key areas of Rhode Island in addition to discussions and clarification of regional geology. Jon Boothroyd, Rhode Island State Geologist, contributed to these discussions along with several photographs. I am very grateful to Teresa Kennedy Gagnon for important contributions to photography, especially in western Connecticut. John Pawloski, executive director of the Connecticut Museum of Mining and Mineral Science in Kent provided detailed information relating to the history of mining in Connecticut, and Robert Hawley, park ranger of Trumbull, provided information on Old Mine Park.

Without the generous financial support and encouragement of the following this volume would never have come to fruition: the Boston College and Campion Center Jesuit Communities and especially John E. Ebel, director of Weston Observatory; Marilyn Bibeau, administrator of Weston Observatory; Katherine Rivera, assistant administrator of Weston Observatory; Vincent J. Murphy and James Lewkowitz of Weston Observatory and Weston Geophysical, Inc.; Randolph J. Martin III; Mark A. S. McMenamin of Mt. Holyoke College; Mary Skehan Watson; Robert and Marie Skehan Cooney; Joseph B. Skehan; and Francis A. Skehan. I am grateful to Rev. Paul Harman of Boston College and Rev. Paul Holland of Campion Center.

I am grateful to the Jesuit Community at Fairfield University, Lynette Aey, and the Gagnon family for their hospitality in connection with field studies in Connecticut.

It is impossible to thank all those who contributed to the production of this book in intangible but important ways, but I would especially like to thank Patricia C. Tassia, my long-time assistant; Nicholas Rast, my long-time colleague and friend; Tracy S. Downing; Maureen Burke; and fellow staff members of Weston Observatory. I am especially grateful to Jennifer Carey of Mountain Press Publishing Company who was very helpful in the editorial process that greatly improved all aspects of the manuscript.

Age	Period	mya	Geological Events in Rhode Island and Connecticut
CENOZOIC	Holocene Epoch	0.01	Sea rises to near modern levels by 3,000 years ago
	Pleistocene Epoch		Glacial Lake Hitchcock exists from 15,000 to 11,000 years ago
			Wisconsinan ice sheet deposits terminal moraine about 22,000 years ago then begins receding
	Quaternary		Wisconsinan ice sheet develops about 80,000 years ago and reaches Conn. and R.I. by 25,000 years ago
			Marine sediments deposited during Sangamon interglacial stage
			Illinoian ice sheet deposited till 140,000 years ago
		1.8	
MESOZOIC	Tertiary	65	Tertiary rocks not exposed in southern New England
	Cretaceous	145	Blocks of Cretaceous Raritan Formation enclosed by Pleistocene-age till on Block Island
	Jurassic	208	Pangea splits apart and Atlantic Ocean opens about 200 million years ago. Rift basins open along the margin of the North American continent, including Hartford Basin
	Triassic	248	
PALEOZOIC	Permian	286	Alleghanian mountain building event, between 300 and 250 million years ago, finalizes assembly of the Pangean supercontinent; Narragansett Pier Granite intrudes 275 million years ago.
	Pennsylvanian	320	Narragansett, North Scituate, and Woonsocket Basins fill with sediment
	Mississippian	355	
	Devonian	417	Rifting begins in Avalon Terrane, producing the 380- to 370-million-year-old Scituate Batholith
			Acadian mountain building event occurs 420 to 375 million years ago when Avalon microcontinent collides with Laurentia, sandwiching the Putnam-Nashoba, Merrimack, Central Maine, and Bronson Hill Terranes in between
	Silurian	443	Sediments deposited in Iapetus Ocean
	Ordovician	490	Taconic mountain building event occurs 485 to 440 million years ago as the Collinsville or Bronson Hill volcanic arc collides with Laurentia
			Island arcs form in Iapetus Ocean
	Cambrian	545	Sediments that will become the Cheshire Quartzite and Stockbridge Marble are deposited on Laurentian continental shelf
			Trilobite-bearing Jamestown Formation deposited on margin of Avalon microcontinent
PRECAMBRIAN	Late Proterozoic	900	Avalon volcanic chain forms on margin of Gondwana about 600 million years ago; magma forms Esmond Igneous Suite, southeastern R.I. granites, and Sterling Plutonic Suite
			Sediments of the Blackstone, Harmony, and Newport Groups and the Plainfield Quartzite deposited on continental shelf and shore of Gondwana
			Rodinia breaks up 750 million years ago, giving rise to Gondwana and Laurentia
	Middle Proterozoic	1,600	Grenvillian mountain building event forms Grenvillian gneisses about 1.2 to 1.1 billion years ago during assembly of the supercontinent Rodinia
	Early Proterozoic	2,500	
	Archean Eon		Earth forms 4.5 billion years ago

mya=millions of years ago

Introduction

Although Rhode Island and Connecticut are small states, they contain a huge variety of rock types, many swirled together in complex patterns. More than one hundred rock formations have official names in Connecticut and Rhode Island, and some of these are further subdivided into named members. Many are difficult for even geologists to identify, and keeping their names straight will challenge anyone. Still, we are lucky that the Collinsville Formation does not occur in the same part of Connecticut as the Collins Hill Formation. Geologists pick names from the local geography where the rock is found, so there is more order to the jumble of names than to the jumble of rocks. For example, Cumberland Granite and cumberlandite both occur in Cumberland, Rhode Island, but they are not related geologically.

The reason so many rocks crop out in such a small area is because the bedrock of Connecticut and Rhode Island has been welded together from at least eight separate landmasses, including continents, microcontinents, island arcs, and ocean basins. Every continent or island had its own beaches, alluvial fans, volcanoes, surrounding ocean floors, and other geologic, environments. Numerous collisions deformed the rocks that made up the landmasses, so now it is hard to recognize what the rocks originally were. A micaceous schist may have originally been a muddy seafloor, and an amphibolite may have been a lava flow.

Once the bedrock was assembled, it almost split in two again as the earth's crust pulled apart and molten lava spilled out from deep faults in what is now the Hartford Basin. Finally, continental ice sheets swept down from the north and buried much of the bedrock in glacial debris, teasing future bedrock geologists.

Connecticut and Rhode Island have some world-class geology. The Westerly Granite is so uniform that it has been called the granite standard. At Purgatory Chasm, boulders of quartzite look as if they've been stretched into oblong shapes. A thick vein of quartz filled a fault and now forms the summit of Lantern Hill in southeastern Connecticut. Dinosaur footprints are preserved in mudstone at Dinosaur State Park in the Hartford Basin. Finding iron ore in the folded and faulted rocks of northwestern Connecticut tested the skills of nineteenth-century miners and would test modern mine geologists today if the ore were still mined. So sit back and enjoy reading about the incredible assortment of rocks and landforms you can see along the roads of Connecticut and Rhode Island.

Understanding the Earth

If we understand how the earth operates today, we can more easily understand the complex geologic history of Connecticut and Rhode Island. In 1788, James Hutton proposed that processes operating at and below the present earth's surface have done so consistently through time, one of the fundamental ideas in geology. This principle is called *uniformitarianism*. Processes actively building mountains today, such as the volcanic mountains of Indonesia, are the same as those that formed mountains long ago. Mountain building events, earthquakes, tsunamis, volcanic eruptions, and other geologic processes currently at work are also responsible for the ancient geological features we observe in Connecticut and Rhode Island.

In the 1960s, geologists developed the theory of plate tectonics, which describes how the outer layers of the earth function. The outermost layers of the earth consist of large slabs of rock called *plates*. These plates are relatively rigid and up to 60 miles thick. Beneath the plates is a warm but solid region called the *mantle*. Convection within the mantle causes the plates to move. Plates, which are made of continental crust or oceanic crust,

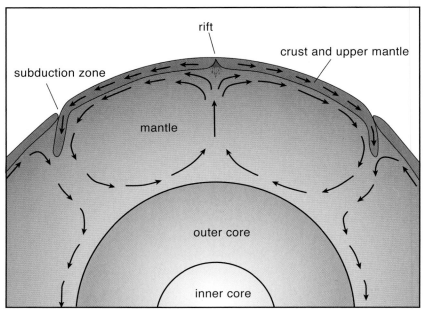

Circulation within the mantle drives the movement of tectonic plates.

can move away from each other, toward each other, or sideways past each other. When they collide, they give rise to mountain chains and volcanoes. The plate tectonic theory has revolutionized the way geologists interpret the rocks of southern New England—a region where at least three plate collisions have occurred in the last 500 million years.

Where plates diverge, or rift apart, new ocean crust forms at spreading ridges. Continued rifting culminates in the formation of an ocean basin. The present Atlantic Ocean began to open up around 200 million years ago. It continues to grow as new crust is added to the rift at the crest of the mid-Atlantic Ridge, visible above water in Iceland. Deep fractures in the earth's crust carry basaltic lavas to the surface along the rift. The Hartford Basin is an ancient rift valley that formed at the same time the Atlantic rifted open. Basalt flows, dating from this time, occupy parts of the valley.

The earth isn't increasing in size with the addition of oceanic crust at rifts, so the crust must be eliminated elsewhere. Where an oceanic plate collides with a continental plate, the denser oceanic plate sinks beneath the continental plate at a subduction zone, and soft sediments on the ocean floor are scraped and pushed into a wedge and accreted to the edge of the continent above the subduction zone. Subduction zones consume large masses of rock. Heat and pressure soften and ultimately melt the sinking oceanic rocks, transforming some of them into magma that rises along

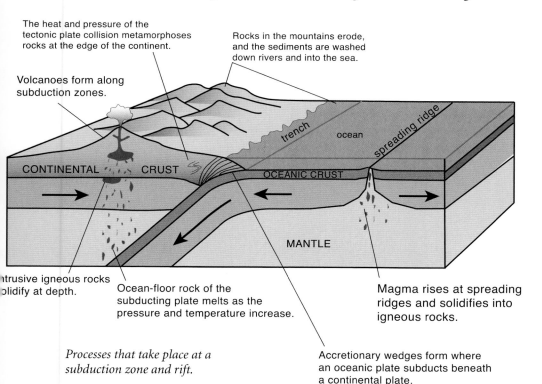

The heat and pressure of the tectonic plate collision metamorphoses rocks at the edge of the continent.

Rocks in the mountains erode, and the sediments are washed down rivers and into the sea.

Volcanoes form along subduction zones.

CONTINENTAL   CRUST

OCEANIC CRUST

trench   ocean   spreading ridge

MANTLE

Intrusive igneous rocks solidify at depth.

Ocean-floor rock of the subducting plate melts as the pressure and temperature increase.

Magma rises at spreading ridges and solidifies into igneous rocks.

Processes that take place at a subduction zone and rift.

Accretionary wedges form where an oceanic plate subducts beneath a continental plate.

fractures and faults. Rising magma heats and metamorphoses continental rocks, forms magma chambers at depth in the earth, and, where fractures reach the earth's surface, erupts as lava, often explosively. A chain of volcanoes typically forms above the sinking plate. Today, an oceanic plate is sinking beneath the coast of Oregon and Washington in the Pacific Northwest, forming the active volcanoes of the Cascade Range.

As the oceanic plate is gradually consumed at the subduction zone, islands or even other continents eventually collide with the continental plate. These landmasses accrete to the edge of the continent. Because they are different from the adjacent rocks, geologists distinguish them with the term *terranes*. A terrane originated in a different place and time than its neighbors and is bound by faults. Some terranes may be much more deformed than others depending on the relative intensity of their past collisions.

Rocks near the surface break brittlely, and the breaks are called *faults* if one side moves relative to the other side. The forces of some mountain building events in Connecticut pushed and lifted huge sections of rock over others, forming thrust sheets—large masses of rock that move a long distance up a low-angle fault called a *thrust fault*. This type of fault often places older rocks on top of younger rocks. Rocks may even shear

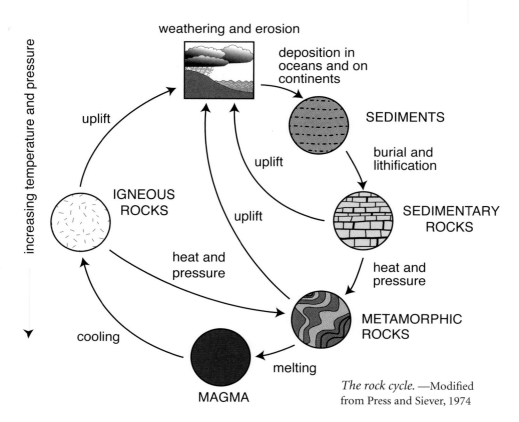

The rock cycle. —Modified from Press and Siever, 1974

and flow during thrust faulting. The top of Canaan Mountain in north-western Connecticut is an older slice of Cambrian rock thrust over the top of younger Cambrian rocks.

Rocks also break where the earth's crust pulls apart. Under these extensional forces, basins form when blocks drop down along breaks called *normal faults*, such as the Eastern Border Fault of the Hartford Basin. Rocks on one side of a normal fault drop down relative to rocks on the other side.

Sometimes blocks of land move past each other along a type of break called a *strike-slip fault*. A noteworthy example is the San Andreas Fault in California. If you stand on one side of the fault and the rocks on the other side moved to your left, the fault movement is said to be left-lateral and if it moved to your right, it is right-lateral. The Beaverhead Fault, which runs up the middle of Narragansett Bay, is a strike-slip fault with right lateral movement. It is no longer active, though, so don't fret!

The Rock Cycle Meets Tectonics

Over 200 years ago, James Hutton, a Scottish geologist and farmer, proposed the concept of the rock cycle to explain how rocks form by geologic processes. The cycle explains how rocks form, break apart, and form again. For example, rocks above sea level become weathered by rain and ice, and then water carries away fragments of the rock and deposits it near the ocean as beach sand. When buried beneath other sediments, the beach sand becomes cemented together as sandstone. If the sandstone is buried deep in the earth, heat and pressure may transform, or metamorphose, the sandstone into quartzite. If mountain building forces push the quartzite high above sea level, the rock cycle begins again. The forces inside the earth drive the rock cycle because compression builds mountains to be eroded and extension forms basins where sediments accumulate.

Geologists divide rocks into three groups: sedimentary, metamorphic, and igneous.

Sedimentary Rocks

Over long periods of time, rocks are broken down by weathering. Wind, water, and ice carry the loose material away and deposit it elsewhere. The sediment may eventually harden into solid rock called *sedimentary rock*. It may be compacted by burial or cemented by a natural agent, such as iron oxide. Conglomerate, sandstone, siltstone, mudstone, and limestone are all sedimentary rocks.

Metamorphic Rocks

When heat and pressure change the minerals and textures of an existing rock, a process called *metamorphism*, the result is a metamorphic rock. Being buried by several miles of rock and sediments can create a lot of pressure! Add to that the force of colliding tectonic plates and the heat of

Folds in Rope Ferry Gneiss, a metamorphic rock, in Waterford, Connecticut.

rising magma, and rocks will be metamorphosed. The types of minerals and sizes of crystals in metamorphic rocks tell us how hot the rocks got and how much pressure they endured. The alignment of the minerals can give a rock a layered texture called *foliation*. Its orientation tells geologists the direction from which the forces were applied and how many times the rock was deformed. The chemistry of the rock can also tell us what the original rock may have been. Geologists learn much of the geologic history of supercontinents, plate tectonics, and mountain building events through careful analysis of metamorphic rocks.

The grade of metamorphism, from low to high, describes the intensity of pressure and temperature that created the rock. For example, if a shale changes to a slate, the metamorphism is low-grade, but if it changes to a schist containing the minerals garnet and sillimanite, the metamorphism is moderate to high-grade. Rocks in direct contact with magma may undergo high-grade metamorphism, while rocks farther away experience lower grades. If the pressures and temperatures are really high, the rock may shear, flow, or even melt, producing mylonites, migmatites, and igneous rocks, respectively.

Mylonite and migmatite are so similar that it can be hard to keep them straight. They are both what we might call "yo-yo rocks." They have been jammed deep within the earth, deformed, and then brought back up to the surface again. Mylonite is a streaky or banded rock formed as rock masses shear past each other during metamorphism. Migmatite forms from a mixture of solid rock and magma. The molten magma is either injected into the solid rock from elsewhere or melted directly out of the rock. As you might expect, mylonites and migmatites grade into one another.

Rocks shear in deep fault zones, where there is so much pressure and heat that some minerals, such as quartz, may lose their original structure, recrystallize, and flow. Trying to determine what the original rock was before it was sheared is a bit like trying to reconstruct an ear of corn from cornmeal. Still, it is possible to tell whether the original rock was pale or dark. And sometimes it is possible to find fragments of the original rock that somehow escaped the shearing.

Igneous Rocks

Igneous rocks solidify from magma. If magma cools slowly at depth, it crystallizes into intrusive igneous rocks. The slow cooling of intrusive igneous rocks permits minerals to grow into crystals visible to the naked eye. Granite, granodiorite, diorite, and gabbro are intrusive igneous rocks, all cooled at depth but differing in their chemistry and cooling history. Large, extensive bodies of intrusive igneous rocks are called *batholiths* or *plutons*. Narrow, planar bodies that fill cracks are called *dikes*.

If molten lava explodes from a volcano or oozes onto the earth's surface, it solidifies quickly into extrusive igneous rocks. Not all of the minerals have time to grow, so some of these volcanic rocks may not have minerals visible to the unaided eye. Obsidian, a rock that cools so quickly that almost no crystals form is essentially glass. Rhyolite, andesite, and basalt are all quickly cooled volcanic rocks, but from magmas with different chemistries. Rhyolite is the chemical equivalent of granite, andesite is the equivalent of diorite, and basalt is the equivalent of gabbro.

Light-colored rocks such as granite have more feldspar and quartz than dark-colored rocks. Light-colored rocks are called *felsic*, a mnemonic adjective from *fel*dspar and *si*lica that describes the general chemistry. It's an odd term but is often used in geology. Its counterpart is the term *mafic*, a mnemonic word derived from *ma*gnesium and *f*erric. These dark-colored rocks contain minerals rich in magnesium and iron, such as amphibole and pyroxene. Diorite and gabbro are mafic rocks. A rock composed almost entirely of mafic minerals is called *ultramafic*.

Ages of Rocks

A thin layer of young glacial till overlies 1.2-billion-year-old Grenville gneisses in southern New England. Many significant events occurred in the billion-plus years between the formation of the gneiss and the deposition of glacial till 20,000 years ago. Geologists invented a time scale to keep track of just such milestones in the earth's story—a story that includes the rise and fall of volcanoes, as well as the evolution and extinction of distinctive life-forms now preserved in rock layers.

Boundaries between periods on the geologic time scale reflect notable changes in life-forms and other important events recorded in the rocks. For example, the boundary between Precambrian and Cambrian times marks the first widespread distribution of marine life-forms with skeletons or hard body parts.

To figure out the age of rocks in Connecticut and Rhode Island, geologists have had to look for the remains of plants and animals preserved as fossils. Although the abundant shelly marine fauna of brachiopods, corals, and bryozoa found in Paleozoic rocks elsewhere in New England must also have existed in southern New England, continental collisions transformed sedimentary rocks here into schists and marbles. Intense deformation favors neither the preservation of fossils nor the motivation of paleontologists to expend the time and laborious effort to find the few fossils that may remain. Even so, fossils have been found, including giant trilobites of Middle Cambrian age in rocks in Jamestown, Rhode Island.

The Norfolk and Narragansett Basins of southeastern Massachusetts and Rhode Island comprise more than 1,000 square miles and contain fossiliferous coal-bearing strata of Pennsylvanian age. These beds contain about three hundred species of fossil plants and animals. The red strata of Mesozoic time in the Hartford Basin yield a rich harvest of dinosaur footprints, a few dinosaur bones, and fossils of other animals, such as fish.

Radioactive elements in minerals in igneous rocks can function as geologic clocks and thus are used to determine the actual time of the boundaries in the geologic time scale. A parent isotope, an atom of a chemical element with a specific mass, decays radioactively to become a daughter isotope. By determining the ratio of parent isotopes to daughter isotopes and measuring the rate of decay of the parent, geologists determine the length of time since the parent mineral crystallized. Such isotopic age determinations are now very accurate.

Bedrock History of Connecticut and Rhode Island

About 750 million years ago, the east coast of North America was at westernmost Connecticut. Everything to the east was added on later, piece by piece. The north-south-trending ridges and drainages in Connecticut reflect in part the north-south orientation of the added bedrock units. The following is a brief geologic history of the events that added the bedrock of Connecticut and Rhode Island to the North American continent. This geologic story of accretion, mountain building, and rifting is presented in chronological order.

Many small continents collided more than 1 billion years ago in Precambrian time to form the supercontinent Rodinia. The collision, a complex series of tectonic events, is called the Grenville mountain building event, a name derived from a region in Canada. The major magmatic and metamorphic pulses of the Grenville event were clustered around 1.2 to 1.1 billion years ago. The rocks affected by the event are now found in North America, Africa, Australia, and Antarctica. A metamorphic rock that records this collision, a certain type of gneiss, is present in western Connecticut.

The large mass of mountains triggered melting in the mantle, and the upwelling magma created a rift. Around 750 million years ago, the rift split Rodinia into several continents—Laurentia, Baltica, and several chunks that rotated and became the supercontinent Gondwana. The Iapetus Ocean began to fill the rift basin between Gondwana and Laurentia. The sea grew so large that migration across it was difficult, and organisms evolved independently on either side, creating divergent flora and fauna.

As mountains eroded and sediment washed down to the sea, the edges of the continents grew outward. Volcanic islands formed along subduction zones and were added to the edges of the continents. Beach sands deposited on the continental shelf of Gondwana in late Precambrian time are now quartzite of the Plainfield Formation of southeastern New England. These sandy deposits were caught up in the Avalonian mountain building event, the deformation that produced the Avalon volcanic island chain along the fringe of Gondwana about 600 million years ago.

Laurentia, named for the Laurentide Highlands of Quebec, became the nucleus for North America. After it broke away from Rodinia, sediments

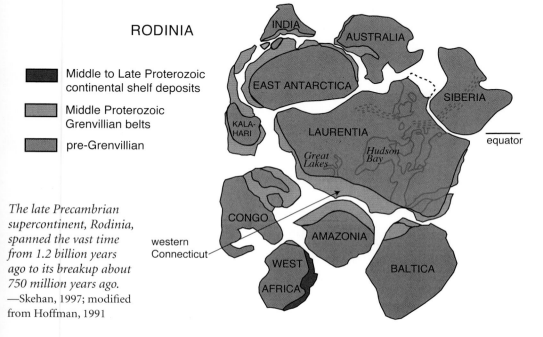

RODINIA

■ Middle to Late Proterozoic continental shelf deposits

▨ Middle Proterozoic Grenvillian belts

■ pre-Grenvillian

The late Precambrian supercontinent, Rodinia, spanned the vast time from 1.2 billion years ago to its breakup about 750 million years ago.
—Skehan, 1997; modified from Hoffman, 1991

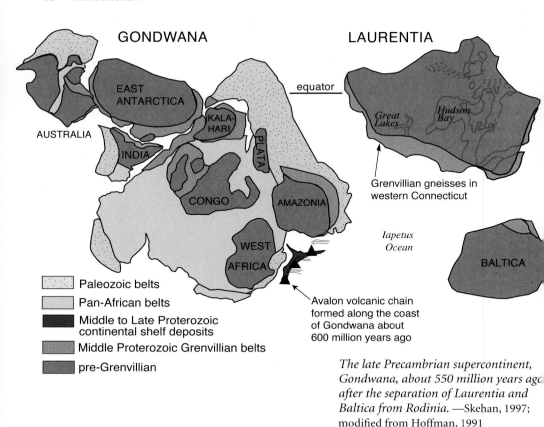

The late Precambrian supercontinent,
Gondwana, about 550 million years ago
after the separation of Laurentia and
Baltica from Rodinia. —Skehan, 1997;
modified from Hoffman, 1991

were deposited on its shelf and volcanic islands grew offshore. These
islands were welded onto the eastern margin of Laurentia during the
Taconic mountain building event between 485 and 440 million years ago,
in Ordovician time. This collision thrusted, pushed, and metamorphosed
the collection of Precambrian to early Paleozoic rocks deposited on the
Laurentian continental shelf. Rocks west of the Hartford Basin show evidence of this collision. Geologists know that volcanic island activity was
associated with the event but continue to debate which of two volcanic
chains—the Bronson Hill or Shelburne Falls—collided with Laurentia
during the Taconic event and exactly when the collision occurred. One
possible scenario is that the Shelburne Falls arc, which formed first, collided first, and later the Bronson Hill arc formed and collided, all during
the lengthy Taconic event. A large accretionary wedge of ocean bottom
sediments was also shoved against the continent and forms a band of rock
west of the volcanic rock.

At some point in early Paleozoic time, Laurentia and Gondwana
reversed course and began moving toward each other. Subduction zones

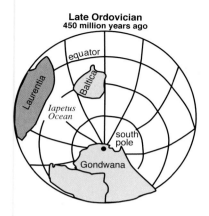

Late Ordovician
450 million years ago

Gondwana was near the south pole and Laurentia was near the equator in Late Ordovician time.

existed on both sides of the Iapetus Ocean. As the Iapetus Ocean closed, several intervening landmasses also moved closer to Laurentia, colliding with one another from time to time along the way. Granite plutons within each terrane record those collisions. Most geologists agree that at least the Avalon and Meguma Terranes were once part of the supercontinent Gondwana. The Putnam-Nashoba Terrane may have been an island arc off the coast of Avalonia. The Gander Terrane, a prominent region in Maine and easternmost Canada, also was present in the Iapetus Ocean.

We know that Avalonia was part of Gondwana because distinctive fossils, trilobites of Cambrian time, exist in the Avalon Terrane in Rhode Island, eastern Massachusetts, Great Britain, and West Africa. Avalonia must have broken away from Gondwana by Ordovician time, or about 450 million years ago, and certainly no earlier than 490 million years ago. Fossils of the Meguma Terrane are also closely related to those of the Avalon Terrane of the northwest African margin.

In Late Silurian and Devonian time, the Central Maine, Merrimack, Putnam-Nashoba, and Avalon Terranes smashed into Laurentia, causing the Acadian mountain building event. This collision, recorded in the extensive plutonic and high-grade metamorphic rocks of eastern Connecticut, firmly welded these blocks of land together. The zone of intense deformation extends north to western Maine and south to Long Island Sound. The mountain building event appears to have swept from the southeast to the northwest across the rocks of New England. Detailed studies in Maine bracket the Acadian mountain building event between 423 and 384 million years ago. Measurements obtained from metamorphic rocks in Connecticut fall within a similar range, from about 425 to 370 million years ago.

Toward the end of Paleozoic time, the Iapetus Ocean was finally swallowed up when Gondwana and the Meguma microcontinent reunited with Laurentia to form the supercontinent Pangea. The collision, called

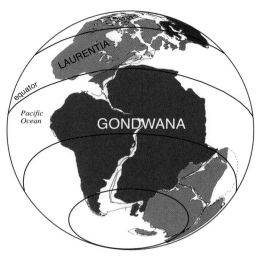

Gondwana docks with Laurentia, forming the Pangean supercontinent.
—Modified from Dalziel, 1997

the Alleghanian mountain building event, began more than 300 million years ago and formed enormous mountains, the eroded remnants of which are the Appalachian Mountains. Pangea was fully assembled by the end of Paleozoic time, about 245 million years ago.

As late as the last quarter of the twentieth century, a number of geologists thought the Alleghanian mountain building event had been relatively insignificant in southern New England. However, it now appears that the Alleghanian mountain building event may have been one of the more widespread and complex tectonic events in this region. It folded, metamorphosed, and thrust faulted sedimentary rocks of the coal basins in Rhode Island and Massachusetts in late Pennsylvanian time. At the same time that the Meguma microcontinent collided with the New England portion of Laurentia, the ancestral African continent collided with land farther south.

Ages of igneous and metamorphic rocks attributed to the Alleghanian event span an enormous range, from 354 to 250 million years ago. The large range probably indicates the episodic nature of major collisions. Geologists now realize this collision renewed compression in the Acadian collision zone; isotopic dates on some metamorphic minerals in the Merrimack and Putnam-Nashoba Terranes give dates within this range. In general, we can say that the Alleghanian mountain building event began before 300 million years ago and peaked somewhat later, giving rise to the 275-million-year-old Narragansett Pier Granite and Westerly Granite of southern Rhode Island and southeastern Connecticut.

Once again, the large continental mass, with its high mountains, heated up the mantle below, and Pangea began to rift apart. The breakup about 200 million years ago gave rise to the modern continents of North America and Europe. The rift cut across the Avalon Terrane, so rocks of Avalonia are found in both North America and Europe. The Atlantic Ocean filled the rift. Early in the opening of the North Atlantic, other basins began to form from Nova Scotia to the Carolinas—including the Hartford Basin. Numerous dikes in Connecticut and elsewhere are the remnants of magma that flowed into the rift basins. The smaller basins pulled apart through Jurassic time but stopped before becoming large enough for the sea to enter. The Atlantic Ocean, on the other hand, continues to widen by rifting to this day.

In the 300 million years since the Alleghanian mountain building event created the Appalachian Mountains, erosion has removed huge volumes of rock from the land and deposited the sediments in the Atlantic Ocean. Sediments from Cretaceous and Tertiary time exist beneath the ocean, forming the coastal plain and continental shelf of North America. There are no intact Cretaceous or Tertiary rocks in Rhode Island or Connecticut, though Block Island has chunks of Cretaceous sediment ripped up by the glaciers.

Glacial History

Every spring in my grandfather's potato field in northern Maine, we discovered a new crop of rocks that had risen to the surface of the ground during winter. We understood how potatoes grew but were confused by the crop of boulders. Continental ice sheets deposited the blanket of clay- to boulder-size sediment across the land, and every winter, frost heaving—the process of subsurface water freezing and expanding—brought more stones to the surface.

The early settlers of Connecticut and Rhode Island were also familiar with the products of glaciation that ornamented their landscape and dictated where they could farm and build. They discovered abundant water in wells dug in sand and gravel deposits that once were deltas in glacial lakes. Unfortunately, sometimes the best sites for wells were already occupied by graveyards, also located in sand and gravel because the digging was easy. Hardpan, a dense rocky clay deposited directly from the base of the ice sheet, was extremely difficult to dig by hand, and if you did manage to excavate a cellar in it, the cellar was often flooded in rainy periods. But if you excavated a well in that same hardpan, it would not provide enough water in times of drought.

Pioneers of North American Glacial Geology

Prior to the nineteenth century there was no glacial theory, although many glacial phenomena were observed and speculated on. A. W. Harris, president of the Liverpool Geological Society, recounted Emmanuel Swedenborg's 1719 interpretation of long, parallel, sinuous lines of sand and clay and large boulders scattered across the Swedish landscape. "He

Reverend Edward Hitchcock.

imagined that a great ocean had broken them, with the sand and clay, from the sea floor, that deep waves had then piled them in ridges, and carried the blocks even to the tops of the mountains."

A few eighteenth-century observers had more plausible explanations. In 1744, Peter Martel wrote in *An Account of the Glaciers of the Savoy* that glaciers are in motion from the higher parts to the lower and carry "great stones even into the valley of Chamonix," including "one of very large size, which several old people assured us they had seen on the ice."

In 1840, Swiss geologist Louis Agassiz published his great work, *Etudes sur les glaciers*, which presented his theory of continental glaciation. In 1846, Agassiz sailed to the United States by way of Nova Scotia. In his book *Geological Sketches*, Agassiz wrote that when his steamer docked in Halifax, Nova Scotia, he "sprang on shore and started at a brisk pace for the heights above the landing. On the first undisturbed ground after leaving the town, I was met by the familiar signs, the polished surfaces, the furrows and scratches, the line-engraving of the glacier, so well known in the Old World, and I became convinced . . . that here also this great agent had been at work, although it was only after a long residence in North America . . . that I fully understood the universality of its action." Agassiz was examining scratches on bedrock that were similar to glacial grooves, or striations, such as he had observed on bedrock in his native Swiss Alpine valleys. "The bases of the glaciers and the sides of the valleys which contain them are found to be polished and scratched by stones found in the lowest regions of the moving ice."

In 1841, Reverend Edward Hitchcock, professor of geology and president of Amherst College in Massachusetts, concluded that European geologists were correct in attributing the formation of such sand and gravel deposits to glacial action. His studies in New England, however, led him to believe that "aqueo-fluvial" processes were more impressive in distributing such deposits than were those of strictly glacial action. His explanation was correct at least in the Connecticut Valley, where abundant sediment was deposited in an enormous glacial lake that occupied the Connecticut River Valley from south of Hartford north to nearly the Canadian border. Little wonder that geologists honor his memory by referring to this great wonder of the Pleistocene world as Glacial Lake Hitchcock.

Ernst Valdemar Antevs (1888–1974) was the first geologist to study varves in Glacial Lake Hitchcock. Sediments laid down on the floor of a glacial lake are composed of a succession of pairs of thin layers called *varves*. A very fine, dark clay layer deposited in the winter when ice covers the lake alternates with a coarser-grained silt layer deposited in the summer when warm weather triggers melting of sediment-laden ice. You can imagine that if you counted every varve couplet in the lake bottom deposits, you would know the life span of the lake. Antevs did just that.

He counted all of the couplets exposed in the Connecticut River Valley from the glacial dam in Rocky Hill and the spillway in New Britain, Connecticut, northward to within a few hundred feet of the Canadian border. In his 1922 study "The Recession of the Last Ice Sheet in New England," he concluded that Glacial Lake Hitchcock existed for 4,000 years. A much more recent study that calibrated the varves with radiocarbon dates found Antevs's estimate to be remarkably accurate.

Glacial Lake Hitchcock existed for 4,000 years.

A Frozen World

When icebergs the size of Rhode Island break off the Antarctic ice cap and melt, climate change takes on more than a theoretical interest. One of the most drastic consequences of global warming is the potential rise in sea level as the ice melts, a process that will affect the coasts of Rhode Island and Connecticut. Sea level has also risen and fallen in the not-so-distant geologic past along our coast. Let's take a look at what happened during the past 1.8 million years, during the Pleistocene ice ages.

The northern half of most of North America has been covered by a continental ice sheet up to 2 miles thick on four occasions in the past 1.8 million years. During at least two of these episodes, the continental glacier spread across the St. Lawrence Valley of Canada, the Green Mountains of Vermont, and Connecticut and Rhode Island.

The Illinoian glaciation, the second to last, left a few deposits that weren't erased by the final glaciation, the Wisconsinan. At Sankaty Head on Nantucket Island, glacial deposits beneath 120,000- to 140,000-year-old fossiliferous marine beds are a terminal moraine of the Illinoian ice sheet. On Block Island, large blocks of older till have been incorporated into moraines of the Wisconsinan ice sheet. These blocks may be Illinoian till. In addition, many drumlins in southern New England may have a core of Illinoian till.

A warm interval, called the Sangamon interglacial stage, peaked around 125,000 years ago and marked the end of the Illinoian glaciation. Coral, which lives in tropical and subtropical climates, lived off the coast of New England during this time, so we know it was warmer than today,

Glacial and Postglacial Events in Quaternary Time

STAGES	YEARS AGO	EVENTS
Holocene	0–11,500	sea-level rise accelerates
	15,000	Connecticut and Rhode Island free of ice
Late Wisconsinan	22,000	ice sheet retreats; terminal moraine deposited on Long Island
	26,000	ice reaches Connecticut
	30,000	warm interval; sea rises
Wisconsinan	80,000	glaciation begins
Sangamon	125,000	warm period; high sea level
Illinoian	140,000–200,000	glaciation
Earlier glaciations and interglacials	200,000–1.8 million	

and sea level was about 10 feet higher. A piece of coral found in a marine sand layer in the Sankaty Cliffs in Nantucket, Massachusetts, was dated at about 128,000 years old. Coral extracts uranium from sea water and fixes it into its skeleton, and uranium has a radioactive isotope that can be used in isotopic age dating. However, the date that uranium in coral provides is the date the coral *lived*, not the date the coral was deposited in sediment.

The most recent North American ice cap, known as the Wisconsinan ice sheet, formed during a cooling period that began about 80,000 years ago. There were several episodes of ice advance during the Wisconsinan, but by about 22,000 years ago, the last ice sheet (Late Wisconsinan) had reached its southernmost position on the east coast of North America, extending to Long Island, Block Island, Martha's Vineyard, and Nantucket. The radiocarbon age of spruce wood found in deposits of the Ronkonkoma terminal moraine at Port Washington, Long Island, is 22,000 years. A terminal moraine marks the maximum extent of the margin of an ice sheet. Although the ice continued to flow south, melting along its southern margin kept up with the forward flow, causing the ice to essentially stand still on Long Island for a few thousand years. The prominent ridge of the Ronkonkoma terminal moraine extends east-northeastward in southern Long Island through the Hamptons into the sea. Segments of

Maximum extent of the continental ice sheets that covered North America during Pleistocene glaciation. The direction of ice flow was perpendicular to the curved lines. —Modified from Oldale, 1992

the terminal moraine to the east form Block Island, Martha's Vineyard, and Nantucket.

The continental glacier was 1 to 2 miles thick at its center, or area of maximum snow accumulation, near Hudson Bay. The ice became progressively thinner farther south. This great ice sheet moved in a south-southeasterly direction toward Connecticut and Rhode Island. At its southern margin, lobes formed at the end of large regional basins such as Narragansett Bay. When the glacial front began to recede, ice lingered in these basins longer than in the uplands.

Retreat of the Ice and Formation of Lakes

The glacial front began to retreat northward from southern Long Island about 21,000 years ago. Moraines that form at the toe of the ice sheet as it is melting back are called *recessional moraines* or *end moraines*. The Harbor Hill moraine, approximately parallel to but a few miles north of the Ronkonkoma moraine, runs along the north shore of Long Island to Orient Point and Plum Island; then it cuts across the east end of Long Island Sound to Fishers Island, and then to the mainland at the Rhode Island–Connecticut line, where it is called the Charlestown moraine. Together, the easterly widening jaws between the Ronkonkoma and the Harbor Hill–Charlestown moraines form Block Island Sound.

As the glaciers melted, meltwater was impounded in glacial lakes and ponds dammed by the retreating ice margin or glacial sediments. The depth, shape, and size of the lakes changed with time as spillway positions changed or the level of spillways lowered due to ice dams retreating and sediment dams washing away. Buried bedrock ridges exposed by erosion stood firm after overlying sediments were stripped away.

Glacial lakes don't fill with water like a bathtub. From the instant of their inception (that is, when the ice margin first retreats back from any potential dam by the tiniest amount), the huge amount of meltwater produced by even the smallest frontal retreat instantly fills the small basin created by that retreat. So the lake is always full and spilling over at the lowest point across the dam. In the northern hemisphere, the constantly full lake usually grows larger in area northward as the ice retreats. Lake levels drop as the spillway lowers by erosion into the dam material, or as new, lower spillways are uncovered by further ice retreat.

Thirty-three glacial lakes have been identified in Connecticut, seventeen of which were dammed by ice and sixteen by sediment. The three largest in Connecticut—Glacial Lakes Connecticut, Hitchcock, and Middletown—were sediment-dammed lakes. Deposits of sediment in each of these lakes, as well as sediments of many smaller lakes and glacially generated stream systems, form a record of the detailed history of systematic ice recession across the region.

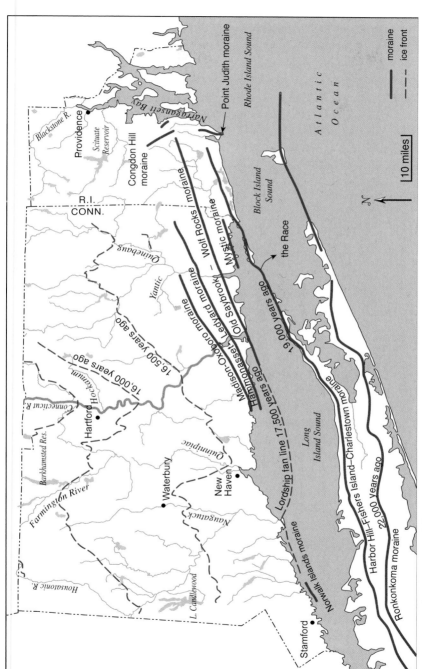

Recessional moraines and the position of the ice front in Connecticut and Rhode Island. —Modified from Stone and others, 2005

Atlantic Ocean

Rhode Island Sound

Point Judith moraine

Congdon Hill moraine

Narragansett Bay

Providence

Blackstone R.

Scituate Reservoir

R.I.
CONN.

Wolf Rocks moraine

Mystic moraine

Quinebaug

Yantic

Madison-Oxoboro Ledyard moraine

Old Saybrook

Hammonasset moraine

Block Island Sound

the Race

19,000 years ago

17,500 years ago

Lordship fan line

16,500 years ago

16,000 years ago

Hockanum

Connecticut R.

Hartford

Barkhamsted Res.

Farmington River

Housatonic R.

Quinnipiac

Waterbury

New Haven

Naugatuck

L. Candlewood

Stamford

Norwalk Islands moraine

Long Island Sound

Harbor Hill–Fishers Island–Charlestown moraine

22,000 years ago

Ronkonkoma moraine

N

10 miles

—— moraine
– – – ice front

Glacial Lake Connecticut

By 19,000 years ago, the ice front was receding northward from the Harbor Hill moraine on Long Island. The shoreline of the Atlantic Ocean was some 70 to 100 miles south of Long Island during the maximum extent of the glaciation, and the Long Island Sound basin was beneath the ice. As the ice melted, the low area between the ice front and the moraine on Long Island contained Glacial Lake Connecticut, which grew larger as the ice retreated toward Connecticut. Initially, this lake connected to a lake in Block Island Sound, which was impounded by the terminal moraine that formed its southern shore. As the spillway over the terminal moraine slowly eroded and lowered, the Harbor Hill–Charlestown moraine became the lake's southern shore and the two lakes were separated. A spillway for Glacial Lake Connecticut formed across the inner moraine at the Race, just west of Fishers Island. The toe of the glacier formed the north shore of Glacial Lake Connecticut until the rocky Connecticut shoreline was exposed. At that time, Glacial Lake Connecticut was slightly larger than Long Island Sound is today. During the life of the lake, the Race spillway slowly lowered, and by 15,500 years ago Glacial Lake Connecticut was completely drained.

Meltwater rivers emptying into Long Island Sound built deltas in Glacial Lake Connecticut. Meltwater also carried abundant silt and clay that settled in deeper parts of the lake. Seismic reflection profiles and drill cores from Long Island Sound reveal that varved clay deposits are locally as much as 300 feet thick. Because so much glacial sediment was deposited here, the sound is now fairly shallow, averaging about 65 feet deep.

Glacial Landforms and Deposits

The continental glaciers scoured away soil, loose sediment, and weathered bedrock from Connecticut and Rhode Island. The glacier smoothed the existing bedrock surface but did not remove a lot of it. The smoothing happened beneath the ice sheet, not out in front of it. Scavenging whatever was in its path, the glacier collected enormous quantities of rocks, trees, and soil. The ice sheet then carried its load in the direction the ice was flowing and deposited it somewhere farther along its path.

Glacial erosion stripped off a substantial amount of soil and loose, weathered rock material from the top of the underlying bedrock. The preglacial, weathered bedrock was probably similar to the reddish, clay-rich, decomposed rocks you can see today in the unglaciated central and southern Appalachian Mountains. Many of the stones in the Wisconsinan glacial debris, however, are unweathered, indicating that earlier advances of the continental glacier, including the Illinoian ice sheet, probably scraped off most of the more deeply weathered material. The interval between the later ice sheet advances was not long enough to allow much weathering of the newly exposed bedrock.

As the ice melted, debris either fell directly out of the ice or was carried away by meltwater to be deposited as sediments in streambeds and lakes. The various deposits occur in such landforms as moraines, drumlins, kames, outwash sands and gravels, eskers, delta plains, kettles, and lakebeds. Sediments deposited by water are generally stratified—they have visible layers, or beds—whereas material deposited directly from the ice is unstratified.

Till

The unsorted glacial debris deposited directly by ice and not moved by meltwater is known as *till*. It consists of a chaotic mixture of silt, sand, gravel, and boulders of various sizes and shapes, all embedded in a silty or clayey matrix of rock flour ground up and carried by the ice sheet. This matrix is composed predominantly of quartz, fresh feldspars, and micas, with some kaolin clay. Till carried short distances characteristically contains rock fragments with irregular fracture surfaces, indicating they were plucked from the exposed bedrock by the ice. Such blocks have not been carried far from the outcrops from which they were snatched. Those that traveled farther are faceted into somewhat rounded shapes and occasionally are striated, grooved, or polished.

One type of till is a loose-textured mass of sandy or silty material containing angular pebbles and boulders of all sizes. This material is deposited directly from the melting ice as the glacier recedes. Another kind of till, laid down beneath the ice sheet, is a more compact material consisting of a smaller proportion of rock fragments of all sizes embedded in a finer-grained matrix. This kind of till, which is difficult to dig with a pick and shovel, is sometimes called "hardpan."

A thin mantle of till, generally less than 15 feet thick, covers a large part of southern New England, especially in upland areas. On steep hillsides and hilltops it may be lacking and bedrock is exposed. On slopes with a northerly aspect that faced the oncoming glacier, till is commonly thicker, having been piled up and plastered against the bedrock hills by the overriding ice sheet.

Drumlins

A drumlin is a streamlined landform composed entirely of till. Drumlins form when moving ice meets enough resistance from till at its base that it is easier for the ice to ride up and over the glacial material than to pick it up and carry it. The skidding movement of ice over the top of the tough, highly compacted till streamlines it into an oval shape, with its long axes pointing in the direction of glacial transport. To visualize the three-dimensional shape of a drumlin, cut a hard-boiled egg in half from end to end and place each half on a flat surface so that the long axes are parallel. In southern New England, the dominant trend of the long axis of the drumlins is south-southeast, which is the direction the glacier was traveling. Local variations in drumlin axes are a result of underlying topographic features that influenced the direction of ice movement as the ice sheet thinned.

Most drumlins in southern New England are composed of two types of till. The lower till is composed of a compact clay, often as hard as cement, and the upper layer is more loosely compacted. Most geologists today agree that the compact clay making up most of the drumlins was probably laid down by the Illinoian ice sheet and was then further shaped by the Late Wisconsinan ice sheet that overrode New England.

The *Quaternary Geologic Map of Connecticut and Long Island Sound Basin* shows more than 1,600 drumlin axes scattered across all of Connecticut. The distribution of some drumlin clusters is due to underlying bedrock consisting of fine-grained rocks like shaley phyllites, micaceous schists, and silty sandstones. Clayey materials in the till, derived from fine-grained bedrock like schist and phyllite, facilitate drumlin formation.

Drumlins range from 0.25 to 1 mile long and may be as much as 200 feet tall. In the Connecticut Valley, younger stratified deposits partially bury many drumlins, so you can't see their full height and thickness at the surface. South- to south-southwest-trending drumlins stick up through stratified lake and stream deposits, confirming that they originated before the melting of the last ice sheet that deposited glacial lake sediments. Wells drilled through the crests of some drumlins reveal thicknesses of up to 200 feet of hardpan. On the flanks of drumlins, the till is usually thinner.

Glacial Boulders

Boulders plucked from bedrock ledges and irregularly strewn over areas covered with till are called *glacial boulders*. These surface boulders tend to occur singly or packed together in groups over the tops of, and on, hill-slopes. Areas with high concentrations of boulders, called *boulder fields*, are mainly useful for the bragging rights of ownership. Farming them is impossible. Landscape architects have skillfully blended a bountiful assortment of glacial boulders with beautiful homes, as, for example, on Masons Island in Mystic and over substantial parts of Ledyard, Connecticut, and Charlestown, Rhode Island.

Glacial Erratics

Glacial erratics are boulders of one rock type that sit in an area of a different bedrock type (hence the term *erratic*). Many erratics within the Hartford Basin are basalt, or traprock, that originated from nearby rugged basalt ridges and are now sitting on areas underlain by sedimentary rock. Basalt erratics have been found as far east as the Thames River (where they sit on metamorphic rock), and also in eastern Long Island and Block Island. Some of these basalt erratics may have been collected by the glacier

Bouldery till exposed along a power line right-of-way north of Whalehead Road in Ledyard.

from basalt dikes, such as the Higganum dike, that intrudes older crystal-line rocks east of the Hartford Basin.

Recessional Moraines

Also known as *end moraines,* recessional moraines are prominent linear mounds or ridges of unsorted rock debris that form at the glacial margin. The classic, simple model of moraine formation describes debris melt-ing out of the ice and piling up into a moraine as the edge of the glacier remains stationary. A large pile of debris accumulates in one place if the glacier continues to move forward at the same rate that it melts back-ward. A surging ice lobe can literally shove the material into place, pushing sheets of stratified outwash sediments in front of it.

End moraines provide a snapshot all along the ice front because the ice receded in a direction at right angles to the trend of the moraine. While the edge of the ice stood at the Harbor Hill moraine on Long Island, it also stood along the Charlestown moraine in southern Rhode Island. The Old Saybrook moraine comes ashore near the mouth of the Connecticut River and runs east-northeasterly into the Wolf Rocks moraine north of West Kingston, Rhode Island. The trend of these moraines helps us form a regional picture of the size and shape of the ice front.

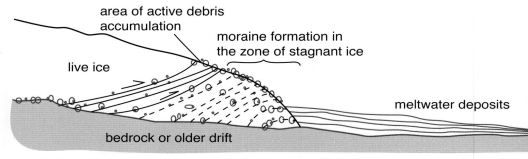

area of active debris
accumulation

moraine formation in
the zone of stagnant ice

live ice

meltwater deposits

bedrock or older drift

Debris picked up and carried by the ice sheet moves to the ice surface along shear planes near the front of the ice. The shear zone acts like a conveyor belt, carrying debris from the base of the glacier to the place of deposition at the stagnant end of the glacier. —Modified from Koteff and Pessl, 1981

Geologists used to look for organic material in glacial moraines to obtain radiocarbon dates for glacial events. However, these dates don't correspond to the time of moraine formation because plants can't live on glaciers. Today, geologists use cosmogenic dating, which estimates the amount of time boulders sitting on the top of glacial sediments have been exposed to sunlight.

Kettles

Stagnant blocks of ice downstream from the glacier margin may become partly or wholly buried by accumulating sand and gravel. As the ice blocks melt, the unsupported glacial outwash collapses, forming craterlike depressions known as *kettles*. A kettle contains water if the groundwater level is higher than the bottom of the kettle or if the base beneath the kettle isn't porous and hence traps rainwater. Kettles that contain water are called *kettle ponds*.

A
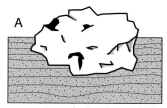

B
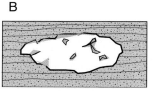

C
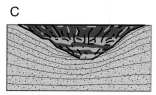

Formation of a kettle. A block of ice breaks off the glacier and sits on outwash (A). Outwash builds up around the ice (B), and when it melts, the sediment collapses into a kettle (C). —Modified from Alden, 1925

Kames

A kame is a low mound or short ridge that originates when meltwater sediment fills depressions or short crevasses in or on the ice. Both water and ice contribute to its structure. Because the sediment in a kame is almost always deposited in ponded water, kames typically have bedding, but the beds deposited directly on or against the ice collapse when the ice melts. As tongues of ice occupied valleys, meltwater streams commonly flowed between the ice in the valley and the valley walls. The resulting meltwater sediments are called *kame terraces.*

Outwash

When glacial ice melts, its runoff forms a series of rivers or braided streams. These rivers carry rock fragments from the end of the glacial conveyor belt, spreading layers of sand and gravel over a broad area and forming an outwash plain. You can see examples of miniature outwash plains along the base of bare sand and gravel slopes, perhaps along a highway, after a heavy rain.

Meltwater from the glacier may distribute an apron of sediment downstream from the ice sheet, the sediment grading with distance from coarse-grained gravel to fine-grained sand and clay. In broad areas free of ice blocks, the outwash plain retains a readily identifiable form. In southern New England, large outwash plains exist only in front of the terminal moraine on Long Island and in front of the Charlestown moraine in Rhode Island.

Deltas

The most common meltwater deposits in southern New England are deltas laid down in glacial lakes. When meltwater streams enter glacial lakes, gravel and sand are deposited in flat-topped deltas as water velocity decreases. Glacial lakes developed in nearly every valley in Connecticut and Rhode Island as the ice retreated. In larger valleys, like Narragansett Basin and the Connecticut Valley, these deposits are especially abundant and widespread. Such relatively flat and easily dug deposits are prized sites for wells, cemeteries,

These sandy, bedded layers were deposited in a glacial lake delta near Bowdish Reservoir in northwestern Rhode Island.

sand and gravel pits, and subdivisions. These deposits are also the principal groundwater aquifers providing public water supply in the region.

Deltas contain beds that slope downward in the direction the meltwater flows into the lake. The sloping layers deposited underwater are called *foreset beds*. As the package of delta foreset beds builds out into the lake, flat-lying beds deposited above lake level by streams feeding the delta are laid on top of the more steeply dipping foreset beds. Because of their position, these beds are called *topset beds*. The surface between the flat-lying topset beds and the dipping foreset beds, called the *topset-foreset contact*, marks the water level in the glacial lake.

Eskers
Eskers are long, sinuous ridges of sand and gravel that resemble stream channels if viewed from above. The steep, narrow ridges can be 35 feet high or higher. In cross section, an esker resembles the St. Louis Arch, with steep slopes of 30 to 35 degrees. Eskers are usually composed of gravelly beds that have collapsed at their steep sides, often with large boulders on the surface. They are deposited as meltwater flows through tunnels in the ice or in open channels—ice crevasses. As the confining ice melts, the sediments slump and form ridges that mimic the shape of the tunnel or crevasse.

Esker tubes contribute substantially to the volume of outwash. The confining ice walls of the tubes are constantly collapsing inward when melting, contributing to the debris flushed out. Meltwater under great hydraulic pressure carries the debris beyond the ice margin, where it is deposited as outwash.

Postglacial History
Strong winds blew along the edge of the North American ice sheet during the melting and recession of the glaciers. Extensive unvegetated meltwater deposits provided ample sand and silt for the wind to transport. Two types of windblown, or eolian, deposits occur in Connecticut and Rhode Island. The first type forms a blanket of sediment up to 3 feet thick across Connecticut and somewhat thicker in coastal Rhode Island. This eolian blanket is fine sand and silty sand. Because these deposits are near the surface, where modern (postglacial) soil has developed, they are commonly oxidized to a light brown to yellowish brown. Severe frost heaving during early postglacial times disturbed the thin windblown layer, so it is usually mixed with stones from the glacial deposits below. The second type of early postglacial windblown deposit is sand dunes. These mostly occur in areas of large glacial lakes, like in the Connecticut Valley, where extensive unforested delta plains provided sand. The shapes of these dunes tell us the wind direction at the time they were built.

Sea Level and the Coast

Sea level was some 350 feet lower during the maximum of the Wisconsinan glaciation because water was tied up in the continental glaciers. As the climate warmed and the ice melted, water flowed into the oceans and sea level began to rise. The land, however, also began to rise because the weight of the ice was no longer depressing the underlying crust. Land to the north, which was buried by more ice, rose more than land at the southern edge of the ice sheet. The postglacial uplift revitalized rivers by steepening them, so that they cut down into glacial meltwater sediments with renewed vigor all across the region.

The rising sea first entered the Long Island Sound basin about 15,000 years ago, after the glacial lakes drained and before the land began to rise significantly. For a while after the ice sheet receded, the land was uplifting at the same rate the sea was rising. This event is recorded in Long Island Sound by an extensive marine delta built when sea level was 130 feet lower than today. By about 9,000 years ago, rebound of the land slowed, so sea level began to rise faster. By about 4,000 years ago the rate of sea level rise had decreased to about 8 inches per century. Scientists have measured 13 to 16 feet of sea level rise during the last 3,000 to 4,000 years in coastal saltwater marsh deposits.

Ice age animals lived in the ice-free region south of the terminal moraine on Long Island, an area that is now under the sea. After the ice sheet withdrew from the region and sea level rose, tundra developed on the recently deglaciated land, and animals and plants moved in. A predominantly coniferous forest followed and was later succeeded by a mixed coniferous-deciduous forest.

South of New York City, the East Coast is characterized by a coastal plain, a gently sloping strip of land near the sea made up of a thick wedge of sediments deposited in Cretaceous and Tertiary time. Farther out to sea, these sediments form the continental shelf of North America. The New England coastline, however, has no comparable coastal plain, although

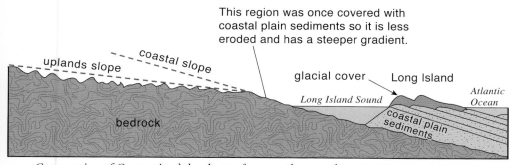

Cross section of Connecticut's landscape from north to south. —Modified from Bell, 1985

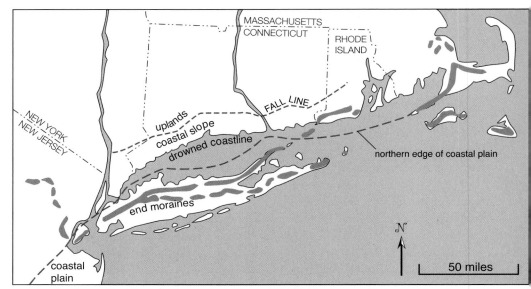

Southern New England has a glacially modified bedrock coastal slope with a drowned coastline. The eroded remnant of Late Cretaceous coastal plain sediments is capped by end moraines and glacial outwash on Long Island. —Modified from Bell, 1985

beneath Long Island and Block Island and farther offshore an erosional remnant of the coastal plain is the foundation of the continental shelf. The rocky headlands and small bedrock hills along the coast of Connecticut and Rhode Island were once covered by sediments of the coastal plain, but erosion has removed the landward portion of these sediments. Preglacial rivers, aided by continental glaciers during the ice ages, accomplished this erosion. The coastal plain sediments formerly extended to the northern limit of the coastal slope, which is sometimes called the *fall line*. The bedrock surface exposed by the erosion is called the *coastal slope*. Because coastal plain sediments covered this area for millions of years, its surface has not been as highly eroded as the bedrock surface farther inland.

Coastal rivers in Connecticut and Rhode Island—the Mianus, Norwalk, Saugatuck, Pequonnock, Housatonic, Quinnipiac, Thames, Connecticut, Niantic, Mystic, Pawcatuck, Pawtuxet, Woonasquatucket, Blackstone, and Sakonnet Rivers—have been flooded for some distance inland, and their water levels respond to the daily rise and fall of the tides. The Connecticut River is tidal for more than 40 miles inland until a bedrock ridge north of Hartford blocks the tidal effect. American Indians gave tidal rivers names ending in "tuck" or "tic." Many of the river valleys originally developed in mid-Tertiary time. The valleys were choked with meltwater deposits as they emerged from beneath the ice. Modern streams have had little opportunity to cut very deep into the meltwater deposits.

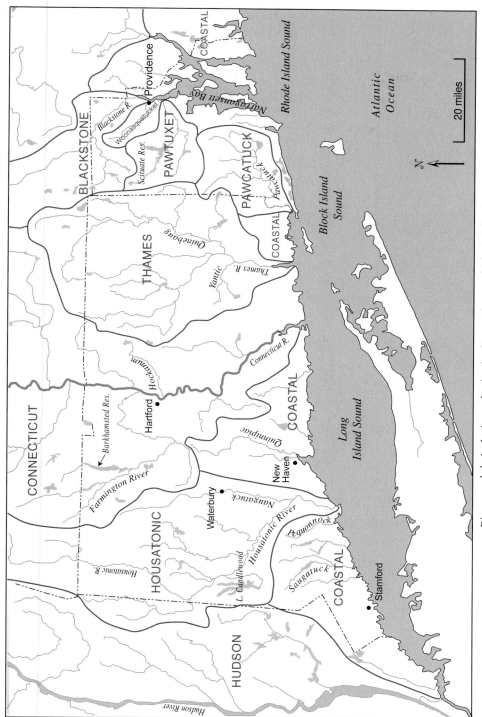

Rivers and their drainage basins in Connecticut and Rhode Island.

Connecticut owes its salt marshes in part to the shelter provided by Long Island and to the drowned coastline. As sea level rose and inundated river valleys, the rivers dumped many tons of nutrient-rich mud in the drowned valleys, nourishing a great variety of creatures of the land, air, and water. Ducks and crabs inhabit the marshes. Soft-shell clams, or steamers, and hard-shell clams such as littlenecks, or quahogs, live in the mudflats. In earlier days, salt marsh grasses fed cattle and were used as roofing thatch.

Some of the most important salt marshes on the Connecticut coast are Barn Island Wildlife Management Area, in Stonington, and Hammonasset Marsh, behind the beach in Hammonasset Beach State Park. The Charles E. Wheeler Wildlife Management Area, at the mouth of the Housatonic River, is one of the most spectacular remaining marshes in Connecticut because it is essentially unaltered by human interventions, such as mosquito-control ditches cutting the grassy flats.

Sea level is again rising at an increased rate. Greenhouse gases from the burning of fossil fuels and other human activities have collected in the atmosphere, trapping the earth's heat and warming the climate. Studies show that global warming has been underway since the end of the Little Ice Age, a period of cold weather from about the fifteenth century to the nineteenth century, but it has accelerated in modern times. Ice caps in Antarctica and the Arctic are melting faster than snow is accumulating, resulting in a net rise in sea level. While much of Connecticut and Rhode Island, with their rock-bound coasts, isn't as susceptible to small rises in sea level as more flat-lying areas, the marshes already have been impacted. Just a few feet of sea level rise can drown a tidal marsh. Marsh vegetation will migrate inland with sea level rise if given the chance, but development along the coast prohibits this in many places. Sea level rise also increases erosion along the coast, cutting bluffs progressively back toward lighthouses and cliffside homes.

Human Activity

The first people in southern New England arrived more than 10,000 years ago and camped near the meltwater rivers and ponds that formed in the wake of the receding glaciers. Evidence of prehistoric people from even earlier times may be submerged in the Atlantic Ocean because sea level rose some 300 feet between 20,000 and 5,000 years ago as the glaciers melted, inundating coastal areas that may have been inhabited.

One of the main rock materials used by prehistoric people in southeastern New England was felsite, a fine-grained volcanic rock with minerals so tiny that they aren't distinguishable with the naked eye. All of the major exposures of fine-grained rocks with felsitic textures were known and used early in the prehistoric period before 8,000 years ago, and they

Homes built near sea level on hard gneiss at Lighthouse Point on the east side of New Haven Harbor.

continued to supply material for many generations. One of the sources was the Spencer Hill rhyolite volcanic flows in Rhode Island. Other lithic materials used in prehistoric times in the region include soapstone, chert, argillite, hornfels, and vein quartz.

The abundant harbors along the Connecticut and Rhode Island coasts attracted a large and courageous seafaring population. Block Island is named for Adriaen Block, a Dutch fur trader who sailed up the Connecticut River in 1614. Nathaniel B. Palmer, a native of Stonington, Connecticut, discovered the Palmer Peninsula of Antarctica in 1820 while on a sealing expedition.

The need for tools, weapons, and furnishings led enterprising colonists to search for and find raw materials in Rhode Island and Connecticut. They discovered iron ores that had formed in swamps in Stafford and in marble beds in the mountains of northwestern Connecticut. Charcoal made from hardwood trees stoked the fires of the forges.

From Hammonasset Beach State Park on the Connecticut shore to Mount Riga in northwestern Connecticut and from Mohegan Bluffs on Block Island to Diamond Hill in northeastern Rhode Island, southern New England is a checkerboard of state parks and state forests, all excellent places to see a part of this land's geologic story, which spans 1.2 billion years.

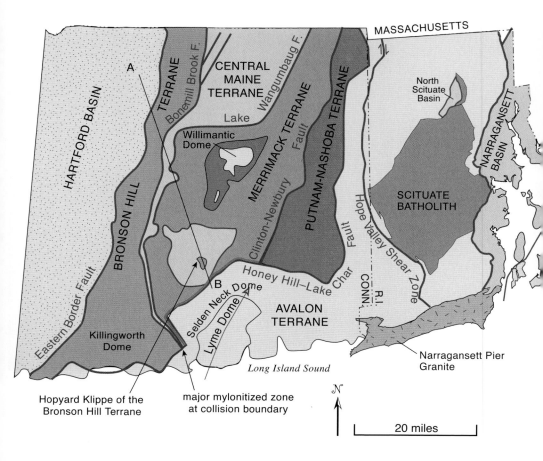

The terranes of eastern Connecticut have been thrust to the east over the large Avalon Terrane.
The line A-B marks the trace of the cross-section below. —Modified from Wintsch and others, 2001

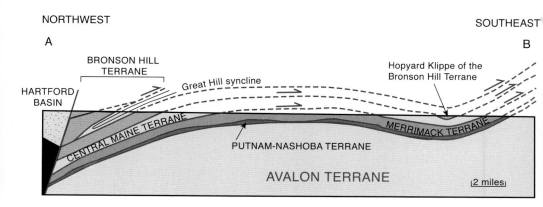

Rhode Island and Eastern Connecticut

Rhode Island and eastern Connecticut have been combined in this book because their geologic stories must be told together. Both consist of terranes added onto the eastern margin of North America. A terrane is a large, fault-bounded body of rock with a geologic history distinctly different from its neighboring rocks. The large Avalon Terrane, a former microcontinent, is well exposed in Rhode Island and extreme eastern and southern Connecticut, and it extends deep below the surface, perhaps as far west as the Eastern Border Fault of the Hartford Basin. Rhode Island is entirely included within the Avalon Terrane. Eastern Connecticut contains parts of the Avalon Terrane, as well as parts of at least four and maybe five other terranes. The presence of the Putnam-Nashoba, Merrimack, Central Maine, and Bronson Hill Terranes is well established. Studies published in 2007 suggest that the Gander Terrane, recognized in Maine and easternmost Canada, may also be present in southern Connecticut.

The Bronson Hill Terrane was a volcanic arc that formed in the Iapetus Ocean off the coast of the continent Laurentia. The Avalon Terrane was a microcontinent that split off the supercontinent Gondwana. The other terranes formed somewhere in the Iapetus Ocean between Laurentia and Gondwana.

The terranes that formed in the Iapetus Ocean were squeezed between Laurentia and its Bronson Hill arc on one side and the Avalon microcontinent on the other side during the huge Acadian mountain building event between 420 and 375 million years ago. Enormous pressures generated by the collision caused rock units to move up from the depths of the earth along faults. Sheets of rock were thrust up and over others in structural forms known as *overthrusts*. The Central Maine, Merrimack, and Putnam-Nashoba Terranes were thrust to the east over the top of the Avalon Terrane, forming a stacked series of thrust sheets known as the Eastern Connecticut Thrust Belt. The great pile of rocks probably formed

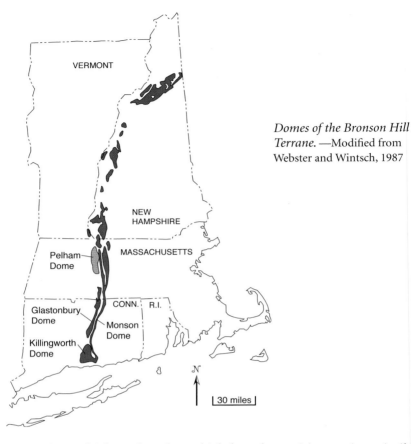

VERMONT

Domes of the Bronson Hill Terrane. —Modified from Webster and Wintsch, 1987

NEW
HAMPSHIRE

Pelham
Dome

MASSACHUSETTS

Glastonbury
Dome

CONN.   R.I.

Monson
Dome

Killingworth
Dome

N

30 miles

mountains as high as the Alps, which have been rising up in a similar tectonic setting much more recently.

Bronson Hill Volcanic Arc

The Bronson Hill volcanic arc, also called the Taconic arc by some, consists of a line of domes thought to be former volcanoes. The Bronson Hill Terrane runs from New Hampshire south to at least Great Hill east of Portland, Connecticut, and possibly all the way to Long Island Sound. In Connecticut, the Bronson Hill volcanic arc consists of two parallel domes of Ordovician crystalline rocks separated by a tightly squeezed syncline of Ordovician to Devonian rocks. The Monson Gneiss of the Monson Dome forms the eastern margin of the Bronson Hill Terrane and the Glastonbury Gneiss of the Glastonbury Dome forms the western margin.

The Bronson Hill volcanic island chain formed either along the margin of Laurentia or much farther offshore between 454 and 442 million years ago in Late Ordovician time. The volcanic arc was probably like the Aleutian Islands or Japan, island chains formed above subduction zones, where an oceanic plate collides with a continental plate. Geologists think the volcanic rocks were deposited on Precambrian to Middle Ordovician gneissic rocks because the Pelham Dome of central Massachusetts contains Precambrian rocks and is in line with the Glastonbury Dome in Connecticut. The Bronson Hill arc may have been the volcanic arc that collided with Laurentia during the Taconic mountain building event between 485 and 440 million years ago.

When Laurentia and Avalonia collided during the Acadian mountain building event between 425 and 370 million years ago, the Bronson Hill volcanoes were squeezed into a narrow band of domes and overturned toward the east. The foliation in the Glastonbury and Monson Gneisses typically dips to the west. All Bronson Hill rocks have been metamorphosed twice, first moderately high, Early Devonian Acadian metamorphism and then low- to medium-grade metamorphism of Pennsylvanian to Permian age from the Alleghanian mountain building event. The western margin of the Bronson Hill Terrane is in fault contact with the eastern margin of the Hartford Basin. The terrane-bounding fault along the east flank of the Bronson Hill Terrane is known as the Bonemill Brook Fault.

The gneisses in the center of the domes crystallized deep below the volcanic arc. The Late Ordovician Glastonbury Gneiss, a biotite gneiss that ranges from homogenous to well-foliated biotite, varies in composition from metamorphosed light-colored granitic rocks to dark granodioritic and dioritic rocks. The light to dark gray, Ordovician Monson Gneiss is made up of stratified and layered gneiss with biotite- and plagioclase-amphibole schist, and gneiss with large lenticular or eye-shaped microcline crystals. Lenses of ultramafic oceanic crust called *peridotite* are also found in the Monson Gneiss.

The domes are mantled by schists and quartzites that originally were layered sedimentary rocks deposited on the volcanic arc rocks after the Taconic mountain building event and before the collision with the terranes to the east. The Collins Hill Formation contains dark mafic volcanic rocks, formerly basalt that poured onto the seafloor in Ordovician time, that grade upward into light-colored felsic volcanic rocks. The Devonian Littleton Formation at the core of the Great Hill syncline is outlined by the distinctive Silurian Clough Quartzite. Schist of the Littleton Formation preserves graded beds even where metamorphosed to high grades, as is the case near the crest of Mount Monadnock in New Hampshire.

Eastern Connecticut Thrust Belt

The next large area of land to be added to the eastern margin of the continent was the Eastern Connecticut Thrust Belt. It consists of great sheets of rock that were thrust to the east over the Avalon Terrane during the Acadian mountain building event, between 420 and 375 million years ago. The major faults separating each thrust sheet formed along areas of weakness, presumably where regions of rock with one history butted up against another region of rock with a contrasting history. Therefore, the faults not only show the structure of the great collision, they also form terrane boundaries.

In the 1950s, H. Roberta Dixon and George Snyder of the U.S. Geological Survey realized that rock formations in eastern Connecticut recorded evidence of having been transported in an easterly direction. The idea was met with some skepticism at the time because *eastward*-directed thrusting had not been recognized as a widespread phenomenon here, and in western New England it was well recognized that the dominant transport direction was westward. In recent decades detailed mapping of geological structures has provided clues to the remarkable story of how eastern Connecticut and Rhode Island became part of North America.

Imagine the colossal folds that formed when two continent-sized blocks of hard rock, Avalonia and Laurentia, were crushed together like jaws of a vice. The rocks caught in the middle moved upward into enormous folded and faulted mountains of strata. Those rocks were extensively penetrated by great masses of molten rock that hardened into igneous bodies that are now gneiss. The region thickened even more during the Alleghanian mountain building event, but later, as extensional forces began to take over, the thrust sheets thinned.

Age (in millions of years)	Bronson Hill Volcanic Arc		Central Maine Terrane		Merrimack Terrane		Putnam-Nashoba Terrane	
Mississippian								
—— 354 ——					Lebanon Gabbro			
Devonian	Littleton Formation				Scotland Schist			
—— 417 ——					Canterbury Gneiss			
Silurian	Clough Quartzite				Hebron Gneiss Southbridge Fm.		Quinebaug Fm. Tatnic Hill Fm.	
—— 443 ——	Collins Hill Fm.							
	Glastonbury Gneiss	BONEMILL BROOK FAULT	Brimfield Schist	LAKE WANGUMBAUG FAULT		CLINTON-NEWBURY FAULT		LAKE CHAR FAULT
Ordovician			Bigelow Brook Fm.					
—— 490 ——	Monson Gneiss							

Rocks of the Eastern Connecticut Thrust Belt.

Putnam-Nashoba Terrane

The Putnam-Nashoba Terrane is named for Putnam, Connecticut, and Nashoba Valley, Massachusetts, where rocks of this terrane occur. This terrane was originally a volcanic arc that developed in the Iapetus Ocean between Ordovician and Silurian time. The narrow, north- to northeast-trending terrane lies east of the Lake Char Fault, north of the Honey Hill Fault Zone, and west of the Clinton-Newbury Fault. The terrane is made up of two main rock formations. The Ordovician Quinebaug Formation contains gray, fine-grained, well-layered schist, quartz-feldspar granular rock, and a light to medium gray, fine- to medium-grained felsic gneiss. These rocks were originally intrusive and extrusive igneous rocks. The other main rock type, the Tatnic Hill Formation, consists of the calc-silicate Fly Pond Member and the gray, fine- to medium-grained schist of the Yantic Member. This formation was originally muddy sediments deposited in Silurian time in a basin next to the arc.

Merrimack and Central Maine Terranes

The Merrimack and Central Maine Terranes feature former sedimentary rocks deposited in basins in the Iapetus Ocean. The west-dipping Merrimack Terrane lies on top of the Putnam-Nashoba Terrane, and the boundary between them is the Clinton-Newbury Fault. The Central Maine Terrane overlies the Merrimack Terrane, and the thrust fault between them is the Lake Wangumbaug Fault.

The rocks of the Merrimack Terrane in Connecticut consist of the Scotland Schist, Hebron Gneiss, and Southbridge Formation. The Silurian-age Hebron Gneiss is interlayered dark gray schist and greenish gray calc-silicate gneiss. These higher-grade metamorphic schists contain abundant sills of granite. The 414-million-year-old Canterbury Gneiss intrudes along the Clinton-Newbury Fault and crosscuts the Hebron Gneiss.

The Central Maine Terrane is the most westerly of the terranes from the Iapetus Ocean. It's also the one that collided head-on with the Bronson Hill volcanic arc on the eastern coast of the Laurentian continent. The Central Maine Terrane is composed predominantly of highly metamorphosed limy and micaceous strata of the Brimfield Schist. High-grade metamorphic minerals in the rocks indicate the strata were buried at great depths when they were heated to high temperatures and pressures. The western margin of the Central Maine Terrane is abruptly cut off by the Bonemill Brook Fault.

The Willimantic Dome within the Merrimack Terrane is a window through the Eastern Connecticut Thrust Belt. Erosion has removed the overlying, attentuated thrust sheets from the core of the dome, exposing older rocks. The center of the dome contains the 600-million-year-old Hope Valley Alaskite Gneiss of the Avalon Terrane. Directly above the alaskite gneiss are rocks of the Waterford Group, also of the

Avalon Terrane. This window has helped geologists see how far west the Avalon Terrane extends below the thrust sheets. A few smaller windows exposing gneisses of the Waterford Group exist south of the Willimantic Dome.

The overlying thrust sheets are preserved, rather than eroded, at the Hopyard Klippe because they make a slight downward dip. In the middle of the fold is a remnant of the Middletown Formation of the Bronson Hill volcanic arc, well east of its main outcrop area.

Avalonia: A Geologist's Paradise

The Avalon Terrane is found in Europe, the British Isles, and Ireland, and from eastern Canada south to Georgia. It takes its name from the Avalon Peninsula in Newfoundland where, in the mid-1960s, Harold "Hank" Williams examined whether Long Peninsula, a major mountain range of western Newfoundland, contains the same rocks as the Avalon Peninsula of eastern Newfoundland. It had been assumed that both mountain ranges were the northern extension of the Appalachian Mountains, which consist of parallel ranges of similar rocks. When the ages of the crystalline rocks of the Newfoundland mountains were dated, Williams discovered that granites in the Long Peninsula were of Middle Proterozoic age or older (1.2 billion years or more), whereas the rocks of the Avalon Peninsula were of Late Proterozoic age (about 620 million years old). Williams concluded that the much younger rocks of the Avalon Peninsula in eastern Newfoundland must represent a block that had become attached to the eastern margin of the northern Appalachians. This was a revolutionary idea in the 1960s, but it fit well with the emerging theory of plate tectonics. Geologists soon recognized many similarities between the rocks of eastern Newfoundland and the 600-million-year-old granites and volcanic rocks of New England's coastal region. And hence the term Avalon Terrane entered the lexicon of New England geologists.

The chemistry of the igneous rocks of the Avalon Terrane is characteristic of igneous rocks that form at convergent plate margins above a subduction zone. Geologists think that Avalonia was a volcanic island chain or small continent off the coast of the supercontinent Gondwana. The granites, known in Rhode Island as the Esmond Igneous Suite, give age dates of 610 and 595 million years. The associated volcanic rocks give dates of 600 million years. These granites intruded the oldest rocks of the Avalon Terrane—volcanic sediments of the Price Neck Formation as well as quartzite, marble, and associated dark schists of the Blackstone and Harmony Groups. These were originally deposited as sands, muds, and lime on the continental shelf of Gondwana, possibly between 800 and 700 million years ago. These Late Proterozoic rocks and fossiliferous early Paleozoic rocks define the Avalon Terrane in New England.

The sedimentary strata overlying the granites of the Avalon Peninsula in Newfoundland contain fossils of animals that lived in Cambrian time, about 540 to 490 million years ago, including trilobites. The very large *Paradoxides* trilobite is considered diagnostic of the Avalon Terrane—if you find it, you've found Avalonian rocks. *Skehanos*, a diagnostic trilobite genus, is assigned an age of 509 to 505 million years.

Since about 1845 a number of trilobites of Avalonian type have been found widely in southeastern Massachusetts as well as in the Maritime Provinces of Canada. In 1975, a coal-related geological investigation turned up complete trilobites in the dark Cambrian phyllites in the vicinity of Jamestown, Rhode Island, on southern Conanicut Island. This was the first report of trilobites in the state and served to identify the Avalon Terrane there. See **RI 138 and RI 24: Tiverton—South Kingstown** for more on the story behind this find.

An extinct type of mollusk known as a *hyolith* occurs in the Early Cambrian strata of Hoppin Hill near Attleboro, Massachusetts, as well as in the Pirate Cove Marble of Newport, Rhode Island. Early forms of these animals lived before trilobites appeared.

The Avalon Terrane of Rhode Island and Connecticut is sometimes referred to as the Avalon Superterrane and subdivided into two subterranes, the Esmond-Dedham and the Hope Valley. The north-trending Hope Valley Shear Zone, which runs from near Framingham, in eastern Massachusetts, southward through eastern Connecticut and western Rhode Island, divides the two subterranes. Along and near the shear

A scale model of a Middle Cambrian, 505-million-year-old trilobite, Skehanos quadrangularis *(Whitfield). The original specimen, collected in 1884 from the Weymouth Formation in Hayward Quarry in Massachusetts, is 1.75 inches long.*

zone, the Esmond rocks have developed conspicuous mineral alignment and prominent foliation, indicating that rocks have slid past one another. The shear zone is younger than the 380- to 370-million-year-old Scituate Batholith of Rhode Island, whose southwest end was sheared away in the shear zone, but older than the 275-million-year-old Narragansett Pier Granite, which truncates the southern end of the shear zone.

The granitic plutonic rocks of the Hope Valley Subterrane have been intensely deformed by folding. These igneous rocks, which alternate with bands of Plainfield Formation, have swirls resembling a layered tectonic stew. They have clearly undergone intense mixing on a remarkable scale. By contrast, the 600-million-year-old granite of the Esmond

Age (in millions of years)	Hope Valley Subterrane	Esmond-Dedham Subterrane
Permian	Potter Hill Granite Gneiss — Westerly Granite — Narragansett Pier Granite (275) *(spanning both subterranes)*	
— 290 —		
Pennsylvanian		Narragansett Bay Group — Dighton Conglomerate, Rhode Island Formation, Wamsutta Formation, Purgatory Conglomerate, Sachuest Arkose, Pondville Conglomerate
— 323 —		
Mississippian		Cumberland Granite
— 354 —		
Devonian		Scituate Igneous Suite (380 to 370) — Spencer Hill Volcanics
— 417 —		
Silurian		
— 443 —		
Ordovician		Conanicut Group — Dutch Is. Harbor Fm., Fort Burnside Fm., Jamestown Fm.
— 490 —		
Cambrian	HOPE VALLEY SHEAR ZONE	East Passage Formation — Pirate Cove Formation
— 543 —		cumberlandite — Newport Neck Formation
600	Sterling Plutonic Suite — Hope Valley Alaskite	Esmond Igneous Suite	BEAVERHEAD FAULT	Southeastern R.I. granites — Newport Granite (595), Bulgarmarsh Granite, Metacom Gr. Gneiss
Late Proterozoic	Waterford Group — Rope Ferry Gneiss, New London Gneiss, Mamacoke Formation / Plainfield Formation	Blackstone Group — Harmony Group		Price Neck Formation

Rocks in rust type originated on the Avalon microcontinent. Those in black formed after Avalonia was melded to Laurentia.

Igneous Suite of Rhode Island and the Dedham Granite of Massachusetts, the main components of the Esmond-Dedham Subterrane, appear more homogeneous and less deformed even though they too are commonly foliated and lineated.

Narragansett Basin

After the Avalon Terrane was accreted to Laurentia, rift basins formed and filled with sediments. The Norfolk Basin is entirely in Massachusetts, the Narragansett and Woonsocket Basins extend from Massachusetts into Rhode Island, and the small North Scituate Basin is entirely in Rhode Island. Rift basins form when the earth's crust is stretched apart by tectonic forces. Most sediments in the basins are of Pennsylvanian age, about 310 to 290 million years old, but the rifting may have begun much earlier. In 2003, it was discovered that the lower layers of the Wamsutta Formation of the Narragansett Basin contains rhyolite volcanics dated at 373 million years, 60 million years older than the sedimentary layers containing late

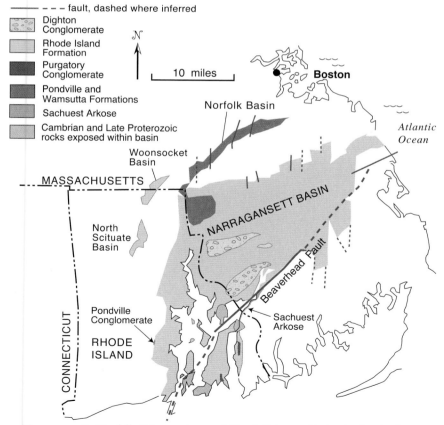

Narragansett, Norfolk, Woonsocket, and North Scituate Basins in the Avalon Terrane. —Modified from Skehan and others, 1986; Murray and others, 2004

Pennsylvanian floras higher up in the basin sequence. The geochemistry of the rhyolite and associated basalt is characteristic of rocks that precede rifting. The 380- to 370-million-year-old Scituate Batholith, which fills much of Rhode Island west of Narragansett Bay, may also be associated with the onset of rifting. This rifting activity produced swampy basins and uplifted fault blocks. Erosion of the uplifted land filled the basins with great thicknesses of sediments—alluvium, sand, and mud—all of which are terrestrial, which means they were deposited on land or in freshwater, not in a sea.

The Narragansett Basin, by far the largest coal basin in the region, occupies almost 1,000 square miles, much of it low-lying, swampy forests in Rhode Island. From 1769, when British troops warmed themselves using coal dug locally in Newport, to recent times, the possibility of mining coal in the Narragansett Basin has attracted attention. In Massachusetts and Rhode Island about forty-two prospects and mines dot the margins of the basin. Coal was once mined for steam engines and domestic use, and several mines in Portsmouth, Rhode Island, produced an estimated 1.1 million tons of coal, primarily for copper smelting, in the nineteenth and twentieth centuries.

During petroleum shortages beginning around 1974, the New England office of the U.S. Department of Energy planned a program to explore the Narragansett Basin resources. In assessing the potential for coal in the Narragansett Basin as an energy resource, a limiting factor is that large parts of the basin have a substantial and increasing population; in addition, large parts are covered with glacial till, outwash, and extensive swamplands. Given these limitations, it seems that short of a severe national energy emergency, it would not be feasible to recover these resources.

Before the Alleghanian mountain building event

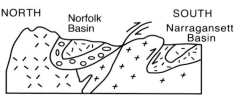

Fault-block basins in Late Proterozoic granites. The basins filled with sediments before the tectonic collision that caused the Alleghanian mountain building event. —Modified from Skehan and others, 1986; Skehan, 1983

Heat and pressure from deep burial metamorphose peat deposits into coal. In this region, enormous peat deposits formed from abundant vegetation growing in great freshwater swamps and marshlands in the basins, similar to the process whereby peat is forming today in the bayous of the lush Mississippi River delta. There are several grades of coal: Bituminous coal forms between 100 and 200 degrees Celsius, anthracite forms between 200 and 300 degrees Celsius, and meta-anthracite forms above 300 degrees Celsius. At even higher temperatures and pressures, the mineral graphite forms.

The rocks of the Narragansett Basin range from essentially unmetamorphosed in the north to high-grade sillimanite zones of metamorphism in the southwest. As recently as the mid-1970s, the metamorphism in the sedimentary rocks of the Narragansett Basin was thought to be contact metamorphism associated with the Narragansett Pier Granite along the southern Rhode Island coast. Geologists now realize that the Alleghanian mountain building event, which peaked about 290 million years ago, metamorphosed the rocks and *triggered* the melting and formation of the Narragansett Pier Granite! During the Alleghanian event, the Iapetus Ocean disappeared as Gondwana collided with the east coast of North America, forming the supercontinent Pangea.

Geologists think another chunk of land also collided with New England. It may have been the Meguma Terrane, which crops out in Nova Scotia and comprises submerged parts of the continental shelf in the Bay of Maine. The collision buckled the Narragansett Basin into a crescent convex to the northwest. Some Cambrian and Late Proterozoic rocks of the Avalon microcontinent were shoved over the top of the basin sediments, while the lower part of the Meguma microcontinent was dragged beneath Avalonia.

Metamorphism swept across the region from west to east over periods of millions of years during late Paleozoic and early Mesozoic time. The effects of the continental collision are most spectacularly developed along the coast of western Rhode Island and, in a much more complex way, in coastal Connecticut south of the Honey Hill Fault Zone.

During metamorphism, clay and associated minerals in shaley rocks are transformed into metamorphic minerals such as chlorite, chloritoid, garnet, staurolite, and sillimanite. The minerals that form depend on the original chemical composition of the rock as well as the temperature and pressure that prevail during the transformation process.

Rocks in the chlorite zone in the northern part of the basin were least affected by the temperature and pressure of the collision. Rocks in the garnet, staurolite, and sillimanite zones south of Warwick experienced the greatest combination of temperature and pressure. The metamorphic minerals tell us that the pile of thrust sheets in the northern part of the

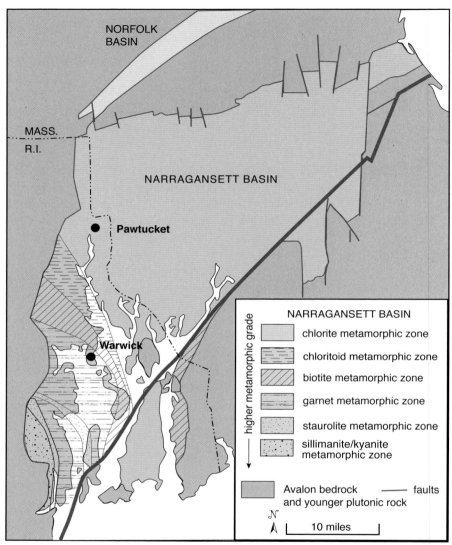

Metamorphic zones of the Narragansett Basin.
—Modified from Murray and others, 2004

Narragansett Basin was rather thin, so the rocks below were not buried as deeply as they were farther south. The zones of higher temperature and pressure near Cranston and Warwick mean that piles of thrust sheets thick enough to form mountains accumulated there. The highest mountains were located in the southwestern Narragansett Basin and farther south and west in the staurolite and sillimanite-kyanite zones. In that direction, temperatures and pressures became so great that rocks melted and formed igneous batholiths.

High temperatures beneath the 20-mile-thick stack of thrust sheets piled on top of the basin drove off most of the combustible gases, such as methane, converting the original coal to meta-anthracite. Its low volatile content makes meta-anthracite very hard to ignite, but once started it burns extremely hot. The sulfur content is also low. In a ditty titled *Meditations on Coal*, William Cullen Bryant wrote unflatteringly of this coal's powers of ignition:

> In the conflagration at the end of the world
> The last thing to burn will be Rhode Island coal.

The deformation of the Narragansett Basin was much more intense than the deformation in the anthracite region of northeastern Pennsylvania and the bituminous Appalachian coal basin, which were also metamorphosed during the Alleghanian mountain building event. The Narragansett Basin was probably much closer to the continent that slammed into North America than either of the other two coal basins. Two episodes of metamorphic heating and pressure, both from the Alleghanian event, have been recorded in the coal of the southern Narragansett Basin.

Rocks of the Narragansett Basin

The sediments of the Narragansett Basin are divided into six major formations. The coal-bearing Rhode Island Formation, in the middle, makes up the bulk of the Pennsylvanian strata.

ROCK UNITS		Geologic Time Period	Millions of years before present
North Narragansett Basin	South Narragansett Basin		
Dighton Conglomerate / Rhode Island Formation	Rhode Island Formation	LATE PENNSYLVANIAN	300
	Sachuest Arkose / Purgatory Conglomerate	MIDDLE PENNSYLVANIAN	310
Pondville Conglomerate / Wamsutta Formation		EARLY PENNSYLVANIAN	320

Rock units by basin and age. —Modified from Murray and others, 2004

Pondville Conglomerate. The Pondville Conglomerate rests on an eroded surface of igneous rocks. It was probably an alluvial fan deposit laid down near the heads of canyons. The basal unit of the Pondville Conglomerate in the northern and western Narragansett Basin is gray to greenish conglomerate in a sandy matrix interbedded with granular sandstone and pebbly sandstone. The conglomerate forms lens-shaped pods along the basin margin. The time of earliest deposition in the western and northern part of the basin is about 310 million years ago. The lack of diagnostic fossils in layers below fossiliferous Pennsylvanian-age coal-bearing strata, however, leaves the door open to possible new information from future research. The Pondville grades laterally into, and is overlain by, redbeds of the Wamsutta Formation.

Wamsutta Formation. Plant fossils 300 million years old have been found in redbeds in the upper part of the Wamsutta Formation in Attleboro, near the Rhode Island border. This site is correlated in age with three nearby fossil localities in the lower part of the Rhode Island formation in Pawtucket, Rhode Island, and nearby sites in the northern part of the basin. These redbeds consist of red siltstone, shale, and conglomerates, with locally abundant volcanic detritus. Rhyolite lava flows in the lower part of the Wamsutta Formation have been dated at 373 million years old, far older than the fossils in the upper redbeds.

Sachuest Arkose. Arkose is a sandstone or conglomerate containing fragments of feldspar, usually weathered from granite. Named for Sachuest Point in Rhode Island, the Sachuest Arkose forms the base of the Pennsylvanian-age coal basin sequence of the southeastern part of Narragansett Basin from Tiverton to Jamestown, Rhode Island. It probably represents the chemically eroded soil that developed on the surface of the older rocks. This pebbly arkosic sandstone with interlayered dark slate contains distinctive dark or smoky quartz grains and white to gray, weathered feldspars that have been converted to fine mica or kaolin clay. Both the smoky quartz and the kaolinized feldspars are probably from the granite below the Sachuest Arkose.

Purgatory Conglomerate. Glassy quartzite boulders and cobbles dominate the coarse conglomerates at Purgatory Chasm in the southeastern part of the basin. The Purgatory Conglomerate was deposited in alluvial fans along the basin's edge prior to deposition of the Rhode Island Formation. This very coarse-grained conglomerate is interbedded with thin sandstone and magnetite-rich sandstone lenses.

The Purgatory Conglomerate is well known for its "stretched" pebbles, which have not actually been stretched but rather were slenderized by dissolution of quartz. Pressure at right angles to the long axis of the ellipse-shaped pebbles and boulders caused the dissolution.

Rhode Island Formation. The Rhode Island Formation, which makes up the bulk of the deposits in both the northern and southern Narragansett Basin, was laid down between 390 and 300 million years ago. The northern part of the formation consists of gray to black slate and phyllite, fine- to coarse-grained quartz sandstone, pebbly sandstone, slate, and interbedded conglomerate with beds of carbonaceous slate, anthracite, and meta-anthracite.

In the southern part of the basin in Portsmouth, Rhode Island, east of the Beaverhead Fault, the rocks are metamorphosed sandstone and conglomerate, and carbonaceous slate. Anthracite and meta-anthracite beds several feet thick were mined to depths of 700 feet and a distance of 2,900 feet down-dip, and for nearly 1 mile perpendicular to the dip. Coal and coaly beds up to 40 feet thick have been reported in the crests of folds. On the limbs of folds, coaly beds are commonly thinner. The thickening and thinning is due to plastic flow, similar to how warm taffy flows. In the southwestern part of the basin, the intensity of metamorphism increases sharply, rising to the sillimanite zone, where deposits that once were coal have been metamorphosed to graphite.

Because of the limited and sporadic exposure of the Rhode Island Formation due to glacial cover and swamp deposits, as well as complications resulting from intense deformation by folding and thrust faulting, reliable estimates of stratigraphic thicknesses are lacking. Estimates of thickness,

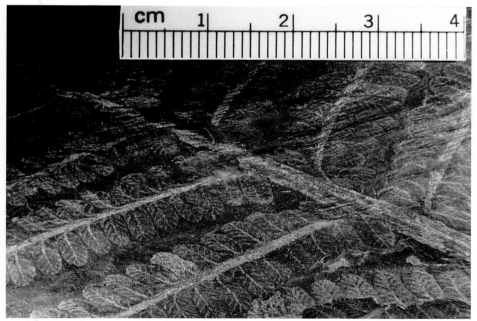

This Pennsylvanian-age fossil of a tree fern (Pecopteris hemiteliodes) *from the Rhode Island Formation at Cliffwalk in Newport, Rhode Island, is now housed in the Pratt Museum at Amherst College.* —Edward S. Belt photo

based on borings, quarries, and mines, range from 10,000 to 20,000 feet. Because of duplication due to complex folding and faulting in various parts of the basin, the actual thickness may be closer to 10,000 feet.

The Rhode Island Formation has yielded many plant fossils useful in determining the relative age of the rocks. Swamp mud buried the plant remains, protecting them from oxidation and erosion. Over time, heat and pressure turned the swamp mud to stone, and the organic plant remains became carbon residue. The plant impressions are visible on bedding surfaces.

Dighton Conglomerate. The 1,500-foot-thick Dighton Conglomerate fills three synclinal structures in the Narragansett Basin. It rests on top of the Rhode Island Formation, capping the basin strata. A gray conglomerate like the Purgatory, the Dighton consists predominantly of quartzite and vein-quartz clasts in a sand-size matrix.

Glaciation

The Late Wisconsinan ice sheet moved south-southeast across eastern Connecticut and Rhode Island about 25,000 years ago and reached as far south as Block Island before melting back. In early stages of deglaciation of the coastal area, the ice front melted back slowly onto the mainland of Connecticut and Rhode Island. This slow ice retreat gave rise to recessional moraines along the coast between 19,000 and 18,000 years ago. At the same time the moraines were forming, deltas were being laid down by rivers in south-draining valleys. At least a dozen lakes ponded behind sediment dams north of the deposits in coastal areas, and ice-dammed glacial lakes formed in north-draining valleys.

Rhode Island and eastern Connecticut were entirely deglaciated between 18,000 and 16,000 years ago, while ice lingered on in the western uplands and in the Hartford Basin. The oldest carbon-14 dates obtained so far in Connecticut are 15,000 years at Rogers Lake in Old Lyme and Totoket Bog in North Branford, and 15,200 years at Cedar Swamp in Ledyard. These dated horizons record tundra vegetation that developed after the ice sheet retreated from the area.

— Road Guides in Rhode Island —

Interstate 95
Pawtucket—Connecticut State Line
50 MILES

Between the Massachusetts border and West Warwick, I-95 crosses the western part of the Narragansett Basin of Pennsylvanian age. The general setting of the basin is discussed in the introduction to this chapter.

Coal Mine Collapse

Coal mining occurred intermittently in Rhode Island throughout the nineteenth and twentieth centuries. Much of this mining was done underground. The urban area around Providence has been built over the top of

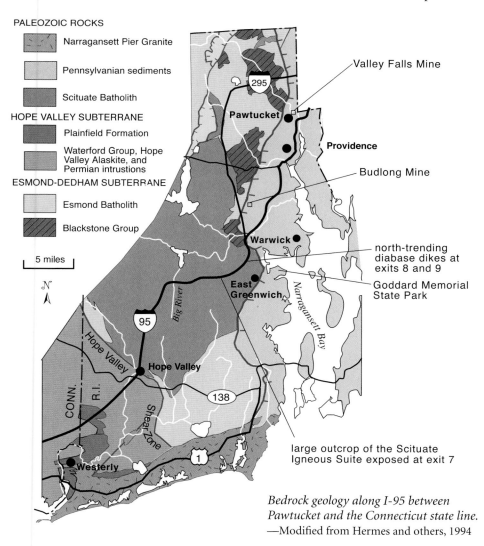

Bedrock geology along I-95 between Pawtucket and the Connecticut state line.
—Modified from Hermes and others, 1994

many of these long-forgotten mines. We are reminded of this hazard only when the ground collapses.

An underground mine has large excavated areas. Miners remove as much of the coal as they can without jeopardizing their safety, leaving behind pillars of coal to support the overburden of rock and soil. Sometimes they remove too much and the ground above collapses or becomes vulnerable to future collapse, especially when burdened with the streets and buildings of a large metropolis.

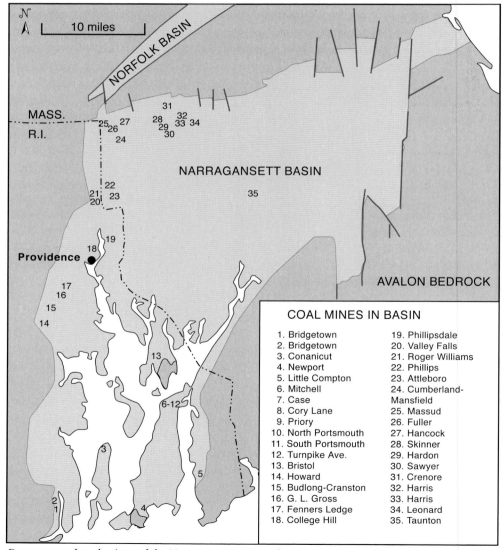

COAL MINES IN BASIN

1. Bridgetown	19. Phillipsdale
2. Bridgetown	20. Valley Falls
3. Conanicut	21. Roger Williams
4. Newport	22. Phillips
5. Little Compton	23. Attleboro
6. Mitchell	24. Cumberland-
7. Case	Mansfield
8. Cory Lane	25. Massud
9. Priory	26. Fuller
10. North Portsmouth	27. Hancock
11. South Portsmouth	28. Skinner
12. Turnpike Ave.	29. Hardon
13. Bristol	30. Sawyer
14. Howard	31. Crenore
15. Budlong-Cranston	32. Harris
16. G. L. Gross	33. Harris
17. Fenners Ledge	34. Leonard
18. College Hill	35. Taunton

Prospects and coal mines of the Narragansett Basin cluster near the western margin, where the coal-bearing portion of the Rhode Island Formation is best exposed. —Modified from Chase, 1978

Notable collapses began in the Providence area in the 1970s. In the spring of 1979, a construction area along the east side of Chase Street broke through into a substantial cavity below. This locality, one block northwest of Cumberland Town Hall and about 0.1 mile from the Blackstone River, is above the Valley Falls Mine. The fairly extensive activity associated with this mine began in 1847 with the production of about 500 tons of coal. By 1853 the underground mine had been extended to a depth of 500 feet, penetrating five coal beds and a 30-foot "nest" of coal. The thick zone of coal was probably created by flowage into the crest of a fold.

In the summer of 1979, the ground collapsed a block and a half northwest of the above site, this time at a home on Macondray Street. That Saturday morning the family's young son looked out his second floor bedroom window then ran to his parents' bedroom shouting, "Daddy, our backyard is gone!" As neatly as if scored by a knife, the remnants of the backyard lawn, outlined by a square white fence, had collapsed. In its place was a hole.

Another collapse occurred in August 1981, this time taking the corner of Club Luzitania with it. The discovery of other areas with the potential to collapse led to a major stabilization effort in 1983 by the U.S. Office of Surface Mining. By December of that year, 500 tons of concrete had been injected into the mine opening. Despite these efforts, collapsing mines continue to be a problem. A parking lot at the Garden City shopping mall collapsed in July 2001 above part of the Budlong-Cranston Mine. The collapsed area has been filled in and stabilized to prevent any further accidents.

Narragansett Bay

The many arms of Narragansett Bay reach far into Rhode Island. The bay is an estuary; rivers carry fresh water into the bay, diluting the seawater. Two large islands sit at the bay's mouth, creating three separate passages into the inner bay. Ships follow the East Passage, between Conanicut and Aquidneck Islands, because it's the deepest, averaging about 44 feet. (Confusingly, the official name of Aquidneck Island is Rhode Island, but it's commonly referred to as Aquidneck Island to distinguish it from the state.) Around 10,000 years ago, after glacial ice was no longer in Rhode Island, the bay had not yet filled with seawater. As sea levels rose due to melting of the ice, the bay probably reached its current level by about 5,000 years ago. The bay is smaller now than it once was as cities have filled in shallow areas near the shore, extending the urban area into the bay. In addition, rivers continue to carry sediment downstream from the uplands, depositing it into the bay.

As the ice melted back to the north, a glacial lake occupied Narragansett Bay. Potowomut Neck in Warwick, the location of Goddard Memorial

State Park, is a delta plain, formed where a river flowed into the glacial lake and deposited sediment. Providence also occupies a delta plain built into the glacial lake in Narragansett Bay.

The Pawtuxet River, which drains nearly one-fourth of Rhode Island, flows eastward in a valley in crystalline bedrock until it reaches the Natick area in West Warwick, where the river flows across glacial meltwater sediments that fill the Narragansett Basin.

Blackstone Group at Warwick

The faulted western edge of the Narragansett Basin brushes the southern ramps of exit 12 of I-95 and runs right through exit 1 of I-295, where the two interstate highways join. Blackstone Group metamorphic rocks, including glassy quartzite, are exposed in large highway cuts on the northward approach to the interchange at exit 12 on I-95. Except for a long set of Blackstone exposures near US 1 in South Kingstown, rocks of that group are not exposed south of Warwick.

Scituate Igneous Suite

Bedrock near I-95 south of Warwick and north of Hope Valley is primarily igneous rocks of the Devonian Scituate Igneous Suite, including volcanic rocks. The granite of the Scituate Igneous Suite intruded the Esmond Igneous Suite of Late Proterozoic age, but the two look very similar, so for many years they were both mapped as the Esmond. Age dates obtained in the early 1990s, however, showed that the Scituate Igneous Suite is 380 to 370 million years old. Its composition is alkaline, which is characteristic of a granite that forms below a rift, an area where the earth's crust is pulling apart. The rifting may have caused the earth's crust to collapse, forming the Narragansett Basin.

The Scituate Batholith contains several varieties of granite that are gray to pink and range from fine-grained to coarse-grained with larger crystals mixed in a matrix of smaller crystals. Most contain biotite. Others also have hornblende, as well as minerals characteristic of alkaline granites, such as riebeckite and aegirine. Some mineral grains are aligned, indicative of compressive flattening or shearing. Foliation is widely present in this region, especially near the Hope Valley Shear Zone, which truncates the Scituate Batholith, indicating that the shear zone is younger than the intrusion.

The discovery that the Scituate Batholith is of Devonian age led to additional searches for igneous rocks of Devonian and Mississippian age in the region. Rift volcanics of Devonian age may lie beneath the Pennsylvanian-age coal basin, and some volcanics are exposed in East Greenwich, especially near the big bend in I-95 near exit 9 and east of RI 4 as far south as RI 402 in Frenchtown. These volcanic rocks, formerly called the Spencer Hill Volcanics after the hill north and west of the junction of I-94 and RI 4, are now mapped as part of the Scituate Igneous Suite.

The volcanic rocks include gray, pink, greenish, and purplish fragmental sediments such as breccia and conglomerate, some of which may have formed as ash flow tuffs or pyroclastic flows. These rocks are typically rich in quartz. Some are pink to gray rhyolite lavas with large crystals of quartz. The presence of volcanic rocks on the edge of the Narragansett Basin suggests that it may have experienced spectacular fireworks in Devonian time.

Granite of the Scituate Igneous Suite on RI 165 on the crest of a hill 0.8 mile east of Escoheag Hill Road and Woody Hill Road in Exeter, 2.7 miles east of the state border. The horizontal lines (bottom photo) are joints. The close-up (right) shows large crystals of feldspar.

Although glacial deposits are widespread over large parts of southern Rhode Island, many substantial outcrops of granite of the Scituate Igneous Suite are exposed in localities accessible from roads other than I-95. Large outcrops in roadcuts just east of exit 7 are near the New London Turnpike at its intersection with I-95 on the East Greenwich–West Greenwich line.

Diabase Dikes

North-trending diabase dikes were exposed during construction of I-95 at exits 9, 8, and 7. These dikes were filled with magma that rose to the surface of the earth during the opening of the Atlantic Ocean beginning about 200 million years ago. This rifting split the supercontinent Pangea apart and occurred nearly 200 million years later than the rifting that generated the Scituate Batholith. Smaller rift basins, including the Hartford Basin, formed at the same time along the edge of the major rift zone in the Atlantic Ocean.

Glacial Doings at Big River

Glacial deposits are widespread over large parts of southern Rhode Island near I-95. Big River, a tributary of the Flat River, flows north through the Big River Wildlife Management Area of West Greenwich. The Late Wisconsinan ice sheet receded through this area about 17,000 years ago as it was melting. Once the southern edge of the ice was north of the southern drainage divide of Big River, meltwater ponded against the edge of the ice because the land slopes north here. Small ponds developed in the Nooseneck River, Raccoon Brook, and Congdon River drainages. A larger lake, called Glacial Lake Mishnock, formed in the Big River drainage and to the east in the vicinity of the present Lake Mishnock, Mishnock Swamp, and Tiogue Lake, north of I-95 between exits 6 and 7.

Nooseneck Hill, on the east side of I-95 north of exit 5, is a drumlin. Other drumlins in the area include Weaver Hill, west of Big River on the border of West Greenwich and Coventry, and Raccoon Hill, Hopkins Hill, and the northern part of Hungry Hill (at exit 6).

Hope Valley Shear Zone

Rock formations of westernmost Rhode Island, part of the Hope Valley Subterrane, are much more intensely sheared and faulted than those of the Esmond-Dedham Subterrane to the east. The rocks in westernmost Rhode Island have been texturized by rock masses sliding past each other along the Hope Valley Shear Zone, a north-trending arcuate feature. I-95 crosses the shear zone near Hope Valley. The south end of the Hope Valley Shear Zone was swallowed up by the intrusion of the Narragansett Pier Granite about 275 million years ago. This means the shear zone is older than the Narragansett Pier Granite. The shear zone is younger than the 380- to 370-million-year-old, Devonian-age Scituate Batholith, which had its southwest end sheared away. The Late Proterozoic igneous and metasedimentary rock units of the Hope Valley Subterrane, west of the Hope Valley Shear Zone, trend in a northerly direction and are parallel to the shear zone.

Southwest of the Hope Valley Shear Zone, I-95 crosses Late Proterozoic granitic gneiss with a calcium feldspar content that indicates it was generated in a subduction-related tectonic event. Just east of the Connecticut border, I-95 crosses over a large patch of the Plainfield Formation, a common rock in the Hope Valley Subterrane.

US 1
Narragansett—Westerly
22 MILES

Prior to the establishment of the Interstate Highway System, US 1 was the main travel route on the East Coast. It went from Houlton, Maine, to Key West, Florida. US 1 in Rhode Island, never more than a stone's throw from Narragansett Bay or Block Island Sound, is now an eccentric mix of partially renovated inner city industrial complexes and historical and recreational parks.

Charlestown Moraine

US 1 follows the southern edge of the Charlestown moraine across most of southern Rhode Island west of Narragansett Bay. This moraine extends from Wakefield to Watch Hill. It's a continuation of the Harbor Hill– Fishers Island moraine, the recessional moraine on the north shore of Long Island. It was deposited about 19,000 years ago during a cold period that momentarily stopped recession of the glacier. Meltwater from the stationary ice flowed into the glacial lake in Block Island Sound.

The Matunuck Hills area, north of US 1 and southeast of Worden Pond, is hummocky terrain along the moraine crest. The many small water bodies are kettle ponds, circular depressions formed where ice chunks from the glacier were buried in till and outwash, and then melted. The hilly Charlestown moraine is a drainage divide. Streams north of it drain into the Pawcatuck River, and streams south of it flow into saltwater ponds behind the barrier beaches along the Rhode Island seashore.

Worden Pond, Watchaug Pond, and Great Swamp

When ice retreated north of the Charlestown moraine, glacial lakes formed as meltwater was impounded by the morainal barrier. Glacial lake sediments of mud, silt, and sand were deposited north of the moraine, and now this flat area is home to many lakes and swamps. Worden Pond and Great

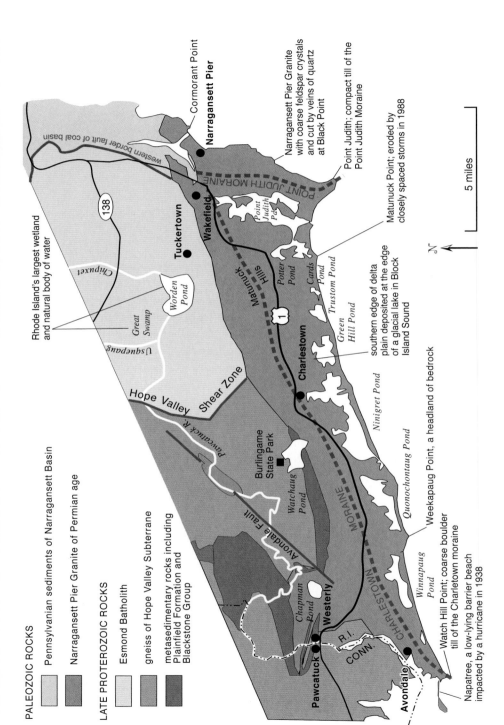

PALEOZOIC ROCKS

Pennsylvanian sediments of Narragansett Basin

Narragansett Pier Granite of Permian age

LATE PROTEROZOIC ROCKS

Esmond Batholith

gneiss of Hope Valley Subterrane

metasedimentary rocks including Plainfield Formation and Blackstone Group

Rhode Island's largest wetland and natural body of water

western border fault of coal basin

Cormorant Point

Narragansett Pier

Narragansett Pier Granite with coarse feldspar crystals and cut by veins of quartz at Black Point

Point Judith; compact till of the Point Judith Moraine

POINT JUDITH MORAINE

Matunuck Point; eroded by closely spaced storms in 1988

Tuckertown

Wakefield

Chipuxet

Worden Pond

Great Swamp

Usquepaug

Hope Valley Shear Zone

Point Judith Pond

Matunuck Hills

Potter Pond

Cards Pond

Trustom Pond

Green Hill Pond

southern edge of delta plain deposited at the edge of a glacial lake in Block Island Sound

Charlestown

Ninigret Pond

Quonochontaug Pond

Weekapaug Point, a headland of bedrock

Burlingame State Park

Pawcatuck R.

Watchaug Pond

MORAINE

Avondale Fault

CHARLESTOWN

Winnapaug Pond

Chapman Pond

Westerly

Watch Hill Point; coarse boulder till of the Charlestown moraine

Pawcatuck

R.I.

CONN.

Avondale

Napatree, a low-lying barrier beach impacted by a hurricane in 1938

5 miles

N

Bedrock geology along US 1 between Narragansett and Westerly. —Modified from Hermes and others, 1994

Swamp occupy a flat expanse of glacial lake bottom sediments northwest of Tuckertown Four Corners. Watchaug Pond in Burlingame State Park also sits on lake-bottom sediments just north of the moraine.

The Usquepaug and Chipuxet Rivers, which flow into Great Swamp and Worden Pond from the north, have well-defined valleys to the north. South of the pond, however, glacial debris of the Charlestown moraine altered the paths of the rivers. Prior to glaciation they flowed south all the way to the sound, but after the pile of glacial sediment was left behind, the water from Great Swamp and Worden Pond flowed west as the Pawcatuck River along the north side of the moraine. Logs of wells nearby indicate that the surface of the bedrock lies at exceptionally great depths at several places along the Charlestown moraine. These deep bedrock surfaces mark the course of preglacial valleys that trended southward across the region.

Point Judith Neck

Point Judith Neck and the point itself are part of a recessional moraine deposit. Waves have carried away much of the finer material of the moraine, leaving behind a beach of mainly boulders. This north-trending moraine was deposited along the western edge of the Narragansett Bay lobe at the same time the Charlestown moraine was deposited. The angled junction between the two moraines is in the vicinity of Wakefield. The Point Judith moraine continues out to sea to the south of the point.

Narragansett Pier Granite

The pluton of the east-west-trending Narragansett Pier Granite is nearly 25 miles long and at least 2 to 3 miles wide along the southern coast of Rhode

Worden Pond is a remnant of a glacial lake.

Pegmatite dikes cut Narragansett Pier Granite at Black Point Fishing Area north of Scarborough State Beach on Judith Neck.

Island west of Narragansett Bay. The granite is mainly hidden beneath a cover of glacial outwash, till, and barrier beaches, but you can see it on the beach at Narragansett Pier and at Cormorant Point. This granite crystallized 275 million years ago. A roof pendant of sedimentary rock caught by the intruding granite contains 296- and 299-million-year-old plant fossils. The granite truncates the Hope Valley Shear Zone, which tells us the shear zone formed before 275 million years ago.

The Narragansett Pier Granite also can be found in small domes along the southern Connecticut shore. In this region, the granite is intimately mixed with quartzite of the Plainfield Formation of Late Proterozoic age, granite gneiss of the Waterford Group of Late Proterozoic age, and Potter Hill Granite Gneiss, which is in the same age range as the Narragansett Pier Granite.

The Narragansett Pier Granite has several distinct phases. The white to gray, fine-grained phase of the granite crops out near the picturesque village of Narragansett Pier. Because this is near the edge of the pluton, it cooled more quickly and has smaller crystals than the other phases. The second major phase of the rock is a medium-grained, pink and light gray granite. In places it contains well-formed large crystals of pink feldspar, commonly about 0.8 inch long. Dominant minerals are smoky quartz, salmon-colored microcline, and white plagioclase. It typically has less than 5 percent biotite. This phase extends westward from the eastern shore of Point Judith Neck north of Scarborough State Beach west for about 14 miles to Ninigret and Watchaug Ponds. The third phase is a colorful pink granite containing crystals of buff-color alkali feldspar and white plagioclase feldspar bigger than the other crystals in the rock. It occurs from 5 miles west of Burlingame State Park to the 12-mile-long, northeast-trending Avondale Fault in Westerly. There are abandoned quarries and roadcuts along RI 78, also known as the Westerly Bypass.

A 2-mile-long dike of Narragansett Pier Granite intrudes the northeast-trending Avondale Fault and forms dike segments parallel to it for 4 miles. The Avondale Fault formed late in the Alleghanian mountain building event, around the same time the Narragansett Pier Granite intruded.

Barrier Beaches and Headlands

From Point Judith to Napatree Point, the southwesternmost corner of Rhode Island, an essentially unbroken line of barrier beaches joins headlands of glacial debris underlain in places by bedrock. The beaches, narrow ridges of sand or gravel shaped by ocean currents, extend parallel to the shore. A body of saltwater usually separates the barrier beach from the mainland. Major salt ponds on the coast of Rhode Island, from east to west, are Point Judith, Potter, Cards, Trustom, Green Hill, Ninigret, Quonochontaug, and Winnapaug Ponds.

Bedrock underlies the headlands between western Winnapaug Pond and the western half of Ninigret Pond. A dike of fine-grained Westerly Granite occurs near Weekapaug Point, and medium-grained amphibolite gneiss occurs at the point. This gneiss resembles the east-trending belt of the Late Proterozoic Mamacoke Formation that extends from Westerly to Watchaug Pond and beyond. Evidence is lacking for the presence of bedrock beneath the beaches from the middle of Ninigret Pond to Point Judith.

Westerly Granite

Dikes of Westerly Granite intrude the rocks of southwestern Rhode Island and adjacent Pawcatuck, Connecticut. The Westerly Granite intruded in Permian time, at about the same time as the Narragansett Pier Granite. The very fine-grained, homogeneous, light gray Westerly Granite is perhaps one of the most thoroughly studied granites in the region from the point of view of its physical properties. The U.S. Geological Survey considers it to be the North American standard for granite because of its homogeneous character and general lack of post-crystallization structures. The structures of other granites are therefore discussed in comparison to the Westerly. Its fine grain and uniformity have also made it a popular building stone.

The east-trending dikes dip south, but some small bodies are irregular. T. Nelson Dale, a geologist with the U.S. Geological Survey in the early twentieth century, had the opportunity to see more active quarries than we do today. In 1908 he observed that the dikes of Westerly Granite vary in thickness from 50 to 150 feet. The rock from any one dike is remarkably uniform.

The Westerly Granite, a beautiful fine-grained rock, is an apt sculpture medium. During the mid-1960s, I had the good fortune to meet an Italian quarryman who at the time was ninety-two years old. In his youth, he had worked at extracting granite blocks that were fashioned into 40-foot

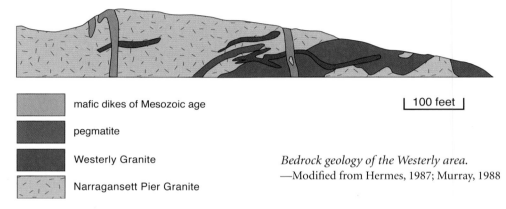

	mafic dikes of Mesozoic age
	pegmatite
	Westerly Granite
	Narragansett Pier Granite

| 100 feet |

Bedrock geology of the Westerly area.
—Modified from Hermes, 1987; Murray, 1988

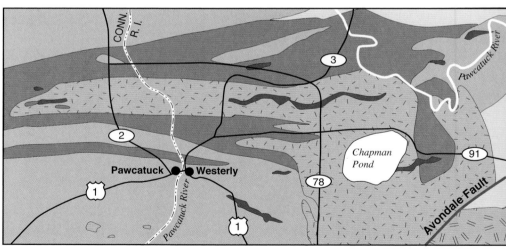

PERMIAN ROCKS

| | Westerly Granite |

Narragansett Pier Granite

| | pink biotite granite with equal grain size |
| | biotite granite with large crystals of feldspar |

LATE PROTEROZOIC ROCKS

	amphibolite gneiss
	granite gneiss
	Plainfield Formation and Blackstone Group

N

| 0.5 mile |

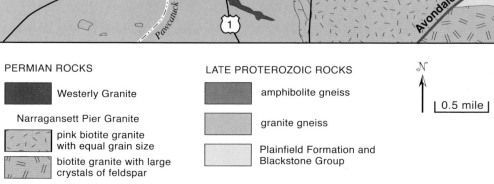

pillars for use, as he told me, in Penn Station, New York City. Sensing my interest in granite for architectural and other purposes, he took me to Sacred Heart Cemetery in Milford, Massachusetts, where he showed me many statues he had sculpted from Westerly Granite.

In Jewett City in Griswold, Connecticut, a 40-foot-high pillar supporting a statue of a World War II veteran stands at the junction of North and East Main Streets (the junction of CT 12 and CT 201). The monument consists of beautifully ornamented, hammered gray Westerly Granite of Permian age.

US 6 and US 44
East Providence—Connecticut State Line
20 MILES

The bedrock of northeastern Rhode Island is magnificently displayed along US 6 and US 44. Off-highway exposures throughout these highlands have been a bountiful source of information for geologists. US 6 and US 44 traverse the Esmond-Dedham Subterrane of the Avalon Terrane. During a subduction-related plate tectonic event, the 600-million-year-old Esmond Batholith intruded Late Proterozoic or older rocks that had formed on the continental shelf of Gondwana.

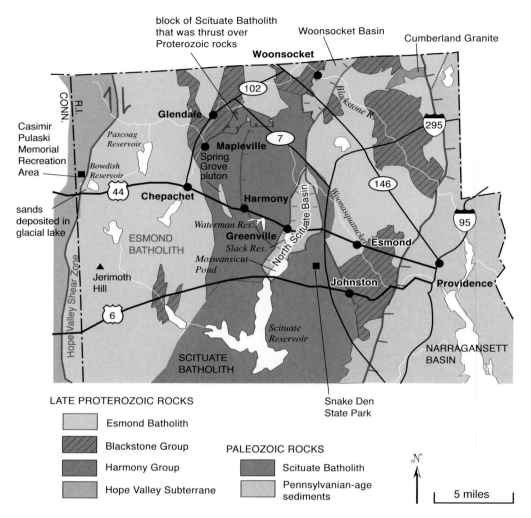

Bedrock geology of northern Rhode Island. —Modified from Hermes and others, 1994

The Late Proterozoic rocks have been strongly metamorphosed into gneiss and schist. They outcrop in northern Rhode Island and in places are roof pendants—pieces of rock that sit on top of, or between, areas of the Esmond Batholith. Geologists have placed the metamorphic rocks into the Harmony and Blackstone Groups. The question of the relative stratigraphic position of the Harmony and Blackstone Groups isn't completely resolved at present. Both groups of strata trend northwest.

The Blackstone Group, named for outcrops near the Blackstone River, consists of volcanic rocks and former sedimentary rocks that are now quartzite (formerly sand), calc-silicate and biotite schist (formerly limy sand), and marble (formerly limestone). The quartzite, called the Quinnville Quartzite, is gray, medium-grained, and homogeneous to thinly bedded.

Volcanic rocks in the Blackstone Group, including greenstone, are called the Hunting Hill volcanics, named for Hunting Hill, north of I-295 in Cumberland. Greenstone, formerly gabbro and basalt interlayered with other volcanic rocks, consists mainly of plagioclase and the green minerals epidote, actinolite, and chlorite. No wonder the rocks are green! Closely associated pillow basalts and serpentinite probably represent rift basin lavas and dikes formed by the breakup of the continental shelf as the 600-million-year-old Avalon volcanic arc was beginning to form along the margin of Gondwana.

The northwest-trending Blackstone sequence is bisected by I-295 in Cumberland, where well-exposed outcrops reveal that the group is in a major syncline. US 44 crosses Blackstone rocks east of the Woonasquatucket River. US 6 traverses a 3-mile stretch of these rocks between the faulted margin of the Narragansett Basin, where the road crosses the Woonasquatucket River, and a point just short of I-295. The first 2 miles are underlain by green to gray epidote and biotite schist interlayered with quartzite and marble. Just east of the Pocasset River on US 6 is a 1,000-foot-wide pluton of the Esmond Igneous Suite, which intruded the schist. West of the Pocasset River, the Blackstone Group is represented by gray, homogeneous to thin-bedded Quinnville Quartzite.

The Harmony Group, the other group of Proterozoic rocks, is named for the village northwest of Waterman Reservoir along US 44. Excellent roadcuts in dark gneisses are widely exposed in hills west of Greenville. The group consists of three distinctive formations in a large fold that extends from just south of US 6 in northern Scituate to the southern end of North Smithfield, north of US 44.

The Nipsachuck Formation, named after Nipsachuck Hill in North Smithfield, is in the core of the regional north-trending fold. This gray to tan, medium-grained granite gneiss has prominent streaks of biotite. The Absalona Formation, named for Absalona Hill just north of US 44 in Glocester, is a gray, medium- to coarse-grained biotite granite gneiss with large distinctive alkali feldspar crystals formed when the rock was metamorphosed. It contains small amounts of schist, amphibolite, and quartzite in layers and as isolated lenses or blocky masses. The Woonasquatucket Formation, named for the Woonasquatucket River, which flows from Smithfield, through Providence, and to the bay, probably represents a north-trending block of rock preserved along a normal fault. This distinctive rock is in part a grayish green, medium-grained schist. It resembles phyllite because the coarser minerals have been mechanically degraded.

Several igneous bodies occur within the roof pendant of Harmony Group rocks. A gabbro-diorite body in Harmony north of Waterman Reservoir may have affinities to a phase of cumberlandite. Near Chepachet, US 44 crosses the 3-mile-long Spring Grove igneous body of the Esmond Igneous Suite, which intrudes the roof pendant of Harmony rocks.

Esmond Granite Quarries

Granite quarries in the 600-million-year-old Esmond Batholith were once big business in Johnston. The town names Greystone and Graniteville speak of its importance, and the rock itself is named after the town of Esmond, just north of Graniteville. The Bare Ledge Quarry, in the northeast corner of Johnston just south of US 44 and east of exit 7 on I-295, is no longer in operation, but it supplied the pillars for the Providence Arcade, built in 1828. The 20-foot-tall columns were the largest in the country at that time. The granite crops out at the interchange of US 44 and I-295. Another good place to see granite of the Esmond Igneous Suite is at Lincoln Woods State Park.

The Esmond Batholith extends from the west margin of the Narragansett Basin west to the Hope Valley Shear Zone. It would make up the bulk of Rhode Island if not for the large Scituate Batholith that intruded it about 380 to 370 million years ago. The many rock types in the Esmond Batholith range from granite and granodiorite to tonalite, quartz-diorite, diorite, and gabbro. The granites vary in color from gray to pink, tan, and greenish. They consist predominantly of microcline, perthite, and plagioclase feldspars, quartz, and small amounts of other minerals. The darker, nongranitic rocks in the batholith, those with more iron and magnesium, are dark gray, purple or black, and medium- to coarse-grained. They contain the minerals plagioclase, quartz, clinopyroxene, hornblende, and olivine.

Scituate Batholith in Johnston and Scituate

The Scituate Batholith, a 30-mile-long by 27-mile-wide body of igneous rocks, punched upward through the Late Proterozoic Esmond Batholith about 380 to 370 million years ago. Rocks of the Scituate Batholith and Esmond Batholith look so much alike that they could not be distinguished until the 1990s, when isotopic dating studies showed the Scituate rocks to be more than 200 million years younger. The Scituate Igneous Suite consists of six different kinds of plutonic rocks. Fine-grained igneous rocks in the suite include rhyolite, porphyritic rocks, and other volcanic rocks.

Note that the Scituate Batholith is not the same thing as the North Scituate Basin of Pennsylvanian age, discussed on page 66. Both, however, are related to extensional tectonics. It's likely that the Pennsylvanian-age sediments filled basins created by the same stretching that brought the magma of the batholith near the earth's surface.

A north-pointing finger of granite of the Scituate Igneous Suite extends north of the main body and is crossed by US 6 and US 44 west of I-295. A 2,000-foot-wide gabbro-diorite body, possibly of Devonian age, extends

Augen gneiss of the Sterling Plutonic Suite with nearly horizontal foliation at Casimir Pulaski Memorial Recreation Area north of US 44.

Sandy beds of a glacial lake delta are exposed in 10- to 20-foot-high outcrops along an unpaved road on the west shore of Bowdish Reservoir about 0.2 mile north of US 44.

north from US 44 where the road runs along the northeastern edge of Waterman Reservoir. Snake Den State Park, west of I-295 between US 44 and US 6, boasts 15- to 35-foot-high cliffs of the Scituate Batholith.

A block of granite of the Scituate Igneous Suite southeast of the intersection of RI 7 and RI 102 in Glendale has been thrust onto rocks of the Harmony and Blackstone Groups, as well as onto the Late Proterozoic Esmond Batholith between Mapleville and Nasonville. The thrusting probably occurred during the Alleghanian mountain building event.

North Scituate Basin

The 4-mile-long and 1.5-mile-wide North Scituate Basin is a rift basin along the faulted, north-tapering edge of the Scituate Batholith. It is probably Pennsylvanian in age and may have formed at the same time as the Narragansett Basin. The two basins may even have been connected before erosion exposed the intervening rocks. Moswansicut Pond on US 6 and Slack Reservoir on US 44 are along the rifted eastern margin of the North Scituate Basin. The Scituate Batholith forms the eastern shore of the Moswansicut Pond.

Along US 44 in Greenville, rocks of the Blackstone Group and the Esmond and Scituate Igneous Suites form a series of thinly sliced fault blocks at the northern and southeastern end of the North Scituate Basin. The normal fault that forms its western margin dips steeply east in Greenville.

Esmond Rocks in Glocester and Foster

The Esmond Batholith lies between the western margin of the Harmony Group gneisses and the Hope Valley Shear Zone. It consists principally of augen granite gneiss with much smaller bodies of related plutonic rocks. *Augen* is German for "eye," and augen gneiss has eye- or lens-shaped potassium or sodium feldspar crystals about 0.4 inch in diameter. This is a tip-off that the rock is strongly deformed, with a foliation or lineation that penetrates the entire rock. If the large feldspars were not deformed, they would have a blocky shape rather than a lens shape. Minerals in the augen granite gneiss include sodium plagioclase, quartz, microcline or orthoclase feldspar, and biotite.

The Hope Valley Shear Zone marks the western edge of the Esmond Batholith. This zone formed during the Alleghanian mountain building event and juxtaposed the batholith against more deformed rocks of the Hope Valley Subterrane, which was once part of the Avalon microcontinent along with the Esmond-Dedham Subterrane. Along US 44 the Hope Valley Shear Zone lies 0.5 mile east of the Connecticut–Rhode Island state line.

Topping out at 812 feet, Jerimoth Hill, near the Connecticut border about midway between US 44 and US 6, is the highest point in Rhode Island. RI 101 crosses the north flank of the hill, which is composed of gneiss of the Esmond Batholith.

RI 138 and RI 24
Tiverton—South Kingston
30 MILES

In earlier times, Rhode Island was governed from two capitals. In winter, the capital was located in Providence, at the head of Narragansett Bay. In the hot summer months, the seat of government moved to Newport, with its cool onshore breezes blowing across a secure natural harbor. Bedrock headlands of Avalonian rocks at Newport Neck and Jamestown guard the harbor like Scylla and Charybdis, two monsters of Greek mythology that lived on either side of a narrow channel of water.

Southern Narragansett Bay has a distinctive sequence of Late Proterozoic and Cambrian strata originally deposited on the Avalon microcontinent. The strata and associated granites and dikes are well exposed in Newport and Jamestown. Pennsylvanian-age beds of the Narragansett Basin cover these older rocks to the north, and faults have disrupted their continuity as well, so southeastern Rhode Island is the only place to see them.

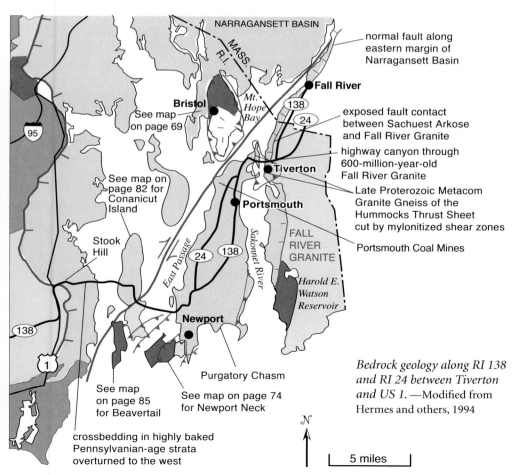

Bedrock geology along RI 138 and RI 24 between Tiverton and US 1. —Modified from Hermes and others, 1994

Fall River Granite at Tiverton

East of Mount Hope Bay, at the state line between Fall River, Massachusetts, and Tiverton, Rhode Island, RI 138 follows an upland of 600-million-year-old granite of the Fall River Batholith. This typically light gray to pink, medium-grained granite has only a small percentage of dark minerals, such as biotite and hornblende.

RI 24 and RI 138 converge just east of the Sakonnet River, an arm of Narragansett Bay. On RI 24 east of the convergence, the highway passes through a canyon of high roadcuts in the Fall River Granite. If you are headed west, the canyon frames the Narragansett Basin lowland in the middle ground and the granitic uplands of western Rhode Island on the skyline.

Sachuest Arkose and Hummocks Overthrust

Downslope and west of exit 5, the Fall River Granite gives way to a 600-foot-wide set of outcrops of Sachuest Arkose, a sandstone containing granules of smoky quartz interbedded with carbonaceous phyllite. It was originally deposited on an erosional surface of the Fall River Granite in the Narragansett Basin in Pennsylvanian time. The arkose, which dips 45 degrees west, is exposed a few hundred feet north of the east end of the Portsmouth Bridge over the Sakonnet River. South of RI 24, the arkose is

Pink 600-million-year-old Fall River Granite containing dark xenoliths of diorite alongside the southbound lane of RI 24 northeast of the deep roadcut.

no longer exposed because it is concealed beneath a remnant of the Hummocks thrust sheet. The irregular, 3-mile-long thrust sheet is composed of Late Proterozoic rocks and was thrust over the sediments of the Narragansett Basin during the Alleghanian mountain building event between 300 and 250 million years ago. The thrust sheet has been considerably eroded, and only a remnant of its once extensive body remains.

Immediately west of the Portsmouth Bridge are dark cliffs of granodiorite gneiss that are part of the Hummocks thrust sheet. These cliffs edge a former quarry called "the Hummocks" on the south side of RI 24. In the southern part of this overthrust sheet, Late Proterozoic basaltic volcanics, possibly equivalent to volcanics of the Price Neck Formation, are exposed on an island in the Sakonnet River.

Bristol Neck

Rocks exposed on Bristol Neck include a highly sheared Late Proterozoic granitic rock known as Metacom Granite Gneiss, overlain by a layer of greenish chloritic schist of uncertain age. Early geologists thought the granite gneiss and schist were a domed fold poking through the cover rocks of Pennsylvanian age. West of Bristol Harbor, Popasquash Neck and Colt State Park are formed of Pennsylvanian-age rocks of the Narragansett Basin.

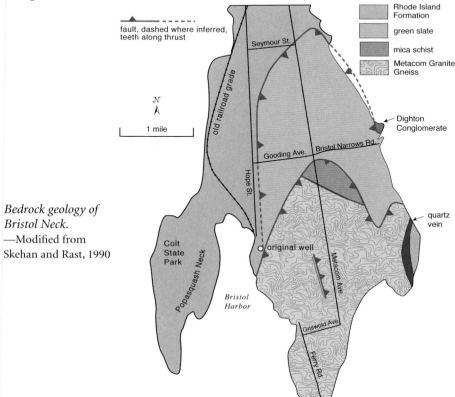

Bedrock geology of Bristol Neck.
—Modified from Skehan and Rast, 1990

In 1899 coal was discovered in a well dug in the west part of Bristol. If the rocks of Bristol Neck formed the core of a simple fold that dipped west, there would be no substantial thickness of overlying coal-bearing strata dipping away from the crystalline core of the Bristol Neck fold. If, on the other hand, the crystalline rocks had been thrust over the top of coal-bearing strata, the overthrust sheet of gneiss could have been hiding a big deposit of Pennsylvanian-age coal. So in the early 1970s, geologists set about testing which hypothesis was correct. They drilled several wells close to the site of the original excavation. They also drilled just west of the contact between the Pennsylvanian strata and the crystalline rocks.

Had the fold hypothesis been correct, a drill hole 500 feet west of the Metacom Granite Gneiss would have encountered the thinly layered green schist and the core gneiss at depths no greater than about 300 to 500 feet. However, only coal-bearing Pennsylvanian sedimentary rocks were encountered, even at depths as great as 800 feet. This provided partial support for the idea that a thin slab of hard rocks had been overthrust onto a thick deposit of fossiliferous Pennsylvanian strata. During the Alleghanian mountain building event between 300 and 250 million years ago, compressional forces from the southeast moved blocks of rock along east-dipping, west-moving thrust faults.

Additional support for the thrust hypothesis was evidenced by the discovery of a 100-foot-wide by 1-mile-long massive quartz vein along the eastern contact of the core granitic rocks with the coal-bearing Pennsylvanian rocks. The quartz vein crops out on the eastern shore of Bristol Neck where a transmission tower is located east of Mount Hope and the Haffenreffer Museum of Anthropology. Hot fluids often move along faults and deposit minerals, so the quartz vein may represent the site of the fault.

RI 24 roadcut just south of the Sprague Street overpass and east of the Portsmouth Coal Mine, through rusty-weathering, Pennsylvanian-age black slate of the Rhode Island Formation with interbedded coal layers

Portsmouth Coal Mine

The Portsmouth Coal Mine is located along the eastern shore of the East Passage near Arnold Point. The westward bulge of the shoreline north of Arnold Point consists in part of grout, or waste rock, from the mine. Two parallel mine shafts begin just east of the tracks of the Providence & Worcester Railroad. The two shafts trend east-southeast a distance of 2,900 feet toward Butts Hill, which is northeast of exit 2 on RI 24. Three principal coal seams were worked here. The middle coal bed was the thickest of the three, on average about 3 feet thick but attaining a thickness of up to 40 feet in places, undoubtedly due to flowage of the coal during heating and folding.

The Portsmouth Coal Mine was the most important mine in the long, sporadic history of mining in the Narragansett Basin. The archives of the Newport Historical Society, located on Touro Street, have a good deal of information on the history of coal mining in Portsmouth. They also contain "occasional papers" by geologists who gathered in Newport during summers over 100 years ago for discussion and fieldwork.

Purgatory Chasm in Middletown

Purgatory Chasm is one of the finest localities in the world for the study of "stretched" pebbles. It features cliffs overlooking Second Beach on Rhode Island Sound in Middletown. The chasm was formed by the erosive power of the sea. During storms, waves pound at the water that remains trapped in the chasm and act like a hydraulic hammer, further eroding the cliff walls.

The cliffs are composed of quartzite and vein quartz-conglomerate of the Purgatory Conglomerate of Pennsylvanian age, deposited as an alluvial fan in the Narragansett Basin. A vast number of white to gray quartzite conglomerate clasts, ranging from sand-sized grains to boulders several feet in diameter, look like they've been stretched in a north-south direction. Pressure generated by the Alleghanian mountain building event

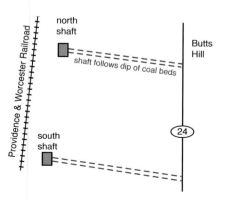

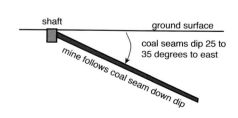

A schematic geological cross section of the Portsmouth Coal Mine shafts dipping east from the adits just east of the Providence & Worcester Railroad.

"Stretched" cobble conglomerate, elongate boulders with "beards" of quartz at their ends, on the cliffs of Purgatory Chasm. The quartz entered solution from sites under high pressure and migrated to sites of low pressure.

Aerial photo of Newport Granite along the south end of Cliffwalk. —Jon C. Boothroyd photo

Aerial photo of Rhode Island Formation along Cliffwalk. —Jon C. Boothroyd photo

forced individual clasts to press against their neighbors. In the high-pressure sites, quartz dissolved and moved in solution to lower-pressure sites, generally at the pebbles' tips, where fibrous crystalline quartz precipitated. The fibrous crystals resemble whiskers on a human chin, so the ends of the slenderized quartzite clasts are called "bearded quartz."

Pocket Beaches of Southern Aquidneck Island

Pocket beaches line the southern end of Aquidneck Island (or, more formally, Rhode Island), where rocky headlands jut south into Rhode Island Sound and protect the beaches from the brunt of the rough seas, allowing sand to collect there. Hazard Beach, Bailey's Beach, Easton's or First Beach, Sachuest or Second Beach, and Third Beach are all pocket beaches.

Newport Granite and the Price Neck Volcanics

Cliffwalk, a 3.5-mile-long public trail along the seashore cliffs facing Easton Bay and Rhode Island Sound, is a good introduction to the geology of Newport Neck. It passes along the edge of private land of the Newport Mansions. Some sections of trail are well maintained and others are difficult at best. Along the northern and central part of the trail, the cliffs are Pennsylvanian-age Rhode Island Formation of the Narragansett Basin. South of Sheep Point, the trail crosses volcanics of the Price Neck Formation, and at Lands End, accessed by Ledge Road, the headland is formed of Newport Granite.

Newport Granite, a 595-million-year-old granite in southern Newport, has also been called Cliff Walk, Lily Pond, and Bulgarmarsh Granite. This

Contact between the flattened conglomerate (right) *and black slate* (left) *of the Rhode Island Formation along Cliffwalk at Forty Steps, near the Administration Building at Salve Regina University.* —Daniel P. Murray photo

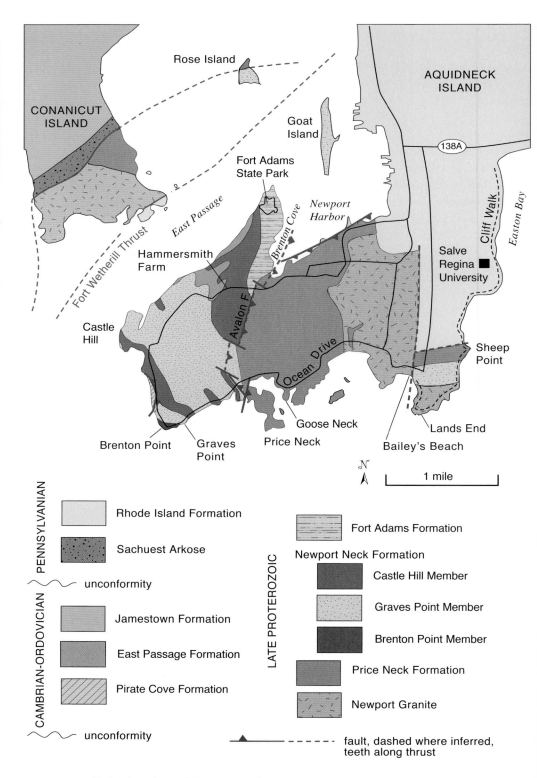

Bedrock geology of Newport Neck. —Modified from Rast and Skehan, 1981

gray, pink, or green granite has large crystals of microcline feldspar set in a matrix of feldspars and quartz with alteration minerals such as epidote, chlorite, and fine-grained muscovite mica. The coarse-grained granitic rock varies from true granite to quartz monzonite, a rock with less quartz than true granite.

The Newport Granite intruded volcanics of the Price Neck Formation. You can see the contact between the granite and the volcanics at Bailey's Beach at the southern end of Cliffwalk, and nearby at Rogers High School, a few blocks from Bailey's Beach. Determining the age of the granite to be 595 million years was key in proving the Late Proterozoic age of the Price Neck rocks.

The Price Neck rocks form extensive coastal outcrops near Ocean Drive on southern Newport Neck and throughout the highlands to the north in the peninsula's interior. It consists of graded beds of feldspar-rich siltstone and sandstone layered with carbonate conglomerate and volcanic tuff. The volcanic rocks typically weather to a buff color and are dark gray to purple on fresh surfaces. Some units may have originated as pyroclastic mudflows, the deadliest of volcanic eruptive deposits. The volcanics are from the Avalon volcanic chain, which formed along the coast of Gondwana more than 600 million years ago.

The intrusion of the Newport Granite metamorphosed the fine-grained graded beds of the Price Neck strata into very hard rocks that resist erosion. The dense Price Neck volcanics sometimes ring like a bell when struck with a hammer. The metamorphism is most intense near the contact zone with the granite. The westward decrease of the metamorphic mineral cordierite, now altered to chlorite, indicates that the Newport Granite was the source of heat.

Graded beds, which form when sediments settle out of water based on their size, are useful for determining what the original top of a bed is. Because the coarser sediments settle out of the water first, the up direction is toward the finer layer. However, in the now-metamorphosed Price Neck strata, large crystals of the high-temperature and high-pressure mineral cordierite grew in the originally fine-grained part of the graded bed. As a result, the original fine-grained layer of the graded bed now appears to have larger grains than the coarse-grained layer! But all is well because when lower temperatures and pressures developed, the cordierite was then transformed into a fine-grained mixture of biotite, muscovite, and calcite, and yet you can still see the shape of the cordierite crystals.

Two cleavages in the Price Neck stratified deposits record two episodes of compression. The main deforming force moved toward the north, compressing the rocks into east-west-trending folds. A good place to see first- and second-generation deformation features is at the boat launch at Goose Neck Cove.

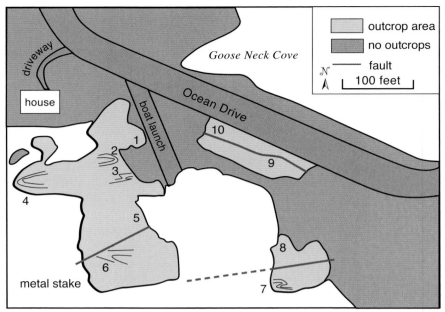

Fine-grained Price Neck volcanic rocks at Goose Neck Cove at the boat launch area show a first generation of folds that are cut by a second generation of cleavage. (1) Soft sediment fold. (2) First-generation fold. (3) Second-generation fold. (4) Fold. (5) Vein of quartz. (6) First-generation fold with fault cutting nose. (7) Second-generation fold. (8) Soft sediment deformation. (9) Graded beds with top to south. (10) Mylonitized area along fault. —Modified from Rast and Skehan, 1981

Folds in the Price Neck Formation in Goose Neck Cove on Newport Neck.

In the central part of the Price Neck outcrop area and east of nearby Hammersmith Road is a fine-grained orangish gray intrusive rock cut by diorite and fine-grained granitic dikes. This intrusion added heat to the system, contributing to the metamorphic intensity.

Avalon Fault

The Price Neck rocks have been thrust to the west along the Avalon Fault over the top of the red and green sequence of the Newport Neck Formation and the green Fort Adams Formation. The north-striking, east-dipping Avalon Fault runs just east of the Newport Country Club. This fault was named not for the Avalon Terrane itself but for the whimsical reason that in the 1980s, the main entrance to the Mansion on Ocean Drive where the fault is located was marked by a rock labeled "AVALON." Deformation of the Avalon Fault may have been contemporaneous with sediment deposition of the Fort Adams Formation. The most chaotic episodes of deformation on the Avalon Fault also produced deep-sea debris flows.

Brenton Point State Park

The Newport Neck Formation forms an almost continuous set of cliff-forming exposures on the southwestern shores of Newport Neck. These rocks are especially accessible at Brenton Point State Park. This formation consists of sequences of gray, green, and maroon, graded sedimentary rocks ranging from fine-grained conglomerate to slate. Two of the three

Quartz veins cut the Graves Point Member of the Newport Neck Formation at Brenton Point State Park.

members of the formation on Brenton Point and Castle Hill consist of magnificently developed graded beds that are 3 to 4 feet thick. These are well exposed in seashore outcrops and rounded headlands. The presence of slump folds, shale-fragment breccias, and other soft-sediment deformation features tells us that the seafloor fringing the Avalon volcanic arc on which these sediments were originally deposited was an unstable slope subject to earthquakes.

The bedded rocks contain textbook examples of multiple generations of folds. The graded bedding reveals the stratigraphic orientation when the sediments were laid down. The tectonic cleavage reveals the first and second episodes of folding. The cleavage also reveals the direction from which the compressive forces were moving when the strata were deformed.

The depositional basin was extending and was unstable enough that deep faults reached magma, which moved up, filling cracks in the rock and crystallizing into dikes. These diabase dikes intruded the Newport

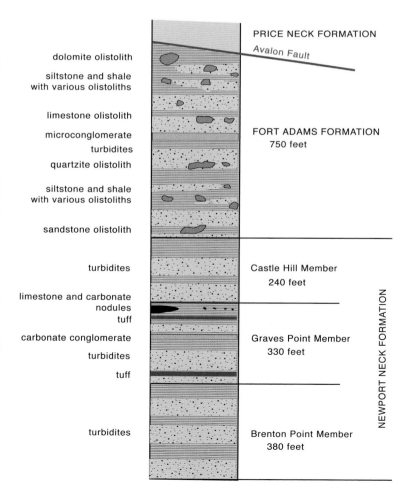

Sequence of the Newport Neck and Fort Adams Formations.
—Modified from Webster, 1986

Folded sedimentary strata of the Graves Point Member of the Newport Neck Formation with graded beds at Brenton Point State Park.

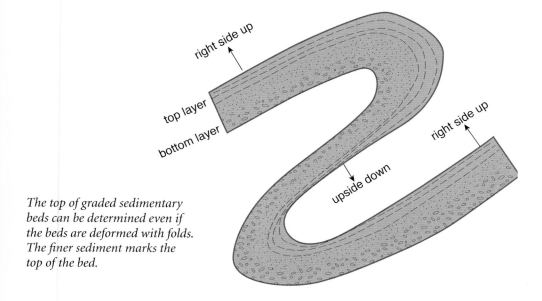

right side up

top layer

bottom layer

right side up

upside down

The top of graded sedimentary beds can be determined even if the beds are deformed with folds. The finer sediment marks the top of the bed.

Neck rocks prior to the second episode of folding. We know this because the dikes contain cleavage that parallels the axial plane of the second generation of folds. Hot water solution has altered these dikes to brilliantly green minerals.

The Pirate Cove Formation of Early Cambrian age is also exposed in cliffs along Ocean Drive in Brenton Point State Park. This sequence of pink to buff and white, thinly laminated, 12- to 15-foot-thick marble beds is interlayered with magenta-colored slate. The marble beds contain tiny fossils of hyoliths, a type of mollusk diagnostic of an Early Cambrian age. If the identification of the hyoliths is correct, these beds are the oldest Cambrian beds in Rhode Island, older than the trilobite-bearing Cambrian beds of the Jamestown Formation.

These fossiliferous beds are located at the strandline near Pirate Cove, about 400 feet north of the northern entrance to Brenton Point State Park and south of Castle Hill. At low tide, the marble beds are exposed at various levels in the sea cliffs for a few hundred feet farther south, where brilliant-colored phyllites of the upper part of the Pirate Cove Formation are well exposed. This striking 50-foot-thick phyllite sequence ranges from brilliant green and gray to maroon, red, and silver.

Fort Adams State Park
The Late Proterozoic Fort Adams Formation crops out in Newport Neck at Fort Adams Beach near the entrance to Fort Adams State Park and also near the Newport Country Club and Hammersmith Farm, once the Kennedy "Summer White House." This formation consists of graded

The upper half of an elliptical quartzite olistolith in the Fort Adams Formation at the level of the entrance road to Fort Adams State Park.

View of Newport Harbor from Harrison Avenue looking at Ida Lewis Yacht Club, built on marble olistoliths in the southern part of the harbor. The two olistoliths supporting the yacht club are separated by a thin layer of maroon slate.

beds composed of conglomerate and slate enclosing large blocks of several different rock types. This type of formation is called an *olistostrome* and likely represents a deep-sea debris flow deposit. Great elliptical blocks of quartzite up to 75 feet long can be observed in the tree-shrouded cliffs along the entrance to Fort Adams State Park. Two great blocks of dolomitic marble in red shale on the south shore of Newport Harbor form the foundation for the Ida Lewis Yacht Club. Other blocks are buff-weathering calcareous siltstone, calc-silicate rocks, and, more rarely, blocks of diorite, gabbro, and ultramafic rocks.

East Passage Formation on Newport Neck

The Cambrian-age East Passage Formation crops out on the northern coastline of Newport Neck near Hammersmith Farm. This formation contains thinly bedded and nongraded red, brown, and gray sandstone and siltstone with sparse phyllite and marble beds and some volcanic layers containing welded tuff. This sequence has strong similarities to parts of the Jamestown Formation on Beavertail. The bottom of the East Passage strata may be a fault because that contact is intensely sheared and overlies the contact between two members of the Newport Neck Formation.

Fort Wetherill State Park

The southern end of eastern Conanicut Island consists of thrust blocks. Pennsylvanian Sachuest Arkose has been thrust onto the Cambrian rocks

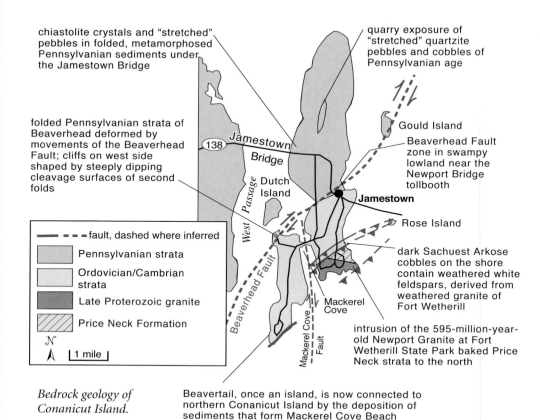

chiastolite crystals and "stretched" pebbles in folded, metamorphosed Pennsylvanian sediments under the Jamestown Bridge

quarry exposure of "stretched" quartzite pebbles and cobbles of Pennsylvanian age

folded Pennsylvanian strata of Beaverhead deformed by movements of the Beaverhead Fault; cliffs on west side shaped by steeply dipping cleavage surfaces of second folds

Gould Island

Beaverhead Fault zone in swampy lowland near the Newport Bridge tollbooth

Jamestown Bridge

138

West Passage

Dutch Island

Jamestown

Rose Island

fault, dashed where inferred

Pennsylvanian strata

Ordovician/Cambrian strata

Late Proterozoic granite

Price Neck Formation

N

| 1 mile |

Beaverhead Fault

Mackerel Cove Fault

Mackerel Cove

dark Sachuest Arkose cobbles on the shore contain weathered white feldspars, derived from weathered granite of Fort Wetherill

intrusion of the 595-million-year-old Newport Granite at Fort Wetherill State Park baked Price Neck strata to the north

Bedrock geology of Conanicut Island.

Beavertail, once an island, is now connected to northern Conanicut Island by the deposition of sediments that form Mackerel Cove Beach

near Jamestown Harbor. The next thrust block to the south, forming the headlands at Fort Wetherill State Park, is composed of Price Neck volcanics intruded by Newport Granite. The southernmost tip of Fort Wetherill State Park is composed of Pennsylvanian conglomerate. The three thrust faults cutting across the Fort Wetherill peninsula extend from the East Passage to Mackerel Cove but are cut off by the Mackerel Cove Fault of probable Alleghanian age, which separates the main part of Conanicut Island from the southern end, known as Beavertail. Steep cliffs of Newport Granite form most of the rocks in Fort Wetherill State Park.

Cambrian Trilobites of Jamestown

Serendipity often plays a significant role in scientific discovery. In the 1970s, as director of the Narragansett Basin Project, I set out to study Carboniferous strata. One of our objectives during this period of energy shortages was to assess the coal-bearing deposits of the Narragansett Basin. The 1971 bedrock geologic map of Rhode Island showed that southern

Conanicut Island was underlain by dark gray to coal-black phyllites. These strata, supposedly Carboniferous in age, were very well exposed along the seacoast all around Beavertail, or southern Conanicut Island. We were convinced that this was an attractive destination for the study.

It was quickly discovered, however, that something was wrong with the "coal basin." Some of the strata of southern Conanicut Island were rhythmically bedded and contained limy concretions and graded beds, hinting of a marine depositional environment, a place where coal was not likely to be found. The structures were also entirely different from those seen in sediments of the Narragansett Basin, which were deposited by meandering rivers. An unpublished manuscript and hand-painted geologic map of Newport and Jamestown prepared around 1900 had recognized that these sedimentary rocks of southern Jamestown were marine, but it offered no opinion on the age of the strata.

A student named Tremaine Smith was hired to map the promising-looking dark shaley rocks on Beavertail. Before long, Tom Devries, a classmate of Smith's who was helping with the field studies, found fossil fragments. They turned out to be from *Badulesia tenera* (Hartt), a Middle Cambrian trilobite. One of the criteria for identifying the Avalon Terrane is the presence of diagnostic Paleozoic fauna, in particular the presence of Cambrian trilobites. Since about 1845, trilobites of Avalonian type have been found widely in eastern Massachusetts, but this was the first trilobite ever found in Rhode Island. The search for coal turned up fossiliferous rocks of Avalonia instead!

The Cambrian strata of Beavertail yielded three trilobite forms: two *Paradoxides* species and a species of *Badulesia*. Of these trilobites the most useful for dating was *Badulesia tenera* (Hartt), a widespread species of Middle Cambrian age (about 505 million years old). This species was known from New Brunswick, eastern Newfoundland, southern Germany, northern Spain, and eastern Turkey. Extrapolation from these partial specimens indicates that the species could grow to be almost 10 inches long! An approximately 6-centimeter-long complete individual trilobite, identified as an infantile form of *Paradoxides*, was found at the top of the Hull Cove Member at or near the contact with the Lion Head Member north of Short Point.

The sequence of rocks at Jamestown was named the Conanicut Group and divided into three formations. From oldest to youngest, the formations are the Jamestown, Fort Burnside, and Dutch Island Harbor. Geologists think these three formations form a unified succession of sedimentary rocks that had an uninterrupted history of deposition; only soft-sediment sliding or faulting disrupts the beds. The ages of these rocks, including those in which no fossils have yet been found, are probably limited to Middle Cambrian time.

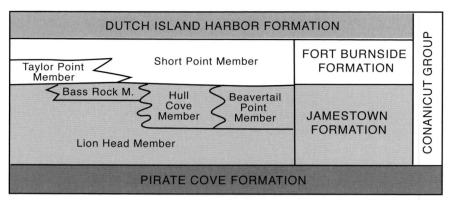

Formations of the Conanicut Group.

The Jamestown Formation has four members: Lion Head, Beavertail Point, Hull Cove, and Bass Rock. However, nowhere are the members in stratigraphic contact with each other. Therefore the stratigraphic position of the Lion Head Member, which contains the age-diagnostic trilobites, is inferred but not known with certainty. The Jamestown Formation consists of fossiliferous green and gray phyllite, with minor amounts of black phyllite and buff- and white-weathering siltstone. It is estimated to be about 650 feet thick. The green and black phyllite consists of the minerals quartz, chlorite, muscovite, and feldspar. Siderite and paragonite are sometimes present. The black color may be due to graphite. Dolomite concretions range from 2.5 to 18 inches in diameter, but are less abundant than in the Dutch Island Harbor Formation.

Most of the more than a dozen fossils collected in the 1970s in Cambrian formations in southeastern Rhode Island were found in the Lion Head Member of the Jamestown Formation north of Lion Head and from just south of the chasm as well. The Lion Head Member is characteristically rich in fossil "hash," small pieces of broken shells from various creatures. The same is true of parts of the Beavertail Point and Hull Cove Members.

Worm burrows also occur in the Beavertail Point Member. The trails can be seen in places where the bedding is essentially parallel to the dominant cleavage, as is the case on the western shore of Beavertail several hundred feet northwest of the lighthouse. Three genera of trace fossils were identified as *Palaeophycus* (=*Buthrotrephis*), *Planolites*, and *Helminthopsis*. Trace fossils also occur in the Hull Cove Member.

Folded Beds at Beavertail

Beavertail's Cambrian rocks contain evidence of multiple episodes of folding. Evidence in these rocks has helped geologists piece together the major tectonic events that affected Connecticut and Rhode Island in Paleozoic time.

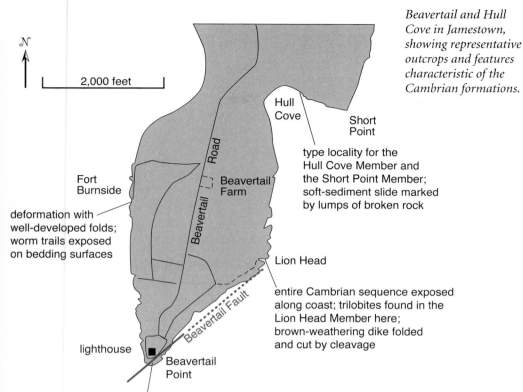

2,000 feet

Beavertail and Hull Cove in Jamestown, showing representative outcrops and features characteristic of the Cambrian formations.

Hull Cove

Short Point

type locality for the Hull Cove Member and the Short Point Member; soft-sediment slide marked by lumps of broken rock

Beavertail Road

Fort Burnside

Beavertail Farm

deformation with well-developed folds; worm trails exposed on bedding surfaces

Lion Head

entire Cambrian sequence exposed along coast; trilobites found in the Lion Head Member here; brown-weathering dike folded and cut by cleavage

Beavertail Fault

lighthouse

Beavertail Point

folded gray and black phyllite beds of the Beavertail Point Member on the southeast side of the fault and pale green phyllite of the Dutch Island Harbor Formation on the northwest side

Rocks at the base of the Beavertail Lighthouse are folded phyllites with well-developed slaty cleavage parallel to the axial plane of the folds. —Daniel P. Murray photo

A refolded fold in an outcrop on Beavertail. —Daniel P. Murray photo

Late in the Alleghanian mountain building event, minette dikes intruded the fossiliferous Middle Cambrian strata of Conanicut Island. Minette is a dark dike rock composed of biotite crystals in a fine-grained matrix of microcline, biotite, plagioclase, and quartz with smaller amounts of other minerals. Interpreted to have formed at moderate depths, minette dikes belong to a family of mafic rocks called *lamprophyres.* At Lion Head Chasm, an altered orange-weathering minette dike up to 13 feet wide cuts these phyllites, hardening them near the contact. At this locality, the minette dike intruded after the first episode of folding and was itself folded and cleaved in the second episode of deformation. On the assumption that these phyllites were primarily folded during Alleghanian mountain building, these minette dikes are most likely Permian or early Mesozoic in age.

Fort Burnside and Dutch Island Harbor Formations

The Fort Burnside Formation is named for the U.S harbor control post that served as the central command site for submarine communications during World War II. The 165-foot-thick formation consists of two members, which together form a distinctive, cyclically bedded unit. The Short Point Member, the basal unit, consists of buff siltstone interlayered with black and gray phyllite. The siltstone beds are typically micaceous and calcareous, and contain conspicuous ripples and crossbeds.

An outcrop on Beavertail with vertical bedding and horizontal cleavage.
—Daniel P. Murray photo

The Taylor Point Member is about 15 feet thick and differs from the Short Point in that the gray phyllite is absent from the sedimentary cycles. South of Lion Head, the siltstone tends to be buff, micaceous, and calcareous. North of Lion Head and at Taylor Point the phyllites are white and cleaner looking and have a notably smaller content of carbonate and mica. Breakup of the layers may be due to soft-sediment deformation.

The Fort Burnside Formation grades upward into the Dutch Island Harbor Formation, with a gradual increase in the amount of unoxidized shaley material and a decrease in the amount of sand. The 355-foot-thick Dutch Island Harbor Formation is uniformly very fine-grained and rhythmically bedded, dark gray to black phyllite, on both weathered and fresh surfaces. Brown-weathering carbonate beds contain carbonate concretions up to 1 foot long.

Beaverhead

Beavertail is mainly composed of Cambrian phyllite. The only exception is Beaverhead, a prominent headland facing the West Passage on the west and Dutch Island Harbor to the north. Here, Pennsylvanian phyllites and conglomerate crop out. Beaverhead is separated from Beavertail by the Beaverhead Fault, a strike-slip fault along which the Beavertail block of Cambrian phyllite moved southwest relative to the Pennsylvanian strata. The northeast-trending, 50-mile-long Beaverhead Fault extends northeast

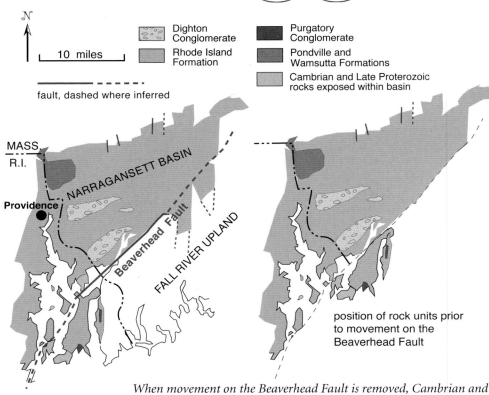

When movement on the Beaverhead Fault is removed, Cambrian and
Proterozoic rocks are closer to rocks of the same age in Bristol Neck.
—Modified from Skehan and others, 1986

along the Taunton River in Massachusetts and southwest from this site
to Rhode Island Sound. This fault, which probably moved during the
Alleghanian mountain building event, is the reason that Avalon rocks on
the east side of the Narragansett Basin differ from rocks on the west side.

Jamestown Bridge Outcrops

Outcrops along the water near the RI 138 Jamestown Bridge on the western shore of Conanicut Island are worth a look. At the east end of the
bridge, find a local street near Seaside Drive heading to the bridge foundation. North of the abutments, seaside outcrops of black chiastolite schist
of Pennsylvanian age can be found. Chiastolite is a variety of andalusite,
a prism-shaped mineral rich in alumina and one of three minerals having
the chemical formula Al_2SiO_5. Chiastolite indicates that these outcrops
have been subjected to moderately high metamorphism. The site near the
bridge is just west of an east-dipping normal fault, which lies just west of
an anticline overturned toward the west. Regional indicators of tectonic
intensity indicate that the grade of metamorphism increases in the westward direction.

Stook Hill

West of the Jamestown Bridge, RI 138 cuts through Stook Hill, the crest of which is 1.3 miles west of RI 1A. On both sides of RI 138 are 20-foot-high outcrops in the Rhode Island Formation of the Narragansett Basin. The mineral assemblages here tell us that the temperature and pressure in the rocks during the Alleghanian mountain building event reached the staurolite-kyanite zone of metamorphism. The high-grade metamorphism extends from the western margin of the basin eastward to the Beaverhead Fault, which cuts through Beaverhead on southern Conanicut Island and then heads south underwater, passing east of the town of Narragansett Pier.

South of RI 138 and Stook Hill, the western fault margin of the Narragansett coal basin lies just east of US 1 and west of the Pettaquamscutt River. South of the US 1/RI 138 intersection, US 1 traverses Proterozoic granite of the Esmond Igneous Suite for about 4 miles before the southwesternmost exposure of the fault cuts through the high-grade, sillimanite- and kyanite-bearing metamorphic rocks of Pennsylvanian age near and south of Indian Lake in South Kingstown.

Wolf Rocks and Congdon Hill Moraines

Two moraine segments deposited at different times lie west of Stook Hill and the RI 138 and US 1 intersection. Congdon Hill, just west of Congdon Hill Road in North Kingston, is the namesake of the north-trending Congdon Hill moraine, which was deposited along the western edge of the Narragansett Bay lobe. The Congdon Hill moraine is probably the same

A roadcut at Stook Hill through conglomerate sandstone metamorphosed at temperatures of at least 600 degrees Celsius and pressures comparable to those at least 15 miles deep in the earth.

Rounded pebbles still visible in the highly metamorphosed rocks at Stook Hill.

age as the Ledyard moraine in Connecticut. Wolf Rocks, 3 miles southwest of Congdon Hill, is at the interlobate angle between the short east- to northeast-trending Wolf Rocks moraine, deposited from the Narragansett Bay lobe, and moraine segments to the west that trend east-northeast to west-southwest and correlate with the Old Saybrook moraine in Connecticut. Interlobate areas such as this often have moraines that meet at angles to each other. RI 138 crosses a segment of the Congdon Hill moraine in South Kingstown 0.2 mile west of the junction with RI 2.

RI 122 and RI 146
Pawtucket—Woonsocket
15 MILES

Bedrock in northeastern Rhode Island is well displayed along RI 146 and US 295. North of Pawtucket, RI 122 and RI 146 cross the faulted margin of the Narragansett Basin. The sedimentary rocks and coal mines in the basin are discussed in depth in the chapter introduction.

Blackstone River

RI 122 follows the Blackstone River upstream to Woonsocket. The river begins near Worcester, Massachusetts, and flows into the Seekonk River, an arm of Narragansett Bay. The Blackstone River has been called the "cradle of the Industrial Revolution." In 1793, the first cotton mill in the United States began operation along the Blackstone, using water power from the river. Nearly two centuries of hard use took a toll on the river, but cleanup efforts have improved the water quality considerably. In 1986, Congress established the Blackstone River Valley National Heritage Corridor, a landscape that features hundreds of natural, historic, and cultural treasures.

The river is named for William Blackstone, who in 1635 became the first Englishman to settle in Rhode Island. Much of the river in Rhode Island flows through rocks of the Blackstone Group, metamorphosed sedimentary and volcanic rocks deposited on the continental shelf of Gondwana in Proterozoic time. The Blackstone River flows through these rocks, as well as Late Proterozoic granite, in a craggy gorge on the border of Massachusetts and Rhode Island.

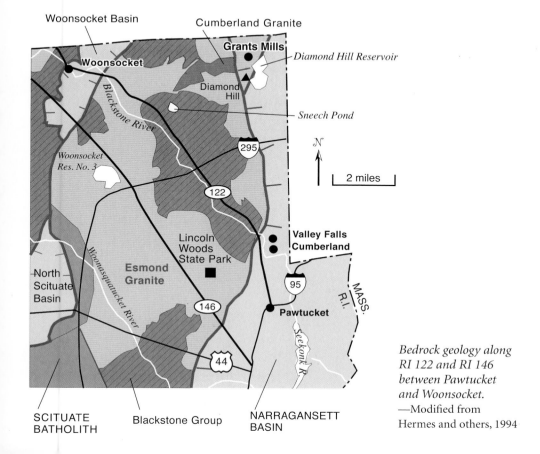

Bedrock geology along RI 122 and RI 146 between Pawtucket and Woonsocket.
—Modified from Hermes and others, 1994

Limerock

Lime was mined from several quarries in northern Lincoln near Limerock, east of the intersection of RI 146 and Wilbur Road. The lime is from marble in the Late Proterozoic-age Blackstone Group. Bowenite, a yellowish green variety of serpentine, is found in marbles of the Blackstone Group and is the Rhode Island state mineral.

Cumberlandite: Rhode Island State Rock

The Rhode Island state rock is cumberlandite, an unusual rock that occurs in the northwestern part of Cumberland. The cumberlandite outcrop is 2 miles northwest of Sneech Pond and forms a 1.5-mile-long, ellipsoid body

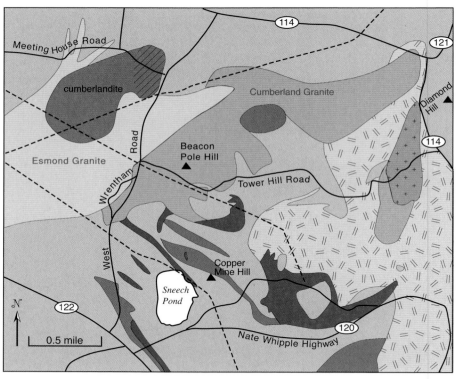

Cumberland Granite of Mississippian age

- granite porphyry
- feldspar, aegirine, and riebeckite granite

Blackstone Group of Late Proterozoic age

- Hunting Hill Greenstone
- Sneech Pond Schist

Precambrian or early Paleozoic plutonic rocks

- Esmond Granite
- Grant Mills Granodiorite
- quartz diorite
- Cumberlandite; hatched area is magnetite-rich melatroctolite
- - - - - - power transmission lines

Geologic map of the cumberlandite and Cumberland Granite intrusions in northern Rhode Island. —Modified from Rutherford and Hermes, 1984

Cumberlandite, the state rock of Rhode Island, is mostly black. The light-colored minerals are feldspar. —Daniel P. Murray photo

Outcrop of cumberlandite, a peculiar magnetic rock in northeastern Rhode Island. —Jon C. Boothroyd photo

at the intersection of West Wrentham and Meeting House Roads. The name *cumberlandite* is now obsolete in geologic circles, but not in Rhode Island! The outcrop is composed of two igneous bodies that crystallized from a common magma. The outcrop is two-thirds anorthositic gabbro and one-third melatroctolite, a dark, dense rock composed of almost 50 percent olivine, 30 percent titanium-rich magnetite, and 15 percent plagioclase. The larger gabbroic body has large crystals of aligned plagioclase feldspar, giving the rock a layered look. Very few other rock bodies in the world have this distinctive composition. The cumberlandite complex is considered Proterozoic in age because it intrudes Proterozoic rocks of the Blackstone Group and the Esmond Igneous Suite.

Cumberlandite Boulder Train

As the continental glacier moved over the cumberlandite outcrop, boulders of all sizes were picked up by the ice. It carried the boulders south, depositing them as the ice melted. This type of distribution of characteristic rocks in a single line is called a *boulder train*. The shape of the area over which the cumberlandite boulders are distributed forms a rough triangle with the upstream end pointed at the outcrop and the downstream area fanning out between two bounding lines. Cumberlandite boulders and cobbles have been found as far south as Block Island.

Cumberland Granite

Cumberland Granite, an intrusive rock that may range in age from Devonian to Mississippian, is unrelated to the nearby cumberlandite intrusion. You can see the granite in a large roadcut along RI 114 about 200 yards west of the intersection with RI 121 in Grants Mills. The granite intrudes the Esmond Igneous Suite and Blackstone Group rocks of the Avalon Terrane. This distinctive gray to bluish gray, medium- to coarse-grained granite contains alkali feldspar, the feldspar with potassium rather than calcium. A granite with this chemistry typically forms at a rift, an area where the earth's crust is pulling apart. This rock resembles the distinctive Quincy Granite near Boston, which also has alkali feldspar. The Cumberland Granite also contains quartz and small amounts of the minerals astrophyllite, zircon, allanite, and fluorite. Plagioclase, the calcium feldspar, is notably absent.

Diamond Hill

Diamond Hill, formerly the site of a small ski area, is a prominent ridge of quartz between RI 114 and Diamond Hill Reservoir in the northeastern corner of Rhode Island. The quartz, including crystals, may have been deposited by hot water circulating along the fault on the western side of the Narragansett Basin. The hard quartz resists erosion, so it now stands 481 feet above the surrounding landscape. Look for cavities within the massive quartz.

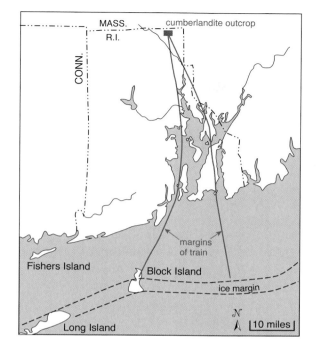

Boulders of cumberlandite, carried by ice from the outcrop in northeastern Rhode Island, have been found within the margins indicated. —Modified from Murray, 1988; Quinn, 1971

Woonsocket Basin

A small sediment-filled basin of Pennsylvanian age straddles the Massachusetts–Rhode Island border at Woonsocket. No coal was mined here. The rift basin contains quartz pebble conglomerate, sandstone, and dark schist, and is an outlier to the larger, coal-bearing Narragansett Basin.

Block Island

Block Island is 12 miles south of Rhode Island and 12 miles east-northeast of Montauk Point, New York, the southeastern prong of Long Island. Because Block Island sits just north of the southernmost point reached by the Wisconsinan ice sheet 22,000 years ago, glacial features figure prominently in the island's geologic story. Sandy morainal deposits, hundreds of feet thick, emerge above the waters of the Atlantic Ocean here, creating the hummocky terrain of the north and central parts of the island. The morainal deposits are complex, in part because the island is located in the interlobate zone where the Narragansett Bay–Buzzards Bay lobe to the east joined with the ice sheet that flowed southeast across Connecticut and western Rhode Island. Sea cliffs on the southern and northeastern shores expose amazing structures within the glacial debris, including blocks of 96-million-year-old Cretaceous sediments bulldozed into place by the glacier. The eastern and northwest coasts are gentler and sandy. Sandy Point is a sand spit extending north into Block Island Sound.

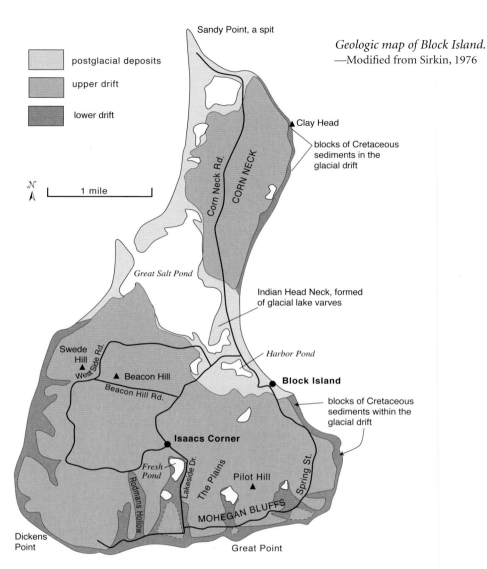

Geologic map of Block Island.
—Modified from Sirkin, 1976

During Cretaceous time, a wedge of sediment thousands of feet thick was deposited on the crystalline bedrock of the coastal plain and continental shelf of New England. The sediment is nearly 1,000 feet thick on the shelf south of the Rhode Island coast and beneath Block Island. Only blocks of Cretaceous sediment surrounded by younger glacial drift are exposed on Block Island. The top of the intact, unconsolidated Cretaceous sediment below the island lies a couple hundred feet below sea level. The exposed blocks of sediment consist of white sands and clays with seams of lignite and iron pyrite nodules. The lignite seams contain a rich microflora that resembles the flora in Cretaceous sediments of eastern New Jersey,

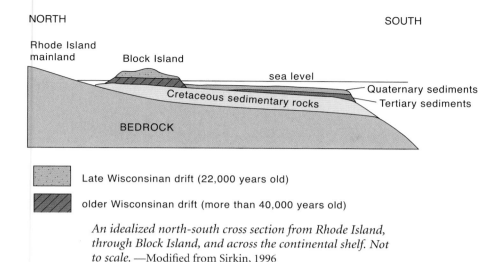

NORTH   SOUTH

An idealized north-south cross section from Rhode Island, through Block Island, and across the continental shelf. Not to scale. —Modified from Sirkin, 1996

namely the South Amboy Fire Clay of the Raritan Formation, which is about 96 million years old.

During much of Tertiary time, between 65 and 1.8 million years ago, the seashore was many miles south and east of Block Island. Tertiary sediments were deposited in the sea and along the coast, but erosion dominated inland. Consequently, there are no Tertiary sediments exposed on Block Island or hidden beneath the island's morainal deposits.

Glacial Deposits and History

Glacial deposits on Block Island consist of an upper drift and a lower drift. *Drift* is a catchall term applied to all sediment associated with glaciers, either deposited directly from the ice or by water. The lower drift, which is mostly below sea level, has been tentatively assigned to the Illinoian glacial stage, which occurred between 200,000 and 140,000 years ago. The upper drift was deposited during the Wisconsinan glacial stage.

The lower drift is generally distinguished from the upper drift by stratigraphic position. Color can also be used, but it isn't as reliable. The upper drift, which blankets most of Block Island, tends to be lighter in color because it contains granitic rock from the Avalon Terrane of eastern Connecticut and Rhode Island. In addition to till, the upper drift contains stratified deposits such as outwash sediments and lakebeds. Granitic boulders are scattered on the surface of the morainal deposits. The Cretaceous blocks are enclosed within the lower drift.

During the Wisconsin glacial stage, the ice pushed south, reaching as far south as Long Island. There, it deposited the Ronkonkoma moraine, the southernmost moraine of the continental glacier, about 22,000 years ago. The moraine heads out to sea at Montauk Point and trends toward the southern edge of Block Island. Low ridges and bouldery gravel on the seafloor are remnants of this terminal moraine. At 22,000 years ago, when enormous quantities of the earth's water were sequestered in ice sheets, the shoreline of the Atlantic Ocean was 70 miles south of the moraine and more than 300 feet below today's sea level. Water melting from the edge of the ice carved canyons across the continental shelf.

Yellowish brown, weathered upper drift in a sand and gravel pit just south of the intersection of West Side Road with Beacon Hill Road. The white pebbles are quartzite, which is more impervious to weathering processes than granitic rocks.

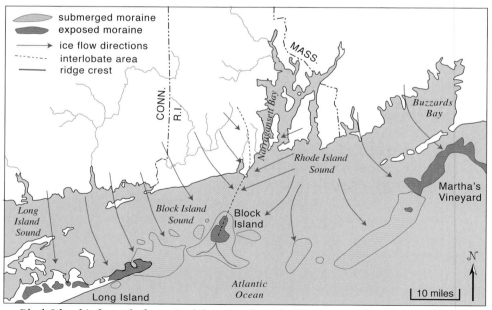

Block Island is formed of morainal deposits where the Narragansett Bay–Buzzards Bay lobe coalesced with the ice to its west. —Modified from Veeger and others, 1996

A coarse-grained pink granitic boulder on the grounds of the Block Island Southeast Lighthouse on Mohegan Bluff is probably porphyritic Narragansett Pier Granite of Permian age, which outcrops on the mainland of southern Rhode Island west of Narragansett Bay.

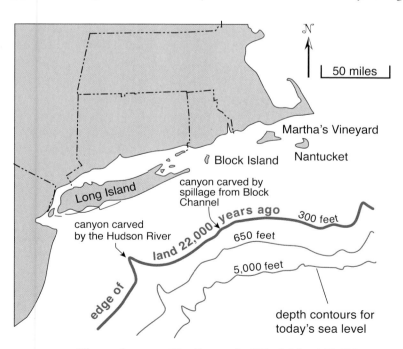

The seashore was 70 miles south of Block Island 22,000 years ago, when the southern edge of the ice was at Long Island. —Modified from Sirkin, 1996

Fresh Pond, to the south of Isaacs Corner and south of Block Island State Airport and Indian Cemetery.

As the ice retreated northward, meltwater flowed into the interlobate area and small lakes formed. The upper drift contains lenses of fine-grained sediment deposited in the lakes and in meltwater channels. Ice chunks that broke off the receding ice sheet were buried by sediment. When they melted, depressions formed, called *kettles*. Many ponds on the southern half of Block Island are kettles. Meltwater also ponded in places, and the flat beds of these former lakes are now flat fields. An example is The Plains, west of Pilot Hill.

While the ice was situated at Corn Neck, meltwater ponded in a lake between the ice and the high morainal deposits to the south at Beacon Hill. Lake bottom deposits called *varves* make up Indian Head Neck east of Great Salt Pond. Varves are alternating layers of dark clay deposited during the winter when a lake is frozen and light silt and sand deposited during summer. Indian Head Neck consists of more than one hundred of these thinly bedded couplets, so the lake must have existed for at least a century.

In the Corn Neck highlands, a hummocky landscape dotted with kettles, the upper drift forms a blanket of till covering the lower drift. At the 141-foot-high sea cliffs at Clay Head, deformed drift sheets and blocks of Cretaceous clays are exposed. High in the northeasterly cliffs is a 40-foot-thick section of fine-grained sediments, likely deposited in another glacial lake that formed at the edge of the ice front.

The eroded gullies south of the Beacon Hill highlands expose areas of older drift, which contains a compact basal till. This impermeable layer, an unsorted and unstratified glacial sediment deposited directly beneath the ice sheet, holds surface water. Fresh Pond is perched on relatively impervious till, a characteristic feature of the lower drift.

Mohegan Bluffs

Mohegan Bluffs, on the southern end of the island, stand more than 140 feet high and are one of the best sites for viewing the glacial debris and impressive deformational structures created by the Late Wisconsinan ice sheet. The lower drift deposits make up the bulk of the cliff exposures between Mohegan Bluffs and Dickens Point, the latter located on the southwestern corner of Block Island. The dark gray, fine-grained sediment has bedding layers and contains lenses of sand and beds of lake clay and silt. This drift was contorted into tight folds, ripped into large blocks, and thrust southward by the younger Wisconsinan ice sheet. Many of the ripped-up blocks are surrounded by light-colored sands of the upper drift.

Sediment slides characterize the steep bluffs. Subsurface drainage near Lakeside Drive and Rodman's Hollow, as well as drainage from surface waters such as Fresh, Peckham, and Mitchell Ponds, may also contribute to the instability of the bluffs.

View toward Great Point from a parking area off Mohegan Trail near its junction with Lakeside Drive. In the distance is the curved profile of a faulted slump block. Note the nearly horizontal layers that can be traced across the gullied cliff faces.

Folds in lakebeds in the lower drift at the base of Mohegan Bluffs near stairs that descend from the parking area to the beach. —Daniel P. Murray photo

A jumble of older and younger drift in a cliff exposure at Mohegan Bluffs.
—Jon C. Boothroyd photo

Postglacial History

Block Island was probably ice free by 19,000 years ago. A radiocarbon date confirms that around the same time, the Hudson lobe had withdrawn to the latitude of White Plains, New York, on the mainland east of Greenwich, Connecticut. With sea level still much lower, Block Island was part of the

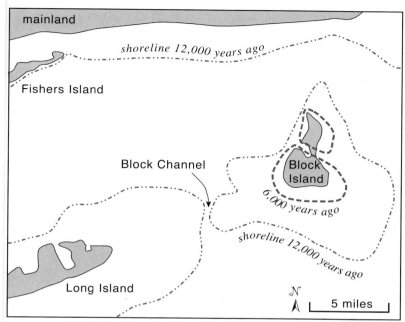

Block Island was finally an island by 12,000 years ago.

mainland and Glacial Lake Connecticut occupied Long Island Sound. At its highest level, Glacial Lake Connecticut probably connected to a glacial lake in Block Island Sound. The outlet of these freshwater lakes spilled over the morainal deposits that connected Block Island to Long Island. The escaping water carved deep channels across the continental shelf into the sea, including a large channel between Long Island and Block Island. The lakes were probably gone by about 15,500 years ago, but seawater soon filled the void.

After the ice receded from Block Island, the climate was still bracing, even severe. A 3-foot-thick blanket of windblown particles overlies the till on Block Island, evidence that the wind blew hard and there was little protective vegetation. Eventually plants began to take root in the barren landscape, and pollen- and spore-producing plants left a rich record of the vegetation. Pollen has been analyzed from the Indian Head Neck varves and from bog sediments of Great Swamp.

Meltwater flowed into the oceans, and by 12,000 years ago, the sea was within 100 feet of its present level. Block Island would have been an island by then, with seawater in Block Island and Long Island Sounds. By 6,000 years ago, sea level was close to its present level. Block Island was actually two islands then—two conspicuous ridges separated by a channel where Great Salt Pond is now located. Ocean currents transported sand from eroding cliffs and united the two islands with barrier beaches.

— Road Guides in Connecticut —

Interstate 84
Massachusetts State Line—Manchester
28 MILES

Between the Massachusetts border and eastern Tolland, I-84 passes over thrust sheets of the Central Maine Terrane. The Central Maine Terrane consists primarily of northeast-trending units of Brimfield Schist of Ordovician age. Northeast-trending thrust faults separate narrow belts of harder and softer units, producing a characteristic hogback topography.

Brimfield Schist of the Central Maine Terrane exposed at the Mobil station near exit 70 on CT 32.

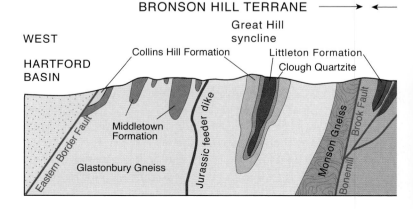

East-west cross section featuring the Bronson Hill and Central Maine Terranes in northeastern Connecticut.
—Modified from Rodgers, 1985

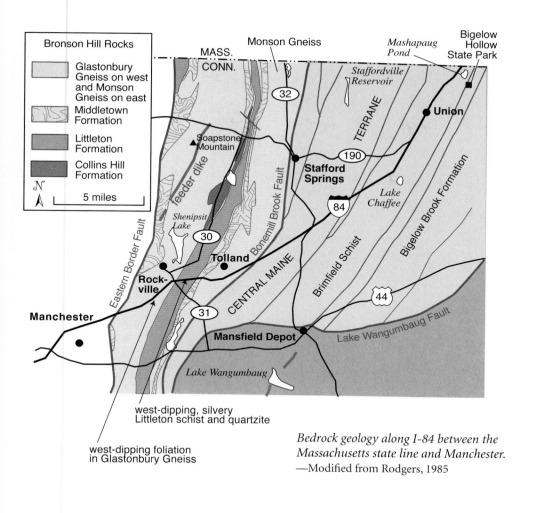

Bedrock geology along I-84 between the
Massachusetts state line and Manchester.
—Modified from Rodgers, 1985

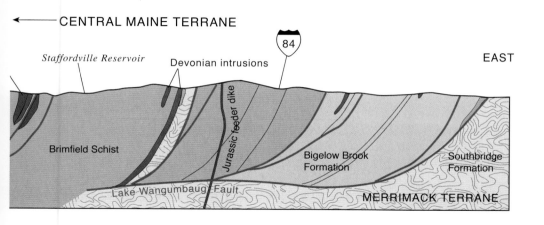

East-dipping thrust faults in Brimfield Schist along CT 32 in Willington near Old River Road.

The linear troughs and irregular ridges of high-grade metamorphosed schist and gneiss were sculptured by erosion in Tertiary time, long before continental ice sheets flowed over the land in Pleistocene time.

Wide zones dominated by sulfidic, biotite-garnet Brimfield Schist are present just east of I-84 from the Massachusetts line to Lake Chaffee in Ashford. The schist weathers to yellowish orange. Large outcrops are found along CT 171, north of the town office of Union, and in Bigelow Hollow State Park.

Iron Mining in Stafford

During the colonial period, bog iron was mined in eastern Connecticut. This type of iron, a soft deposit of hydrous iron oxides, is formed by precipitation of iron from water. In Connecticut, the bog iron is usually found in swamps fed by iron-rich springs. The bog iron ores are associated with iron-rich bedrock, mainly the rusty-weathering Brimfield Schist.

Stafford Hollow, simply labeled "Stafford" on maps, is the site of an iron furnace built in 1737. Stafford Hollow is situated on the upper reaches of the Willimantic River at the junction of CT 319 (Orcuttville Road) and CT 19 near Riverside Pond. This furnace gave way to the Lafayette Furnace, named in gratitude to the French general of Revolutionary War fame. The first stoves manufactured in Connecticut were made here from superior quality ore beds. The furnace was closed around 1837 when the ore beds of Stafford were exhausted.

Staffordville, on CT 19 at the southwest end of Staffordville Reservoir, had an iron foundry in 1830 and was known as the New Furnace. Stafford

Springs, located at the confluence of the Middle River and Furnace Brook, is now the main center of Stafford. Colonists called the sulfurous warm springs here "Indian Spring," and they were indeed frequented by the Narragansetts, Wampanoags, and Pequots.

Bonemill Brook Fault

I-84 crosses the north-trending Bonemill Brook Fault between exits 69 and 68. This fault zone, which forms the western margin of the Central Maine Terrane and the eastern margin of the Bronson Hill Terrane, is where Laurentia and the Bronson Hill volcanic arc welded to the eastern Connecticut thrust sheets between 425 and 370 million years ago. This

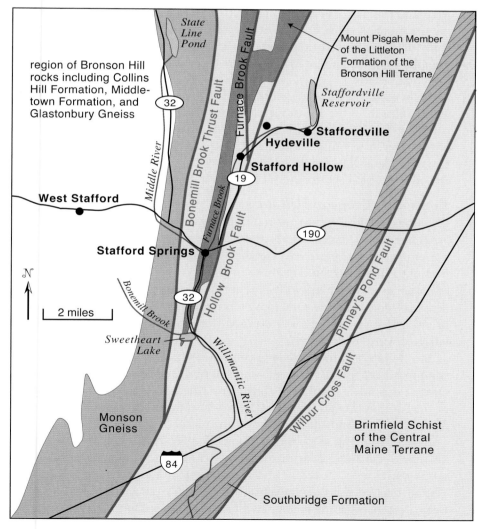

The Bonemill Brook Fault, with its many branches, separates the Bronson Hill Terrane from the Central Maine Terrane.

broad fault zone consists of a complex of three faults located where the Middle River and Furnace Brook join to form the Willimantic River.

Soapstone Mountain in Shenipsit State Forest

The 1,075-foot-high Soapstone Mountain, in the southeast corner of Somers, is composed of gabbro that was later altered to soapstone, a massive rock made primarily of the mineral talc. Another 0.5-mile-diameter body of soapstone forms the hill to the northwest of Soapstone Mountain. At least eight smaller, north-northeast-trending gabbro plutons form a linear zone in this part of the Bronson Hill volcanic arc. The plutons are Ordovician in age and are part of the Middletown Formation or intruded it. The alteration to soapstone probably took place in the Acadian mountain building event. Native Americans carved bowls from the soapstone. A series of three fire-control observation towers have been constructed on Soapstone Mountain, the first of which was built in 1930. The blue-blazed Shenipsit Trail passes over Soapstone Mountain en route to Massachusetts.

To the east, a north-northeast-trending, 10-mile-long diabase dike passes within 0.1 mile of the Soapstone Mountain pluton. This dike is essentially parallel to the famous Higganum dike that crosses Connecticut from east of New Haven to Union, near the Massachusetts line. About 200 million years ago, these dikes fed the basalt flows that filled the Hartford rift basin, and covered some of the eastern Connecticut thrust sheets.

Rockville's Bronson Hill Rocks

The Bronson Hill Terrane runs continuously from western Maine through New Hampshire, Massachusetts, and Connecticut. In Connecticut, it forms a prominent north-northeast-trending upland ridge that rises abruptly from the Hartford Basin. The Bronson Hill Terrane was originally a chain of volcanic islands that lay offshore to the east of the Laurentian continent in Ordovician time. Outcrops of formations that comprise part of the Bronson Hill Terrane are well exposed close to Rockville, a well-named village in Vernon along I-84.

The Bolton syncline, called the Great Hill syncline at its southern end, is a prominent feature that runs the length of the terrane. Throughout most of this fold's length, the Devonian Littleton Formation is outlined by the Silurian Clough Quartzite. Near I-84 and the Vernon-Tolland line, glacial outwash sand and gravel cover the rocks.

A superb outcrop of garnet-bearing Bolton Schist, a local name for the Littleton Formation, occurs just north of I-84 northeast of exit 67. Follow CT 31 north to CT 30 and head east on CT 30 for 1 mile. At the Tolland-Vernon line, go right on Industrial Park Road West and follow Gerber Drive to roadcuts at the junction with Research Way. The dark gray schist was originally deposited as a marine mudstone rich in iron, alumina, and organic material in Late Silurian to Early Devonian time. It was then deformed by folding and metamorphosed twice. The first time, during the Acadian mountain building event in Late Devonian time, garnet crystals formed. Small, blocky staurolite crystals, although not abundant here, formed during the second metamorphic event, the Alleghanian mountain building event that occurred about 300 to 250 million years ago, in Permian time.

Top: *Quarry in dark gray Bolton Schist, a local name for the Littleton Formation.*

Right: *Chunks of Bolton Schist with small garnets and larger staurolite crystals, formed by metamorphism in the Acadian and Alleghanian mountain building events, respectively.*

Burgundy Hill Quarry

Burgundy Hill Quarry, located on private property in western Tolland within 2 miles of the garnet-bearing Bolton Schist outcrop described on page 108, was excavated in the Late Silurian Clough Quartzite. The name Burgundy was given by the quarry owner because of the burgundy-tinted splotches that characterize the larger blocks of quartzite. It is also the color of the abundant 0.4-inch-long garnets that were mined from the quarry more than one hundred years ago for use as abrasives. The quartzite has also been used for architectural stone. Because quartzite consists predominantly of silicon dioxide, it doesn't contain enough iron and alumina to form garnets when subjected to elevated temperatures and pressures. The garnets formed in a micaceous schist layer adjacent to quartzite. When the schist layer breaks off, garnets remain on the surface of the quartzite.

Eastern Border Fault

I-84 crosses the Eastern Border Fault 0.5 mile east of exit 65 in Talcottville. Here the Jurassic Portland Arkose and older Mesozoic rocks of the Hartford Basin have been dropped downward relative to the Bronson Hill rocks to the east.

About 0.5 mile northwest of Vernon Center, angular rock fragments form a breccia along the Eastern Border Fault, especially near the New York, New Haven & Hartford Railroad crossing of Ogden Brook. East of Talcottville, where the railroad crosses the fault, you can see folded and faulted schists and redbeds of the Portland Arkose in the railroad cut. Within 1 mile of the Eastern Border Fault, hot fluids associated with the fault have converted iron-bearing minerals in the Glastonbury Gneiss and amphibolite of the Middletown Formation to chlorite.

Interstate 95
Rhode Island State Line—Branford
60 MILES

In southern Connecticut, I-95 crosses several long bridges over drowned river valleys, the most prominent of which are the Mystic, the Thames, and the Connecticut. The Pawcatuck River, on the state border, and the Niantic, on the border of East Lyme and Waterford, are also drowned river valleys. The melting of most of the Wisconsinan ice sheet increased sea level, so seawater inundated these valleys, creating harbors.

Between the Connecticut border in North Stonington and Branford, I-95 crosses primarily rocks of the Hope Valley Subterrane of the Avalon Terrane. Most of these rocks are Late Proterozoic gneisses and stratified

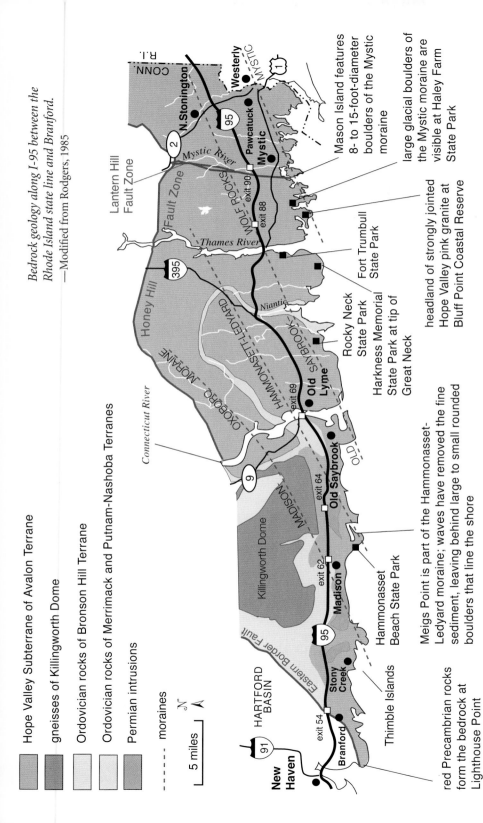

Bedrock geology along I-95 between the Rhode Island state line and Branford.
—Modified from Rodgers, 1985

Hope Valley Subterrane of Avalon Terrane

gneisses of Killingworth Dome

Ordovician rocks of Bronson Hill Terrane

Ordovician rocks of Merrimack and Putnam-Nashoba Terranes

Permian intrusions

– – – – moraines

N

5 miles

Mason Island features 8- to 15-foot-diameter boulders of the Mystic moraine

large glacial boulders of the Mystic moraine are visible at Haley Farm State Park

headland of strongly jointed Hope Valley pink granite at Bluff Point Coastal Reserve

Fort Trumbull State Park

Rocky Neck State Park

Harkness Memorial State Park at tip of Great Neck

Meigs Point is part of the Hammonasset-Ledyard moraine; waves have removed the fine sediment, leaving behind large to small rounded boulders that line the shore

Hammonasset Beach State Park

Thimble Islands

red Precambrian rocks form the bedrock at Lighthouse Point

CONN.
R.I.

Westerly

MYSTIC

N. Stonington

Pawcatuck
Mystic

2

95

1

Lantern Hill Fault Zone

Mystic River

Fault Zone

WOLF ROCKS

exit 90

exit 88

Thames River

395

Honey Hill

Niantic

HAMMONASSET-LEDYARD

OXOBORO MORAINE

Connecticut River

Old Lyme

exit 69

9

SAYBROOK

OLD

Old Saybrook

exit 64

MADISON

Killingworth Dome

exit 62

Madison

95

HARTFORD BASIN

91

New Haven

exit 54

Branford

Stony Creek

Eastern Border Fault

An outcrop of Plainfield Formation at the junction of Cow Hill Road and CT 184, 0.75 mile west of the Mystic River. The layered gneiss has pink boudinaged pegmatite layers.

metamorphic rocks, but some younger granites intrude the Avalon rocks. Late Proterozoic rocks include the Plainfield Formation and the Waterford Group, of which the Mamacoke Formation, the Rope Ferry Gneiss, and the New London Gneiss are a part. These formations occur as east-west-trending bands and great sills between the coast and the Honey Hill Fault Zone, about 15 miles to the north. Younger rocks of Permian age, including the Potter Hill Granite Gneiss and the Narragansett Pier Granite, intrude the older rocks.

Rocks of the Hope Valley Subterrane have been repeatedly deformed by northwest-directed collisions and doming. For a distance of 4 miles south of the Honey Hill Fault Zone, east-striking, north-dipping foliation characterizes rocks that have been tightly compressed into folds as long as 35 miles and with both limbs dipping north. The foliation parallels the axial planes of the folds. Farther south and closer to the coast, however, the same strata have been domed and appear to be more complexly deformed.

Potter Hill Granite Gneiss

I-95 crosses the Permian-age Potter Hill Granite Gneiss between the Rhode Island border and Anguilla Brook in Stonington. This medium- to coarse-grained, equigranular rock consists of quartz, sodium and potassium feldspar, and a bit of biotite. It is found discontinuously over some 60 miles from southwestern Rhode Island to the Connecticut River. Foliated portions are intimately mixed with undeformed granite. Redistribution of the magma during crystallization probably gave rise to the gneissic portions, which look like wavy bands. Because of this, the Potter Hill Granite Gneiss had long been grouped with the Late Proterozoic igneous rocks of the Hope Valley Subterrane. More recent studies, however, yielded a date of 279 million years ago for its crystallization, indicating it formed during the Alleghanian mountain building event.

From Anguilla Brook in Stonington through Groton, I-95 follows the westward trend of the stratified group of formations, including gneiss of the Mamacoke Formation in the Precambrian Waterford Group, rocks that the Potter Hill Granite Gneiss intruded.

Stonington

Stonington, a coastal town on a rocky point of Rope Ferry Gneiss of the Waterford Group, was named Pawcatuck or Mistick by the Indians but was renamed Stonington by colonists in 1666. It was an early shipbuilding center known as the "Nursery of Sea Men." The Pegleg Brown House, at 94 Water Street, is the birthplace of Nathaniel B. Palmer, who in 1820 discovered Antarctica. The Old Stone Custom House, 10 Main Street, is constructed of Hope Valley Alaskite Gneiss. The Old Stone Lighthouse with its octagonal tower, located at Stonington Point, is also constructed of the rock.

Lantern Hill Fault Zone

About 0.25 mile west of the Mystic River, I-95 crosses the north-trending Lantern Hill Fault Zone, which broke rocks about 200 million years ago during the formation of the Hartford rift basin. The fault zone cuts a highly contorted complex of quartzite and quartz schist of the Plainfield Formation, stratified gneiss of the Mamacoke Formation, and the plutonic Hope Valley Alaskite Gneiss. See **Connecticut 2: Stonington— Glastonbury** for discussion of the fault zone.

Moraines along I-95

I-95 crosses three recessional moraines and parallels three others between the Rhode Island border and Branford. All of them trend east-northeast and formed along the edge of the receding ice sheet. The moraines are not continuous features but rather occur in segments, with parts eroded away in places and perhaps never well developed in other places. Some feature a double line of parallel segments.

Fishers Island–Charlestown moraine. This large recessional moraine, the first moraine north of the Ronkonkoma terminal moraine, was deposited about 19,000 years ago. It forms Fishers Island of New York.

Clumps-Avondale moraine. This chain of small bouldery islands and shoals lies about 0.5 mile north of the Fishers Island–Charlestown moraine.

Mystic moraine. The Mystic moraine extends from Pine Island off Avery Point in Groton through Mason Island and southern Stonington to Westerly, staying south of I-95. You can see large glacial boulders at Haley Farm State Park and on Mason Island.

Glacial boulders from the Mystic moraine were used to make this stone fence at Haley Farm State Park.

Old Saybrook–Wolf Rocks moraine. I-95 crosses the line of the Old Saybrook–Wolf Rocks moraine near the bridge over the Thames River, but the moraine isn't well developed here. The moraine heads out into Long Island Sound at Cornfield Point in Old Saybrook. When traced offshore, it curves, following the former curved edge of an ice lobe that sat offshore of New Haven Harbor about 17,500 years ago.

Hammonasset-Ledyard moraine. I-95 crosses the Hammonasset-Ledyard moraine near exit 65. It heads out to sea at Meigs Point. A submerged extension of this moraine is marked by a buoy on the trend toward Falkner Island. See the discussion of Hammonasset Beach State Park later in this road guide.

Madison-Oxoboro moraine. This moraine isn't well-developed, perhaps because it's partially buried by fluvial and ice margin deposits. Ridges and mounds, each less than 0.5 mile long, extend from Hogshead Point in Guilford east to the Hammonasset River. I-95 crosses the line of the Madison-Oxoboro moraine at exit 62.

Bluff Point Coastal Reserve

Strongly jointed Hope Valley Alaskite Gneiss forms the headland at Bluff Point Coastal Reserve. Bushy Point, a 1-mile-long spit, is a sandy beach that fronts the Poquonnock River. Wind and waves have moved the coarse sand into dunes that override the marshes.

Pink granitic rock of the Hope Valley Alaskite Gneiss forms a headland at Bluff Point in Groton. Parallel fractures in the rock are joints.

Thames Harbor

New London and Groton are located along the drowned river valley of the Thames River, one of the deepest harbors on the Atlantic. From the New London Ledge Lighthouse, the Thames River extends north 16 miles to the confluence of the Quinebaug and Yantic Rivers. Great Neck, on the west side of the harbor, is made primarily of Rope Ferry Gneiss of the Waterford Group, which is easily observed at a headland in Harkness Memorial State Park. The New London Ledge Lighthouse, to the southeast of Great Neck, is also built on gneiss of the Waterford Group. A large area of outcrops of

New London Gneiss is visible north of I-95 at exit 84 and east of CT 32. Mamacoke Hill, an island peninsula in the New London Harbor about 2 miles north of the I-95 bridge, is the type locality of the Mamacoke Formation of the Waterford Group. A type locality is the specific geographic place where a geologic feature or rock unit was first recognized and described.

Fort Trumbull, on the west side of the New London Harbor south of I-95, is built on a foundation of New London Gneiss.

New London Gneiss near exit 84 just west of the Thames River.

Headland of Rope Ferry Gneiss cut by pink pegmatite veins of Narragansett Pier Granite at Harkness Memorial State Park.

Darker gneissic banding is present in this large outcrop of New London Gneiss near exit 84.

Lyme Dome

West of the Thames River, the swirls in the bedrock get even more complex. Geologists have identified a number of structures in this region, including Lyme Dome, Montville Dome, Selden Neck Dome, and the New London synform. A synform is a complex fold structure in which it is difficult to tell which direction is up. A dome is an upward bulge in the rock layers. These structures in southeastern Connecticut formed when the collision with Gondwana shoved the hard rocks of the Avalon Terrane toward the hard buttress of the Killingworth Dome during the Alleghanian mountain building event.

Rodgers's 1985 *Bedrock Map of Connecticut* shows the 10-mile-long Lyme Dome, which trends northeast through Old Lyme and East Lyme,

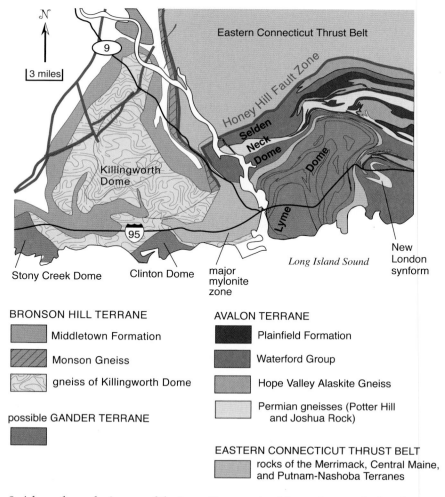

Swirls on the geologic map of the Lyme Dome region hint at the complexity of the geology here. —Modified from Walsh and others, 2007

to be primarily Late Proterozoic rock of the Avalon Terrane intruded by Permian granites. Work published in 2007 suggests that the Late Proterozoic rocks in the Lyme Dome may actually belong to the Gander Terrane. This work theorizes that the Avalon Terrane was wedged between the Gander Terrane and the eastern Connecticut thrust sheets.

Highly deformed rocks of the Merrimack Terrane wrap around the east, north, and west sides of the Lyme Dome. The Selden Neck, Montville, and New London structures, composed of Avalonian rocks, also seem to bend around or into the Lyme Dome, suggesting that the Lyme Dome structure formed first. On geologic maps, it looks like the New London synform forcibly indented the east side of the Lyme Dome like a battering ram. This collision likely took place during the Alleghanian mountain building event. Ongoing geologic studies in this area are attempting to understand its complexity.

Rocky Neck State Park

At Rocky Neck State Park, a crescent-shaped pocket beach nestles between two rocky headlands of gneiss in the Lyme Dome. You can witness erosion and deposition at work with every tidal cycle, as waves wash against the headlands. The sand, derived from gneiss and quartzite, is mainly quartz, along with some feldspar. Look for dark bands of the mineral magnetite, which is heavier than the quartz and feldspar and congregates in layers when washed back and forth by waves.

Griswold Point

Griswold Point, a 0.75-mile-long spit at the mouth of the Connecticut River in Old Lyme, is a westward extension of White Sands Beach. It is reaching west toward Great Island marshlands but has not yet connected. The spit, which changes dynamically from year to year, partially protects the marsh.

Killingworth Dome

The Connecticut River forms a quasi boundary between the wide band of Late Proterozoic rocks to the east and the large Killingworth Dome to the west. The Late Proterozoic rocks actually do cross the river and continue west along the coast, wrapping around the south end of the Killingworth Dome, hugging the coast to New Haven Harbor, and then disappearing beneath the waters of Long Island Sound. The Killingworth Dome, a former volcano cored by hard gneiss, formed a buttress that stopped the Avalon Terrane in its tracks during the Alleghanian mountain building event. The geologically young Connecticut River did not, of course, have anything to do with determining the point of the collision, but the river, too, has avoided the Killingworth Dome, eroding a path to the east of these hard rocks.

Softer rocks caught between the Killingworth buttress and the hard rocks of Avalonia were sheared and slenderized almost beyond recognition. How could it be that the more than 50,000 feet of strata of the four combined eastern Connecticut thrust sheets, which occupy the eastern half of Connecticut farther north, have been so drastically thinned? These "softer" rocks were probably pushed up and out along faults. Individual areas of rock may not have been softer than the gneiss of Avalonia or the Killingworth Dome, but the rocks in the thrust sheets are less homogeneous, with more breaks and changes in rock type, making them more likely to be pushed out of the way. Presumably the missing rocks ended up in the enormous mountains that formed during the collision and have since eroded away. Some of these excessively thinned rock formations were thickened by folding; they can be seen near and along I-95 at exit 69. They extend west along I-95 from Old Saybrook to exit 64, at CT 145 in Westbrook.

Between exit 64 in Westbrook and exit 54 in Branford, I-95 crosses back and forth between gneisses of the Killingworth Dome and the Late Proterozoic rocks of either Avalonia or the Gander Terrane, as well as Permian granites that intruded during the Alleghanian mountain building event. For more about the Killingworth Dome, see **Connecticut 9: Old Saybrook—Middletown.**

Hammonasset Beach State Park

Hammonasset Beach State Park, south of exit 62 in Madison, is the most visited state park in Connecticut, and at 919 acres, also the largest. Its 2-mile-long beach and dune complex extends landward to the northwest from Meigs Point. Sand for this beach and dune complex, called

View east across the Hammonasset River and marshlands to Cedar Island, a spit, in the distance. A spit is a beach that extends away from a headland in such a way that open water or a marsh lies between the beach and the shore.

Hammonasset Beach, is generated by wave action reworking the glacial delta deposits underlying much of the state park. The bouldery headland at Meigs Point is the southwest end of the emergent part of the Hammonasset-Ledyard moraine.

The Hammonasset-Ledyard moraine crosses I-95 near exit 65. Near Hammonasset, this boulder moraine forms two linear, aligned belts that consist of parallel segments of boulder till more than 1 mile long. The southern belt is at Meigs Point, a bouldery prominence with splendid views all around. The northern belt is to the right along the trail to Willard Island. Large boulders in the marsh are part of the northern belt.

The Hammonasset-Ledyard moraine extends east-northeast from Meigs Point to Westbrook (and beyond). The till of the moraine is exposed around the viewing platform at Meigs Point, but the finer-grained components have been lost due to winnowing by the surf, leaving behind large boulders. Some segments of the moraine stand at the head of delta deposits that built into Glacial Lake Connecticut along the coast between Clinton and Old Saybrook. Toward the southwest, a linear array of small shoals marks the crest of the moraine where it extends offshore into Long Island Sound.

At Meigs Point you can look north and east across the large wetlands between Meigs Point and Clinton Harbor. A nature center, located in a farmhouse built in 1828, is connected to Willard Island by a nature trail. A self-guided trail also explores the moraine at Meigs Point.

Boulders from the Hammonasset-Ledyard moraine at Meigs Point. —Janet Stone photo, U.S. Geological Survey

Stony Creek

Stony Creek Granite Gneiss, a well-known architectural stone, was quarried at several sites in Branford and Guilford in the early twentieth century, and at least one quarry is still active. This red to pink, medium- to very coarse-grained granite gneiss intruded the Late Proterozoic rocks hugging the southern margin of the Killingworth Dome. Although it was long thought to be a Late Proterozoic igneous pluton, recent studies suggest that the magma that became the Stony Creek Granite Gneiss probably derived from melting of Late Proterozoic basement rocks just prior to 275 million years ago, during the Alleghanian mountain building event. It is called a "stitching pluton" because it intrudes the boundary between two older units. A large body of Stony Creek Granite Gneiss underlies southeast Branford.

The Thimble Islands, in Long Island Sound off Branford, are in large part composed of a complexly mixed assemblage of Late Proterozoic rocks, Stony Creek Granite Gneiss, and red to pink, medium- to coarse-grained Narragansett Pier Granite.

Eastern Border Fault and Lighthouse Point

The Eastern Border Fault, which formed during the opening of the Atlantic Ocean basin about 200 million years ago, separates the Avalonian and Bronson Hill volcanic arc rocks from the Hartford Basin rocks of Triassic and Jurassic age. I-95 crosses the Eastern Border Fault at exit 54. South of I-95, the fault trends west-southwest through East Haven and into the eastern part of New Haven Harbor at the northern margin of Lighthouse Point. The lighthouse sits on a colorful Late Proterozoic granite gneiss aptly named Light House Gneiss. This is the farthest west that Avalonian rocks are visible, though presumably they extend farther west beneath the waters and sediments of Long Island Sound. Light House Gneiss is a red to light pink or gray, medium-grained, well-foliated granitic gneiss.

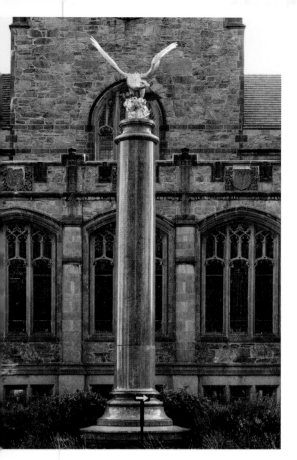

This 35-foot-tall pillar of polished Stony Creek Granite Gneiss is now at Boston College with the Boston College Eagle perched on top. Prior to the construction of I-93, the pillar was once located in Dewey Square, at South Station in downtown Boston, where it upheld a statue of Admiral Dewey. —Gary Gilbert photo

The lighthouse at Lighthouse Point at the southeast end of New Haven Harbor sits on a red Late Proterozoic rock called Light House Gneiss.

Interstate 395
Massachusetts State Line—Interstate 95
60 MILES

Between the Massachusetts border and the Honey Hill Fault Zone south of Norwich, I-395 primarily passes through the Putnam-Nashoba Terrane of Ordovician age. The eastern edge of the terrane is marked by the Lake Char Fault, the major thrust fault that separates the eastern Connecticut thrust sheets from the Late Proterozoic rocks of the Avalon Terrane. The

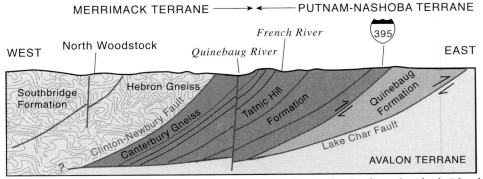

East-west cross section about 2 miles south of the Massachusetts border from the Rhode Island border west to Woodstock. The Merrimack and Putnam-Nashoba Terranes are thrust toward the east onto Late Proterozoic formations of the Avalon Terrane. The Paleozoic formations are truncated at depth by the Lake Char thrust fault. —Modified from Rodgers, 1985

Well-layered, gray to dark gray gneiss and schist of the Tatnic Hill Formation at exit 100 in Thompson. View looking northeast along the northbound exit ramp north of Wilsonville Road. These rocks weather dark, but their fresh surfaces are very light because of the quartz and feldspar minerals.

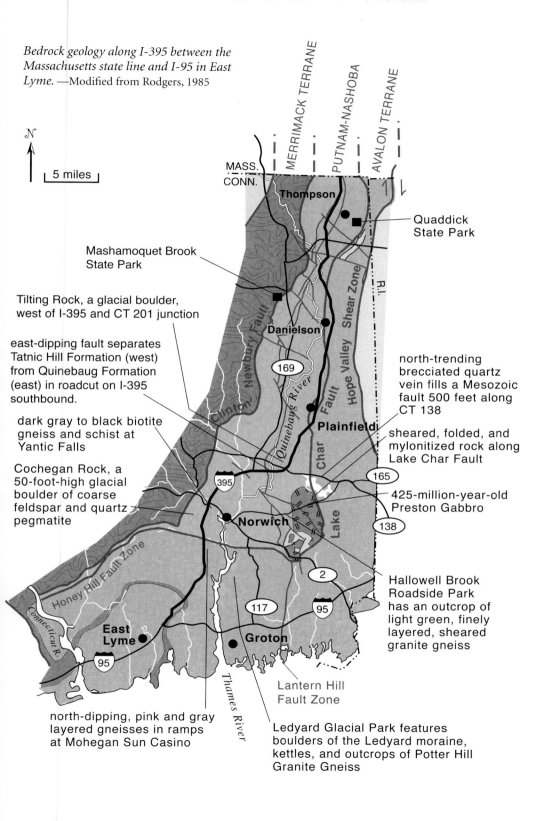

Bedrock geology along I-395 between the Massachusetts state line and I-95 in East Lyme. —Modified from Rodgers, 1985

N

5 miles

MERRIMACK TERRANE

PUTNAM-NASHOBA

AVALON TERRANE

MASS.
CONN.

Thompson

Quaddick
State Park

Mashamoquet Brook
State Park

Tilting Rock, a glacial boulder,
west of I-395 and CT 201 junction

Newbury Fault

Hope Valley Shear Zone

R.I.

Danielson

169

east-dipping fault separates
Tatnic Hill Formation (west)
from Quinebaug Formation
(east) in roadcut on I-395
southbound.

Clinton

Quinebaug River

north-trending
brecciated quartz
vein fills a Mesozoic
fault 500 feet along
CT 138

dark gray to black biotite
gneiss and schist at
Yantic Falls

Plainfield

Char Fault

sheared, folded, and
mylonitized rock along
Lake Char Fault

Cochegan Rock, a
50-foot-high glacial
boulder of coarse
feldspar and quartz
pegmatite

395

165

Norwich

Lake

425-million-year-old
Preston Gabbro

138

Honey Hill Fault Zone

2

Hallowell Brook
Roadside Park
has an outcrop of
light green, finely
layered, sheared
granite gneiss

Connecticut R.

East
Lyme

117

95

Groton

95

Lantern Hill
Fault Zone

north-dipping, pink and gray
layered gneisses in ramps
at Mohegan Sun Casino

Thames River

Ledyard Glacial Park features
boulders of the Ledyard moraine,
kettles, and outcrops of Potter Hill
Granite Gneiss

Putnam-Nashoba Terrane contains two west-dipping thrust sheets, each composed of a single formation. The Quinebaug Formation, the eastern and lower thrust sheet, is a gray layered gneiss. The Tatnic Hill Formation, the western, overlying thrust sheet, is a gray gneiss and schist with interlayered grayish green calc-silicate gneiss.

Our traverse along I-395 begins in Thompson on the Tatnic Hill Formation. At Mechanicsville, I-395 crosses onto the Quinebaug Formation and then crosses the Lake Char Fault at Dayville. East of the Lake Char Fault, I-395 crosses the Plainfield Formation and Late Proterozoic gneiss of the Avalon Terrane. From exit 90 in Danielson to southern Plainfield, I-395 follows the Lake Char Fault Zone, which is nearly 0.5 mile wide here. The zone contains intensely recrystallized rocks and mylonite of Paleozoic age. In Plainfield, I-395 crosses back onto rocks of the Putnam-Nashoba Terrane.

Glacial Lakes in the Quinebaug River Basin
South of Putnam, the interstate follows the Quinebaug River for much of its length. The Quinebaug River joins the Yantic River at Norwich, and the combined streams flow to Long Island Sound as the Thames River. When the ice margin retreated into the broad valley of the Quinebaug River, Glacial Lake Quinebaug formed south of the ice and north of a pile of glacial sediments that filled the modern bedrock gorge of the present Quinebaug River south of Jewett City. The water level of the lake was controlled by a bedrock spillway at 134 feet elevation next to the gorge, giving the lake more than ordinary durability. The glacial lake lengthened northward in the Quinebaug lowlands to about US 6 in Brooklyn. As the ice front receded northward from Danielson, the level of the deltas at the edge of the ice was controlled by small bodies of water, including ice-dammed ponds.

A good place to see delta sands is east of exit 89 and south of Central Village at the entrance to the Hopkins Sand and Gravel Pit near the Providence & Worcester Railroad, about 0.25 mile west of CT 12. The deposits cover a large area east of the Quinebaug River.

Glacial Lake Oneco was dammed by ice in tributary valleys to the Quinebaug River valley about 16,500 years ago. The lake filled the Moosup River and Quanduck Brook drainages, extending into Rhode Island near CT 14 and RI 14.

Pachaug, Glasgo, and Beach Ponds
Heading east from I-395 at exit 85, CT 138 travels past Pachaug and Glasgo Ponds, which sit on glacial lakebeds. When ice still filled the Quinebaug River valley, meltwater draining from the higher country along the Rhode Island border backed up against the ice and filled the Pachaug River valley. Glacial Lakes Voluntown and Pachaug were two of these

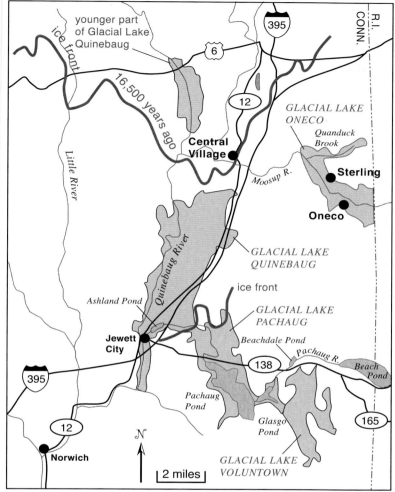

Glacial lakes formed in the Quinebaug River drainage basin as the ice front receded to the north. —Modified from Stone and others, 2005

ice-dammed lakes. Ponds such as Beachdale and associated sand plains near Mount Misery are remnants of Glacial Lake Voluntown. Hopeville Pond and Ashland Pond, also drained by the Pachaug River, are situated on the extensive sand plain.

CT 138 crosses the Lake Char Fault near the middle of Pachaug Pond, and the pond inherits a part of its north-northwest trend from the broad mylonite zone of shearing in the fault zone. South of Pachaug Pond, the Preston Gabbro of Ordovician age forms Bay Mountain, which is skirted on its north flank by CT 165. You can see the gabbro in roadcuts along CT 165.

View to the east of a Z-shaped fold in gneiss of the Ordovician Tatnic Hill Formation in a roadcut at exit 83 from I-395. The roadcut is at the entrance to the eastbound lane of CT 97. The fold measures about 25 to 30 feet from top to bottom.

Continue east on CT 165 to see cliff-sized igneous rocks of the Avalon Terrane east of Beach Pond. Elongate quartz grains in the foliated Late Proterozoic gneiss form spectacular deformation structures that are elongate in a northerly direction. The foliation strikes west-northwest and, near the Hope Valley Shear Zone farther east, dips at high angles both east and west. Beach Pond fills a prominent dip in the landscape that follows the southeast-trend of the granitic bedrock.

Norwich Area

In Norwich, between exits 80 and 83, I-395 passes through roadcuts exposing folds in the Tatnic Hill Formation. You can see this rock unit up close at Yantic Falls, on the Yantic River just above its confluence with the Thames. See **Connecticut 2: Stonington—Glastonbury** for more information about Yantic Falls and the Norwich area.

Honey Hill Fault Zone at Fort Shantok

I-395 crosses the Honey Hill Fault Zone at the border of Norwich and Montville, about 0.5 mile south of exit 80. Here, Trading Cove Brook follows the trend of the fault. The Honey Hill Fault is basically the westward continuation of the Lake Char Fault. The two faults separate the underlying Avalon Terrane to the south from the overlying, eastern Connecticut thrust sheets. Originally, a single fault formed during the Acadian mountain building event when Avalonia collided with

View of west-dipping Tatnic Hill Formation containing sills and lenses of granite, which in turn contain xenoliths of mafic gneiss. The roadcut is along the southbound lane of I-395 between exits 81 and 80.

Laurentia. The startling change in trend where the Lake Char Fault becomes the Honey Hill Fault Zone, developed when Gondwana collided with Laurentia during the Alleghanian mountain building event. Rocks of the Merrimack and Putnam-Nashoba Terranes have been smeared for a distance of 18 miles along the north side of the Honey Hill Fault Zone west of the Connecticut River.

Along the Thames River

Alternating layers of east-west-trending metasedimentary and igneous rocks of the Hope Valley Subterrane of the Avalon Terrane extend south along the Thames River from the Honey Hill Fault Zone. Closer to the coast, however, the layers are intensely folded and refolded. Some of these fold structures are tens of miles long.

Cochegan Rock, a 50- by 50- by 40-foot glacial boulder, is one of the biggest in Connecticut, with an estimated weight of 10,000 tons. It's located off Raymond Hill Road in a wooded area about 0.5 mile west-southwest of the Mobil Station between exits 79 and 79A in Montville. The rock is a coarse-grained, quartz-feldspar pegmatite. The quartz is predominantly smoky, and many rounded feldspar crystals are associated with sparse muscovite crystals and gray to black biotite.

Cochegan Rock, a huge glacial boulder, in Montville west of I-395.

In the Thames River Basin, early meltwater deposits were graded to the water level in Glacial Lake Connecticut in Long Island Sound, but most were eroded by later meltwater. Glacial Lake Uncasville was impounded behind a segment of the Ledyard moraine that crosses the Thames River valley at Uncasville. Ice margin deposits and river deltas were built into this lake as the ice retreated northward to the Norwich area. Segments of the Ledyard moraine exist east and west of I-395, but there is no ridge in the path of the highway. You can see the moraine, as well as outcrops of Potter Hill Granite Gneiss at Ledyard Glacial Park, on the east side of the Thames River near the junction of Whalehead Road and Vinegar Hill Road in Ledyard.

US 6 and US 44
Rhode Island State Line—Manchester
45 MILES

US 6 and US 44 cross all four terranes that were thrust to the east over the Avalon microcontinent, stacked one on top of the other, during the Acadian mountain building event. The terranes form north-trending bands separated by north-trending faults, so both highways pass over similar

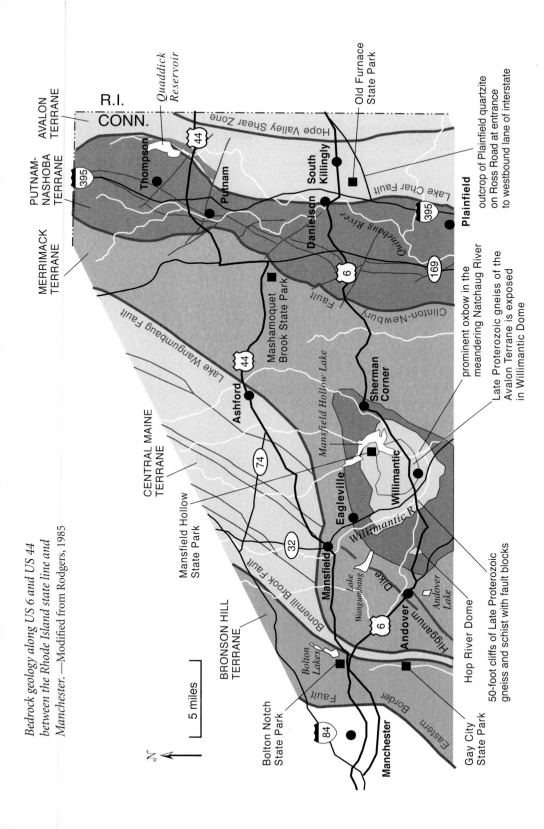

Bedrock geology along US 6 and US 44 between the Rhode Island state line and Manchester. —Modified from Rodgers, 1985

N

5 miles

R.I.
CONN.

AVALON TERRANE

PUTNAM-NASHOBA TERRANE

MERRIMACK TERRANE

CENTRAL MAINE TERRANE

BRONSON HILL TERRANE

Quaddick Reservoir

Hope Valley Shear Zone

Thompson

Putnam

Danielson

South Killingly

Plainfield

Old Furnace State Park

outcrop of Plainfield quartzite on Ross Road at entrance to westbound lane of interstate

Lake Char Fault

Quinebaug River

Clinton-Newbury Fault

prominent oxbow in the meandering Natchaug River

Late Proterozoic gneiss of the Avalon Terrane is exposed in Willimantic Dome

Lake Wangumbaug Fault

Mashamoquet Brook State Park

Mansfield Hollow Lake

Sherman Corner

Ashford

Eagleville

Willimantic

Willimantic R.

Mansfield Hollow State Park

Mansfield

Lake Wangumbaug

Dike

Andover

Andover Lake

Higganum

Hop River Dome

50-foot cliffs of Late Proterozoic gneiss and schist with fault blocks

Bonemill Brook Fault

Bolton Lakes

Eastern Border Fault

Bolton Notch State Park

Gay City State Park

Manchester

geology. The general geology is discussed from east to west with specific sites noted along each road.

Between the Rhode Island Border and I-395

US 6 crosses the Hope Valley Shear Zone 1.7 miles west of the Rhode Island state line, and US 44 crosses it 0.5 mile east of the state line. This major north-trending fault in the Avalon Terrane divides the Esmond-Dedham Subterrane from the Hope Valley Subterrane. The shear zone formed between 380 and 275 million years ago—no one has yet pinpointed the timing more accurately.

The Ponaganset Gneiss, a well-foliated rock with large crystals of feldspar, occupies the region east of the Hope Valley Shear Zone along US 6. West of the shear zone, three bands of the Late Proterozoic Plainfield Formation, each about 0.3 mile wide, crop out in South Killingly. The middle band consists of thin-bedded quartzite, mica schist, and dark gray gneiss, whereas the other two consist of glassy quartzite. Look for quartzite about 700 feet west of the Margaret Henry overpass and 1,000 feet east of the Snake Meadow overpass. A fourth band of glassy quartzite, a few hundred feet thick and sandwiched between light gray to pink granite gneiss of Late Proterozoic age, occurs at the intersection of US 6 and I-395.

You can see the quartzite and other rocks at Old Furnace State Park, south of US 6 and east of I-395. You can reach this historic mill by Ross Road, which ends at a parking lot at North Ross Pond at the foot of Half

Glassy quartzite of the Plainfield Formation along US 6 in Killingly.

Thin-bedded quartzite of the Plainfield Formation on Ross Road in Killingly at the entrance ramp to CT 695 westbound.

Hill. This locality consists of a 0.5-mile-long series of clifflike exposures of the pink to gray granite gneiss of Late Proterozoic age with thin-bedded glassy Plainfield Formation at its eastern base. The quartzite and quartz schist of the Plainfield Formation are well exposed between North Ross Pond and Ross Pond and are also found along and near Hubbard Hill Road south of US 6 and north of CT 695.

It's Danielson's Fault

US 6 crosses the north-trending Lake Char Fault in Danielson near the bridge over the Quinebaug River, which follows the fault there. US 44 crosses the fault 0.1 mile west of Munyan Road. The fault zone is characterized by a zone of mylonite, a rock that has been intensely milled or worked over by earth-deforming movements. A prominent zone of mylonitization along the fault more than 0.5 mile wide is visible on the northwest side of Five Mile River Road, which is south of US 44 in Putnam. The zone is almost as wide along US 44 on either side of Munyan Road.

The Lake Char Fault separates the Avalon microcontinent from the Putnam-Nashoba Terrane. These great blocks of rock, now stacked vertically, were originally separated by an as yet unknown distance. During the Acadian mountain building event, the Putnam-Nashoba Terrane was shoved east over the top of Avalonia. The Putnam-Nashoba Terrane is the lowest in the stack of four eastward-moving thrust sheets that occupy eastern Connecticut.

The name "Char" is an abbreviation for the Indian name of Lake Webster, about 15 miles north of here in Massachusetts, whose full forty-five-letter spelling is Chargoggagoggmanchauggagoggchaubunagungamaugg, reputed to mean "You fish on your side, we fish on our side, and nobody fishes in the middle."

Putnam-Nashoba Terrane

The map shape of the Putnam-Nashoba Terrane in northeastern Connecticut is that of an unevenly balanced dumbbell. US 44 crosses the terrane just north of the dumbbell's narrowest part where it has been thinned to about 1.25 miles, and US 6 crosses a 6-mile-wide swath in the lower wide part. The dumbbell appears to be a large-scale boudinage—a structure in a metamorphic rock in which a layer has been stretched and broken so it looks like a string of fat sausages. The thickening and thinning of the terrane is due to stretching of the belt in a north-south direction. Thinning, or "necking," happens in hot, stretched rock just as is does in taffy.

The Putnam-Nashoba Terrane consists of two distinct formations, the Quinebaug and Tatnic Hill. The Quinebaug Formation, the eastern, lower unit, consists of gray to dark-gray, medium-grained, well-layered gneiss. The Quinebaug rocks are in the sillimanite-muscovite grade of metamorphism. The Tatnic Hill Formation, the western, upper unit, is similar in color and grain size but includes more aluminous and schistlike rocks because it was derived in part from rocks rich in clay. When clay is metamorphosed, it often becomes mica, a platy mineral that forms the flaky texture of schists. The lower part of the Tatnic Hill Formation is made up of micaceous gneisses containing the iron- and alumina-rich minerals garnet, staurolite, and sillimanite. The latter two minerals typically occur in schist layers and form coarse, prismatic grains. They grow at very high temperatures and pressures, indicating that these rocks were buried in the depths of Himalayan-scale mountains before rebounding back to the present-day surface of the earth as the mountains eroded. Kyanite, a pale blue alumina-rich mineral, occurs as coarse grains in some parts of the rock. The middle part of the Tatnic Hill Formation is a greenish calc-silicate gneiss formed by metamorphism of lime- and silica-rich limestone layers.

US 6 crosses the west-dipping, 6-mile-wide Putnam-Nashoba Terrane between Danielson and Stetson Corner in Brooklyn, passing about 1 mile north of Tatnic Hill, the namesake of the upper formation. At Stetson Corner, the Tatnic Hill Formation disappears beneath the Merrimack Terrane at the Clinton-Newbury Fault. But this isn't the last you will see of the Tatnic Hill Formation along US 6; it is exposed again farther west in the

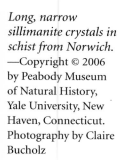

Long, narrow sillimanite crystals in schist from Norwich.
—Copyright © 2006 by Peabody Museum of Natural History, Yale University, New Haven, Connecticut. Photography by Claire Bucholz

Willimantic Dome. US 44 crosses a number of faults around Putnam then travels onto rocks of the Merrimack Terrane just west of the big hairpin bend near the Putnam hospital.

Merrimack Terrane

Rocks of the Merrimack Terrane in northeastern Connecticut include the Hebron Gneiss, an interlayered dark-gray schist and greenish gray, fine- to medium-grained, calc-silicate rock, and the Scotland Schist, a gray to silvery, rusty-weathering, fine- to medium-grained rock of Silurian to Devonian age. The Hebron Gneiss has been traced as part of a broad band of strata of Ordovician to Silurian age from New Hampshire and eastern Massachusetts into northeastern Connecticut. The 413-million-year-old Canterbury Gneiss, a distinctive light gray, medium- to coarse-grained plutonic rock, intruded the Hebron Gneiss. The Canterbury Gneiss and enclosing Hebron Gneiss dip gently to the west in eastern Connecticut, but dip east away from the crest of the Willimantic Dome in Chaplin and Windham. The Canterbury Gneiss appears to occupy the structural position of the Clinton-Newbury Fault. In other words, the Canterbury igneous rocks may have been emplaced by thrust faulting during Devonian time, and if the Clinton-Newbury Fault were evident here, it would be located where the Canterbury Gneiss formed.

Mashamoquet Brook State Park and Wolf Den

Mashamoquet Brook State Park, located 2.6 miles south of Pomfret Center, lies in the Merrimack Terrane. The eastern gateway to the 781-acre park is at the right-angle bend of US 44 at its junction with CT 101. Between the right-angle bend and Abington, US 44 straddles the interbedded gray schist and greenish calc-silicate gneiss of the Hebron. This poorly exposed unit extends southward about 1,200 feet to a contact with the Canterbury

Gneiss, which intruded the Hebron Gneiss 413 million years ago. The Canterbury Gneiss underlies all but the easternmost margin of Mashamoquet Brook State Park and forms rugged crags and the Wolf Den. In 1742, Israel Putnam, who came to be one of the most prominent Revolutionary War heroes, tracked a sheep-stealing wolf west to the Connecticut River and then back to its den. No-nonsense Putnam confronted the wolf eyeball to eyeball in the wolf's den, a narrow crawl space in Canterbury Gneiss. A well-marked trail along Wolf Den Road in the southwestern part of the park is also accessible from US 44, 0.6 mile east of Abington. A viewpoint at the southeastern margin of the park is on the top of a steep east-facing cliff of Hebron Gneiss, east of which is Wolf Den Brook. The cliff overlooks the eastern, down-dropped side of the Wolf Den Fault.

Willimantic Dome

The Willimantic Dome, bisected by US 6, forms a bull's-eye map pattern 7 miles in diameter in the middle of the Merrimack Terrane. Late Proterozoic rocks are exposed in the center of the dome. Here, erosion has removed the rock of the eastern Connecticut thrust sheets, which had been displaced over the Late Proterozoic rocks during the Acadian mountain building event. Geologists refer to such a structure as a "window" because you can see through the otherwise overlying rock formations. The window in the Willimantic Dome exposes the Tatnic Hill Formation of the Putnam-Nashoba Terrane and, below that, Late Proterozoic gneisses of Avalonia, indicating that the Avalon microcontinent moved at least this far west beneath the thrust sheets of eastern Connecticut.

US 6 crosses gneiss and schist of the Tatnic Hill Formation between Sherman Corner and North Windham. To the west, US 6 crosses onto Late Proterozoic gneisses. Here, the Tatnic Hill Formation is in direct contact with the Late Proterozoic gneisses. The Quinebaug Formation, the unit that is in contact with the Late Proterozoic rocks at the Lake Char Fault, is missing below the Tatnic Hill Formation in the Willimantic Dome. A fault at the base of or in the lower part of the Tatnic Hill may have removed the Quinebaug Formation. Fracture and rotation of mineral grains caused by faulting is pronounced in the lower part of the Tatnic Hill Formation, supporting the notion that a fault is present. This fault, named the Willimantic Fault, occupies the same position as the Lake Char Fault to the east but is warped across the dome. US 6 crosses the Willimantic Fault in North Windham just east of the intersection with CT 203.

The Late Proterozoic rocks in the core of the Willimantic Dome are exposed in the spectacular east-west roadcuts along US 6 between North Windham and just west of the Willimantic River crossing. In this stretch, US 6 crosses a 1.5-mile breadth of gneiss of the Waterford Group, followed by a 3-mile breadth of light pink to gray, well-foliated Hope Valley Alaskite

View to the north to folded thrusts of Tatnic Hill Formation and granite sills in Coventry east of Hop River.

A view to the north of splendid geological structures along the westbound lane of US 6 in southernmost Coventry approaching Hop River. A series of west-dipping normal faults gave rise to folds in the layers of the Tatnic Hill Formation. Vertical lines are dynamite drill holes.

Gneiss, a 600-million-year-old granitic rock characteristic of the Avalon Terrane. These Late Proterozoic rocks are extraordinarily well exposed in clifflike highway cuts along the westbound lane of US 6 near its intersection with Mansfield Avenue in southernmost Mansfield.

On the west flank of the Willimantic Dome, US 6 crosses the Willimantic River at the fault contact between gneiss of the Waterford Group and the overlying sequence of Tatnic Hill gneiss and schist. Roadcuts up to 40 or 50 feet high alongside the westbound lane of US 6 provide a spectacular display of these structures.

Three other domes, miniature versions of the Willimantic Dome, occur in the Merrimack Terrane and expose Late Proterozoic rocks of Avalonia: the Hop River, Chestnut Hill, and Williams Pond Domes. The Hop River Dome spans the Hop River at the village of Hop River and is crossed by US 6.

Mansfield Hollow State Park

Mansfield Hollow State Park features a man-made impoundment that enlarged a natural lake originally called Naubesatuck, Algonquin for "lake at the pond." Stone implements found in the park, made by the Nipmuck group of Algonquians, suggest that people have occupied this region for thousands of years. In 1952 the U.S. Army Corps of Engineers completed construction of an earthen dam and concrete spillway to impound the Fenton, Mt. Hope, and Natchaug Rivers. Normally covering 440 acres, Mansfield Hollow Lake can expand to inundate 1,950 acres during floods. It's one of Connecticut's best canoeing lakes and fishing spots. The blue-blazed Nipmuck Trail begins here and travels north along the Fenton River. Large outcrops of pegmatite in the Hebron Gneiss occur southwest of Chaffeeville along the trail.

Clough Quartzite in Eagleville

In Eagleville, on CT 32 at its intersection with CT 275 in Mansfield, the exterior of St. Joseph's Catholic Church is clad with a locally quarried Clough Quartzite. This unusual rock consists of a thinly bedded micaceous layer and a garnet-bearing layer, both sandwiched between thicker quartzite layers. Garnets don't grow in quartzite, but the quartzite tends to split into slabs along the mica-rich layers in which garnets do grow, leaving the surface of the quartzite studded with garnets from the micaceous layer. Although use of this beautiful rock as an architectural stone may not be unusual, the church in Eagleville is the first building that I have encountered as such. Also known as "Bolton stone," it is quarried in Bolton, Vernon, and Tolland, including the Burgundy Hill Quarry in Tolland. See **Interstate 84: Massachusetts State Line—Manchester.** This buff to rusty-weathering quartzite is found in the two west-dipping limbs of the Bolton syncline in the Bronson Hill Terrane.

St. Joseph's Catholic Church in Eagleville contains multicolored, garnet-studded, iron-stained slabs of Clough Quartzite of Silurian age.

Close-up views of two different colors of the Clough Quartzite studded with garnets.

Higganum Dike in Andover

Two parallel, staggered segments of the Higganum dike of Jurassic age intrude the Hebron Gneiss in Andover north of Andover Lake. US 6 crosses one just east of the intersection with CT 316 at the town of Andover. About 200 million years ago, magma flowed through a fracture in the rock and fed the basalt sheets that filled the Hartford Basin. When the remaining magma in the fracture cooled, it crystallized into a dike composed of diabase, a rock with the same chemical composition as basalt but with visible crystals because it cooled more slowly beneath the surface of the earth.

Lake Wangumbaug Fault

The Lake Wangumbaug Fault, north and west of the Willimantic Dome, forms the eastern margin of the Central Maine Terrane. The mainly west-dipping stratigraphic units that comprise the Central Maine Terrane are continuous from Massachusetts southward to Eastford, Ashford, northern Mansfield, and northern Coventry, where they are all cut out by the westward-curving, northwest-dipping Lake Wangumbaug Fault 2 miles north of the Willimantic Dome. As this fault extends westward to near Bolton Notch, it approaches the Bonemill Brook Fault, which forms the eastern boundary of the Bronson Hill Terrane. The Central Maine rocks have been reduced to a breadth of 0.75 mile here, between the Coventry-Bolton line and the south end of Bolton Lakes, along US 44. Because the Lake Wangumbaug Fault curves west and US 44 heads southwest, US 44 crosses this major fault zone several times. US 6 crosses the fault 1 mile northwest of the Coventry-Bolton line.

Bolton Notch State Park

Bolton Notch State Park, between Bolton Notch Pond and the southern end of Bolton Lakes, is north of the junction of US 6 and US 44. The rugged underlying Bronson Hill Terrane, a volcanic arc in Ordovician time, is much narrower here than elsewhere in Connecticut. Bolton Notch, a narrow pass through the hard rocks of the Bronson Hill Terrane, was eroded by a deeply incised preglacial stream. The passage through Bolton Notch has long been known as the Connecticut Path and was used by generations of Native Americans, stagecoaches drivers, and post riders. The New York, New Haven & Hartford Railroad also exploited the passageway, and the old railway bed is now part of the East Coast Greenway, a biking and hiking trail from Maine to Florida.

Magnificent, 100- to 200-foot-high cliff ledges are exposed in Bolton Notch State Park. The rock, which was quarried along the abandoned railway at the base of the cliffs, is Devonian Littleton Formation, a metallic gray micaceous garnet and/or staurolite metasedimentary schist as well as interbedded fairly pure quartzite and fine- to medium-grained micaceous quartzite. These rocks, originally sediments deposited on the ocean floor, were metamorphosed during the Acadian mountain building event.

Native Americans occupied sites at Bolton Notch for thousands of years. One site shows evidence of use 8,000 years ago, and another was occupied 200 to 300 years ago. A natural shelter, Black Sal's Cave, was named for one of the last of the Mohegan tribe. Another cave sits about 100 feet above the railroad bed on the south-facing cliff.

The Littleton Formation is at the center of a syncline, a squished downward-bending fold. This fold, known as both the Great Hill syncline and the Bolton syncline, runs the length of the Bronson Hill Terrane as far south as Great Hill. The former sedimentary rocks in the syncline were caught between hard blocks of Monson Gneiss and Glastonbury Gneiss. A thin but persistent layer of Clough Quartzite occurs in both limbs, and the Littleton Formation forms the 1-mile-wide core.

Another place to see rocks of the Bronson Hill Terrane near the Bonemill Brook Fault is at Gay City State Park, south of Bolton on CT 85. Rocks of the Collins Hill and Middletown Formations are exposed there.

Connecticut 2
Stonington—Glastonbury
53 MILES

The Pawcatuck River forms the state boundary between Westerly, Rhode Island, and Pawcatuck, a historic whaling and seafaring center in Stonington, Connecticut. The Pawcatuck River cuts across the grain of the bedrock formations. As the river approaches Long Island Sound, it flows parallel to the Charlestown moraine, which has diverted it to the west.

Small patches and east-trending dikes of Pennsylvanian and Permian granite occur in the Hope Valley Subterrane in the southeastern corner of Connecticut. The 275-million-year-old Narragansett Pier Granite trends east-northeast in southern Rhode Island and is at least 3 miles wide west of the Avondale Fault, but narrows to 0.5 mile wide at the Connecticut border. The 275-million-year-old Westerly Granite is centered in Westerly, Rhode Island, but several patches occur in Connecticut. The Potter Hill Granite Gneiss is much more extensive in southeastern Connecticut. It was formerly interpreted as Late Proterozoic in age but more recently has produced late Paleozoic to early Mesozoic isotopic dates.

Between Pawcatuck and Lantern Hill in North Stonington, CT 2 crosses no fewer than seven formations of igneous and metasedimentary units. Here they trend generally east-west, but to the northeast of here, the same formations run north-south. This section of CT 2 crosses the "Big Bend" of the Hope Valley Subterrane of the Avalon Terrane, where the rock layers from the north, in Voluntown, make a right-angle turn toward the west and continue through New London and Montville to the Connecticut River. One of these elongate bodies, the Plainfield Formation, has been intruded in sill-like fashion by granitic rocks such as the 600-million-year-old Hope Valley Alaskite Gneiss.

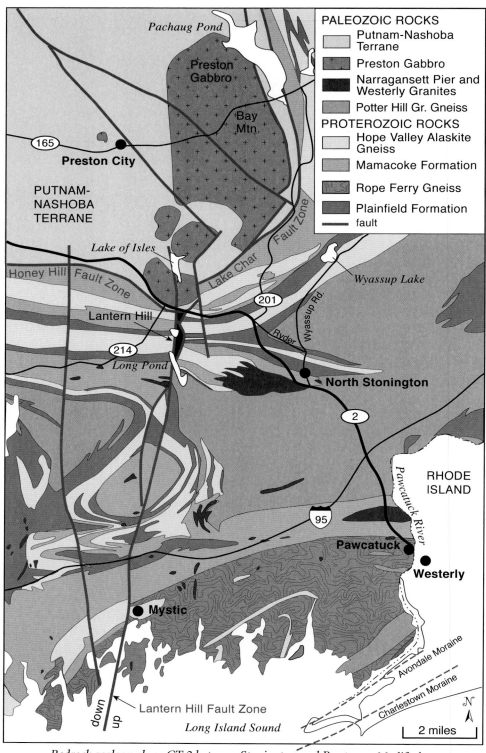

PALEOZOIC ROCKS
- Putnam-Nashoba Terrane
- Preston Gabbro
- Narragansett Pier and Westerly Granites
- Potter Hill Gr. Gneiss

PROTEROZOIC ROCKS
- Hope Valley Alaskite Gneiss
- Mamacoke Formation
- Rope Ferry Gneiss
- Plainfield Formation
- fault

Pachaug Pond

Preston Gabbro

Bay Mtn.

165 **Preston City**

PUTNAM-NASHOBA TERRANE

Lake of Isles

Honey Hill Fault Zone

Lake Char Fault Zone

201

Wyassup Lake

Wyassup Rd.

Lantern Hill

214

Ryder

Long Pond

North Stonington

2

RHODE ISLAND

Pawcatuck River

95

Pawcatuck

Westerly

Mystic

Avondale Moraine

Charlestown Moraine

down up Lantern Hill Fault Zone

Long Island Sound

N

2 miles

Bedrock geology along CT 2 between Stonington and Preston. —Modified from Rodgers, 1985

These formations have been complexly deformed during several episodes of folding. The geologic map shows the point of an 8-mile-wide, Z-shaped open fold 0.25 mile east of the intersection of CT 2 and CT 201 (Cossaduck Hill Road). This fold is formed of the 0.5-mile-wide, gray to pink, tan-weathering, foliated, porphyritic Potter Hill Granite Gneiss. This and other large folds in the Big Bend area provide clues to the intensity of igneous intrusion and the complexity of deformation throughout this region of the Hope Valley Subterrane.

Lantern Hill Fault Zone

Although the neighboring Mohegan Sun Casino on CT 2 appears to exert a greater attraction on the general public than the Lantern Hill Fault Zone east of Lantern Hill Road, this 12-mile-long fault zone is one of the truly spectacular geological features of the region. The shimmering white quartz summit of Lantern Hill, part of the fault zone, rises to almost 600 feet east of Long and Lantern Hill Ponds.

The glittering white quartz crystallized from hot, silica-rich mineral waters that welled up into the fault zone. This normal fault was caused by the stretching of the earth's crust that opened the Atlantic Ocean, as well as the Hartford rift basin, about 200 million years ago. The pod of vein quartz at Lantern Hill fills a fracture 1,500 feet wide and 1.5 miles long, and the walls of most steep-dipping brittle fractures in the fault zone

View to the northeast from Lantern Hill Road across Lantern Hill Pond toward the white quartz at the crest of Lantern Hill, in the northern part of the north-trending Lantern Hill silicified zone in North Stonington.

are coated with quartz crystals. A large commercial quartz quarry once known as the Silex Mine, located on the south side of Lantern Hill and east of Long Pond on Lantern Hill Road, is now owned by the Pequot Indian Tribe.

The Lantern Hill Fault Zone extends northward from the mouth of the Mystic River, on Long Island Sound, to Preston. The Mystic River follows the fault for 4 miles, and Long and Lantern Hill Ponds also occur in the fault zone, a zone of weakness that facilitates erosion. The vertical displacement along the fault increases from over 330 feet in the south near Mystic to about 1,400 feet near CT 2 in the north at Wintechog Hill, North Stonington. The Lantern Hill Fault Zone splays into several faults that start near the head of the oval-shaped Mystic basin and fan out to the north, offsetting rock formations of the basin and those to the north as far as Long Pond.

Lantern Hill, also called Tar Barrel Hill, has long been known for its spectacular southward view of Long Island Sound and eastward view of the Atlantic Ocean. Sassacus, the Pequot chief of the Algonquin tribes, used it as a lookout. During the War of 1812, the United States established a watch on the summit. Huge barrels of tar were lighted during the night of August 11, 1814, as a timely warning to defend Stonington's harbor against a fleet of British ships clustered offshore attempting a surprise bombardment. The United States repulsed the attack, sending the English sailing for the open sea. To the delight of the citizens of Stonington, the poet Philip Freneau penned this lyrical phrase about the battle:

> It cost the king ten thousand pounds
> To have a dash at Stonington.

Foxwoods and the Honey Hill Fault Zone

Perhaps best known for its Foxwoods Casino, the Mashantucket Pequot Reservation, whose eastern portal is on CT 2 at its junction with CT 214, also includes the Mashantucket Pequot Museum and Research Center and a lookout tower. The swiftest way to Foxwoods is to follow the fleets of casino tour buses. While most visitors to Foxwoods may not be preoccupied with the geology, it should be noted that the junction of CT 2 and CT 214 is the location of the northwest-striking Honey Hill Fault Zone, the boundary between the Hope Valley Subterrane of Avalonia to the south and the abutting Putnam-Nashoba Terrane.

Preston Gabbro

The 450-million-year-old Preston Gabbro, a 7.5-mile-long by 3-mile-wide pluton that nestles in the southeast corner of the Putnam-Nashoba Terrane, lies just north of the terrane-bounding Honey Hill Fault Zone and just west of the Lake Char Fault, which are continuations of each

Roadcut along CT 2 of gray gneiss of the Preston Gabbro just east of the intersection of CT 214 near Wintechog Hill and Milltown Roads. The foliation of the dark gray gabbro and associated light gray diorite dips 20 degrees to the northeast and strikes west northwest.

other. The pluton is cut off by the faults at depth, indicating the final movements along the Lake Char and Honey Hill Faults were more recent than the mid-Silurian age of the pluton. Swantown Hill, Ayer Hill, Prentice Mountain, Barns Hill, and Cossaduck Hill, clustered around the Lake of Isles in North Stonington, are made of the Preston Gabbro. A splay of refracted younger faults of varying trends in the Preston Gabbro indicates the difficulty the Jurassic-age Lantern Hill Fault Zone may have encountered in penetrating the hard rocks of the pluton.

This massive to mylonitized mafic pluton intruded the Ordovician Quinebaug Formation, a dark gray, medium-grained, well-layered gneiss that forms the base of the Putnam-Nashoba Terrane. The Preston Gabbro consists of 50 percent labradorite feldspar and 50 percent clinopyroxene, which often is the only mafic mineral except for magnetite-ilmenite and small amounts of olivine. A dioritic phase coexists with the gabbro. You can get a good look at the gabbro in roadcuts along CT 165 near the center of the pluton.

A 425-million-year-old granitic dike intrudes the northwest contact between the pluton and the intensely sheared Ordovician Quinebaug Formation, so we know the shearing occurred prior to 425 million years ago. The dike is probably a late-crystallizing phase from the same magma that became the gabbro and diorite.

Norwich and the Putnam-Nashoba Terrane

Norwich sits at the confluence of the Yantic and Quinebaug Rivers, where they become the Thames River, which flows from Norwich to Long Island Sound. Till from the Illinoian glaciation is exposed at the north end of Jail Hill in downtown Norwich, just north of the confluence. Norwich also lies in the middle of the Putnam-Nashoba Terrane, the most easterly sheet that is thrust over the Avalon Terrane. The Quinebaug Formation is the lower unit, and the Tatnic Hill Formation, containing the Fly Pond and Yantic Members, is the upper unit.

A good place to view Tatnic Hill Formation is at Yantic Falls on the Yantic River, just upstream of its confluence. Yantic Falls, also known as Uncas Leap, can be reached via Lafayette and Yantic Streets and Heritage Walk. Legend has it that Uncas, a Mohegan warrior, leaped across the gorge. The presence of faults and fault blocks in the Ordovician Tatnic Hill Formation enabled the river to more readily erode the gorge.

Splendid 60-foot-high roadcuts in the Tatnic Hill Formation dominate the views from CT 2 in the vicinity of I-395, and especially around exits 25, 26, and 27, west of I-395 and in and near the village of Yantic. The interchange of CT 2 and I-395 has large outcrops of gray to dark gray gneiss

View looking downstream at Yantic Falls where the Yantic River cut a gorge through the Tatnic Hill Formation 0.6 mile upstream of its confluence with the Quinebaug River.

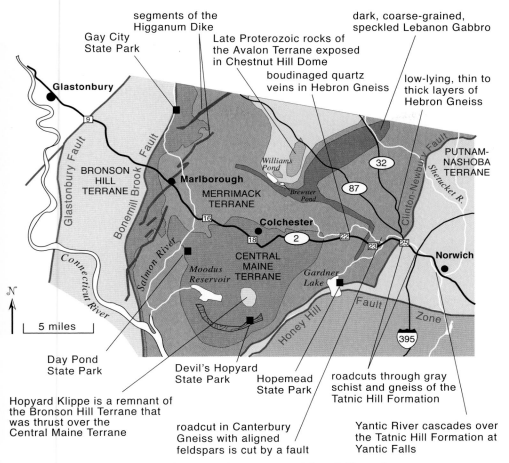

segments of the
Higganum Dike

Gay City
State Park

dark, coarse-grained,
speckled Lebanon Gabbro

Late Proterozoic rocks of
the Avalon Terrane exposed
in Chestnut Hill Dome

boudinaged quartz
veins in Hebron Gneiss

low-lying, thin to
thick layers of
Hebron Gneiss

Glastonbury

PUTNAM-
NASHOBA
TERRANE

Williams
Pond

BRONSON
HILL
TERRANE

Marlborough

MERRIMACK
TERRANE

Brewster
Pond

Colchester

CENTRAL
MAINE
TERRANE

Moodus
Reservoir

Gardner
Lake

Norwich

N

5 miles

Connecticut River

Salmon River

Honey Hill

Fault

Zone

Day Pond
State Park

Devil's Hopyard
State Park

Hopemead
State Park

roadcuts through gray
schist and gneiss of the
Tatnic Hill Formation

Hopyard Klippe is a remnant of
the Bronson Hill Terrane that
was thrust over the
Central Maine Terrane

roadcut in Canterbury
Gneiss with aligned
feldspars is cut by a fault

Yantic River cascades over
the Tatnic Hill Formation at
Yantic Falls

Bedrock geology along CT 2 between Norwich and Glastonbury.
—Modified from Rodgers, 1985

Roadcut opposite the Episcopal steeple at exit 25 in Yantic, in western Norwich, revealing 25 feet of the Yantic Member of the Tatnic Hill Formation.

Roadcut in the Tatnic Hill Formation at exit 25 along the eastbound off-ramp.

of the dominant Tatnic Hill Formation with prominent dikes and sills of granite. The very high and large outcrops near exit 25, where CT 2 and CT 32 split, consist of the greenish gray calc-silicate Fly Pond Member to the east and the gray to dark gray, fine- to medium-grained schist of the Yantic Member to the west. The latter member can be located easily because you can see the prominent steeple of the Episcopal chapel rising above it. The total breadth of the Tatnic Hill Formation along CT 2 through the center of Norwich and beyond is about 11 miles.

Chestnut Hill Dome in the Merrimack Terrane
The Merrimack Terrane, a broadly exposed thrust sheet, lies above and west of the Putnam-Nashoba Terrane and below and east of the Central Maine Terrane. It consists mainly of the Silurian to Ordovician Hebron Gneiss and the Devonian Canterbury Gneiss, which intruded the Hebron Gneiss as a large sheetlike igneous mass.

The Chestnut Hill Dome, northeast of Williams Pond in Lebanon, is a smaller, north-northeast-trending, asymmetric version of the large Willimantic Dome to the north. Erosion has removed the rocks of the thrust sheets here, revealing the underlying rocks. Late Proterozoic rocks of the Avalon Terrane are exposed in the middle of the dome, evidence that Avalonia was shoved this far west beneath other terranes. On the bedrock map, you can see that rocks of the Putnam-Nashoba Terrane surround the gneiss, which are surrounded in turn by rocks of the Merrimack Terrane.

Vegetation lines a fault in the Canterbury Gneiss along the westbound lane of CT 2 in eastern Bozrah.

Boudinaged quartz veins in Hebron Gneiss along the westbound lane of CT 2 in Bozrah 0.5 mile east of exit 22.

Lebanon Gabbro and Diorite

About 1 mile west of Fitchville and west of exit 23, CT 2 crosses a narrow tentacle of Lebanon Gabbro, a dark, coarse-grained mafic pluton of Devonian age. A white to black, streaked, medium-grained dioritic gneiss coexists with the gabbro. The Lebanon Gabbro lies on the southern edge of the Willimantic and Chestnut Hill Domes, and a major northeast-trending, northwest-dipping thrust fault may exist between the pluton and the domes. The orientation of foliation in the Tatnic Hill Formation south of the dome centers does not match that of the Lebanon pluton near Brewster Pond. In addition, remnant slivers of the Canterbury Gneiss are found along the contact between the Tatnic Hill Formation and the Lebanon Gabbro. The hypothesized thrust fault may be responsible for imparting the northwest-dipping regional foliation to the gabbro and the associated rocks to the southeast.

Central Maine Terrane and the Hopyard Klippe

Although the Central Maine Terrane generally occurs as a north-south band *west* of the Merrimack Terrane, a large circular area of Central Maine Terrane occurs in the middle of the Merrimack Terrane south of CT 2. Within the area is a small circle of Middletown Formation of the Bronson Hill Terrane. These rocks are part of the Hopyard Klippe. A klippe is a piece of a once-continuous thrust sheet that has been isolated from the rest of the sheet by erosion.

Devil's Hopyard State Park and Day Pond State Park are accessible places to view Brimfield Schist, the uppermost rock of the Central Maine

John Chapman Falls spills over gneiss of the Brimfield Schist at Devil's Hopyard State Park.

Bashan Dam, which impounds the Moodus River east of Bashan, is built on Brimfield Schist of the Central Maine Terrane.

Terrane. To reach Day Pond State Park, take exit 16 from CT 2 and head south on CT 149 to Westchester. The dam at Day Pond is regarded as a splendid example of the classic stonework that characterizes structures built or restored by the Civilian Conservation Corps. The park is adjacent to Salmon River State Forest and has many trails. Glacial till covers much of the land, but look for dark gray, rusty-weathering Brimfield Schist along the park's trails.

Glacial Lake Colchester

Glacial Lake Colchester was an ice-dammed lake that formed along the glacial front 16,500 years ago. Its south end abutted segments of an unnamed glacial moraine near Colchester. The lake filled the Meadow Brook valley, which CT 2 follows between exits 18 and 16.

Higganum Dike at Marlborough

Two forks of a 3.5-mile-long, northeast-trending segment of the Higganum diabase dike are exposed along CT 2, 0.4 mile east of exit 13 in Marlborough. This dike, which cuts diagonally across eastern Connecticut from North Branford to Stafford, fed the sheets of basalt in the Hartford Basin in Jurassic time. The lavas must have covered many of the crystalline rocks of eastern Connecticut as well, but have since eroded away.

Bronson Hill Terrane and the Glastonbury Gneiss

CT 2 crosses the Bonemill Brook Fault just west of Dickinson Creek. This fault forms the western boundary of the Central Maine Terrane and the eastern margin of the Bronson Hill Terrane. West of the fault, CT 2 crosses thin units of the Monson Gneiss and the rocks of the Great Hill syncline. After the highway crests the drainage divide west of Dickinson Creek, it crosses onto a wide expanse of Glastonbury Gneiss. The northeast-trending, resistant gneiss forms a mountainous band that includes Kongscut Mountain and Minnechaug Mountain, north of the highway, and Meshomasic Mountain south of the highway. This lofty ground drops off rapidly along CT 2 between East Glastonbury and Glastonbury. Near exit 9, CT 2 crosses the 20-mile-long Glastonbury Fault, which forms part of the eastern margin of the Hartford Basin.

Connecticut 9
Old Saybrook—Middletown
23 MILES

Ice Retreat and Glacial Lake Essex

The continental ice sheet melted back from Long Island Sound about 17,000 years ago, depositing moraines on its northward retreat and producing large volumes of meltwater that deposited outwash. CT 9 passes over the trend of two recessional moraines in Old Saybrook and Essex, but you can't see any segments of them from the highway. The Falls River, which flows into the Connecticut River from the west at Essex, was impounded by ice at the end of the last stage of continental glaciation. Ice melted back from the uplands faster than it melted from the Connecticut River Valley, so there was a tongue of ice in the valley that dammed streams flowing from the hills. Deltas formed where streams entered the lake, and lake water spilled over low points in the Falls River drainage divide. Essex hosts the Connecticut River Museum, which features exhibits about the history of the area.

Hope Valley Subterrane

A quick glance at the bedrock map seems to show that the Late Proterozoic Avalon rocks end on the east side of the Connecticut River, but a closer look shows they appear on the west side, too, near Deep River and Essex. Though CT 9 doesn't actually cross over rocks of the Avalon Terrane, they are just east of the road. The Hope Valley Subterrane of the Avalon Terrane features alternating layers of igneous and metamorphic rocks, some of them arranged in folded swirling patterns.

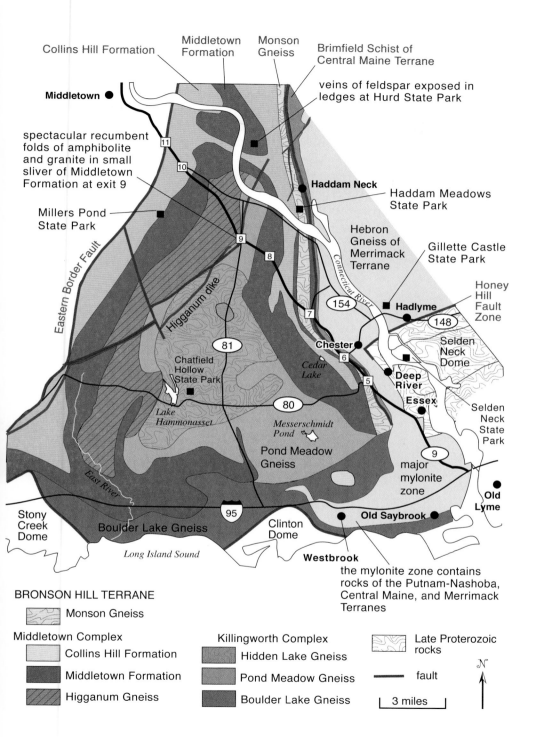

Collins Hill Formation

Middletown Formation

Monson Gneiss

Brimfield Schist of Central Maine Terrane

veins of feldspar exposed in ledges at Hurd State Park

Middletown ●

spectacular recumbent folds of amphibolite and granite in small sliver of Middletown Formation at exit 9

11

10

Haddam Neck ●

Haddam Meadows State Park

Millers Pond State Park

9

Hebron Gneiss of Merrimack Terrane

Gillette Castle State Park

8

Eastern Border Fault

Higganum dike

7

154

Connecticut River

Honey Hill Fault Zone

148

Hadlyme ■

81

Chatfield Hollow State Park

Cedar Lake

Chester

6

Selden Neck Dome

Lake Hammonasset

80

Messerschmidt Pond

5

Deep River

Essex

Selden Neck State Park

East River

Pond Meadow Gneiss

9

major mylonite zone

Old Lyme ●

95

Stony Creek Dome

Boulder Lake Gneiss

Clinton Dome

Old Saybrook ●

Long Island Sound

Westbrook

the mylonite zone contains rocks of the Putnam-Nashoba, Central Maine, and Merrimack Terranes

BRONSON HILL TERRANE

Monson Gneiss

Middletown Complex

Collins Hill Formation

Middletown Formation

Higganum Gneiss

Killingworth Complex

Hidden Lake Gneiss

Pond Meadow Gneiss

Boulder Lake Gneiss

Late Proterozoic rocks

fault

3 miles

N

Bedrock geology along CT 9 between Old Saybrook and Middletown.
—Modified from Rodgers, 1985

Killingworth Dome

Between Old Saybrook and Middletown, CT 9 follows the Connecticut River valley, skirting the eastern side of a rugged upland formed by crystalline rocks of the Killingworth Dome. Although surrounded by population centers of considerable density, the rocky terrain is relatively unpopulated and is covered by large tracts of Cockaponset State Forest. The continental glaciers scoured off the dome's soils and covered the hard rocks with a thin veneer of glacial till, so the uplands aren't hospitable to farming. Logging by early settlers cleared the hills and provided views of Long Island Sound. Today, with much of the land reforested, views are harder to come by, but you can see Long Island's Montauk Point on a clear day from two spurs of Chestnut Hill, southwest of Chatfield Hollow, and from Roast Meat Hill. Stands of laurel, which are at their most colorful in June, grace many back roads in this area. Cedar Lake in western Chester, north of CT 148 and east of Cedar Lake Road, is one of two swamps in Connecticut that support Atlantic white cedar, a wetland species at the northern edge of its range.

The Killingworth Dome had long been grouped with the Bronson Hill Terrane. It is broader than the other Bronson Hill domes, but its large core of hard gneisses resembles the Ordovician Monson Gneiss. However, recent age dating reveals that, quite surprisingly, the core gneisses of the dome are about 339 million years old, or of Mississippian age. Igneous intrusions of this age occur in Rhode Island but have not been recognized previously in the Bronson Hill Terrane. As with the other domes in the Bronson Hill Terrane, the Ordovician-age Collins Hill and Middletown Formations appear to mantle the core gneisses.

The dome sits just west of a geologically complex region where rocks of several different pedigrees—Late Proterozoic rocks of either the Avalon or Gander microcontinents, eastern Connecticut thrust sheets, and Bronson Hill volcanics—have been squished together in close proximity, folded and domed, and smeared and mylonitized. During the Acadian mountain building event, between 420 and 375 million years ago, the Avalon microcontinent collided with Laurentia and the Bronson Hill volcanic arc. All the terranes caught in between were thrust up and over the Avalon microcontinent. In northeastern Connecticut, these thrust sheets make north-south, parallel bands that, while complex in their own right, at least agree with the accepted geologic story. In the lower Connecticut River region, however, the outcrops have no predictability—they swirl around and are extremely thin.

Geologists now think that during the Alleghanian mountain building event, between 300 and 250 million years ago, Gondwana smashed into southern Connecticut from the southeast and pushed hard Late Proterozoic rocks against the buttress of the Killingworth Dome. At that time,

This roadcut in the Tatnic Hill Formation on CT 9 northbound in Old Saybrook illustrates the complexity of the region. A vertical sill at left is intruded by a northwest-dipping granite dike, which is in turn crosscut by a thicker granite sill.

the three major thrust sheets between the two blocks of hard rock were slenderized to a mere 0.25-mile thickness in places, bent into folds, and mylonitized. This collision probably flattened the south end of the Killingworth Dome, gave rise to the molten rock of the Mississippian-age pluton in the dome's core, and wrapped the Late Proterozoic rocks around the coastal formations underlying nearby Long Island Sound, possibly as far west as New Haven. The effects of a continental collision are like the effects of a hammer pounding a metal object on an anvil. Although the continental hammer collides with the anvil very slowly, perhaps a fraction of an inch a year, it moves inexorably over millions of years.

In 2007, Robert Wintsch and colleagues divided the dome into two complexes, the Middletown and the Killingworth, which they suspect are separated by a fault. They propose that the Middletown Complex, which includes the Middletown Formation, the Collins Hill Formation, and the Higganum Gneiss, formed in a volcanic arc associated with a back-arc rift. They think the Killingworth Complex, which includes the Hidden Lake Gneiss of Mississippian age and the Pond Meadow Gneiss and Boulder Lake Gneiss of Ordovician age, formed in a volcanic arc above a subduction zone.

The foliated gneisses of the Killingworth Complex are gray plagioclase, quartz, biotite, and/or hornblende gneiss with little or no pink or buff potassium feldspar. Plagioclase and potassium-feldspar-rich veins a few inches thick are nearly everywhere and have been folded along with the

Granite sills cut a 60-foot-high outcrop of dark gray, rusty-weathering Middletown Formation along the northbound entrance ramp to CT 9 at exit 6.

gneissic foliation. The presence of these veins and the mineral hornblende in the gneiss, both of which require certain temperatures and pressures to form, tell us that these rocks must have been buried to depths of about 20 miles, where temperatures were 700 degrees.

The extremely compressed but complete sequence of the eastern Connecticut thrust sheets forms a 0.5- to 4-mile-wide, 15-mile-long band that snakes around between Deep River and Westbrook, on the coast. The band contains Brimfield Schist of the Central Maine Terrane, Hebron Gneiss of the Merrimack Terrane, and Tatnic Hill Formation of the Putnam-Nashoba Terrane. Examples of this mylonitized strata appear along CT 9 between Old Saybrook and Chester except between 0.1 mile south of exit 5 and exit 6, where rocks associated with the Killingworth Dome crop out.

Chatfield Hollow State Park
Chatfield Hollow State Park is located in the south-central part of the Killingworth Dome, where the gneiss foliation dips gently to the east. Numerous ledges and outcrops are visible along the trails. The first part of the Chimney Trail/Indian Caves Trail, which begins at CT 80, explores

a chaotic jumble of gneiss blocks ripped up by the passage of the Wisconsinan ice sheet. An escarpment in the eastern part of the park is broken up by large joints or cracks, in places forming caves, some of them with their own cool, moist microclimates. Rock climbers use a technique called "chimneying" to scale the inside of large fractures between blocks of rock, and the Chimney Trail is named accordingly; it abruptly enters one of these fractures and climbs out the top.

Chatfield Hollow State Park is the site of Connecticut's first Civilian Conservation Corps camp, which opened in 1933 and was appropriately named Camp Roosevelt after Franklin D. Roosevelt.

Ferry Crossing below Gillette Castle State Park

The ferry *Selden III* crosses the Connecticut River, connecting CT 148 between Chester, near exit 6 on CT 9, and Hadlyme on the east bank. Every day between April 1 and November 30, except for Thanksgiving, this 65-foot-long white ferry with a black skirt carries about seventy thousand passengers on the 0.25-mile, 2- to 6-minute trip. According to Jenna Cho of the *New London Day* (August 15, 2005), Captain Tom Darcy's philosophy as to why people choose the ferry over the I-95 Baldwin Bridge is precisely "because they want to use the ferry."

Gneiss of the Killingworth Dome in Chatfield Hollow State Park.

Schist of the Hebron Gneiss at Gillette Castle State Park.

The high bedrock cliff on the east bank, below Gillette Castle State Park, is formed of Hebron Gneiss of the Merrimack Terrane. This state park is a good place to view this rock, which is well-layered and cut by numerous pegmatite veins here.

Middletown Amphibolite along CT 82

A short trip north on CT 82 at exit 7 is geologically rewarding, especially if combined with Scenic Highway 154 along the Connecticut River. Exit 7 is located on Monson Gneiss, but CT 82 heads north into a north-trending roadcut that exposes several hundred feet of amphibolite and gray gneiss of the Middletown Formation of the Bronson Hill Terrane and then rusty-weathering Brimfield Schist of the Central Maine Terrane. The fault that forms the eastern boundary of the Brimfield Schist is located in the roadcut where CT 82 bends to the east. The Brimfield Schist has been thrust eastward along this fault over the Hebron Gneiss of the Merrimack Terrane.

Bronson Hill Rocks

Between exits 7 and 8 along the northwest flank of the Killingworth Dome, CT 9 traverses Bronson Hill rocks. For 1 mile north of exit 7, CT 9 crosses the light to dark, medium- to coarse-grained Monson Gneiss. Farther north, the road traverses dark gray amphibolite and hornblende

A large outcrop of Monson Gneiss in the median of CT 9 about 1 mile north of exit 7, near the Chester-Haddam line. View is from the northbound lane.

A Z-fold in alternating layers of dark gray amphibolite and light granitic sills in the Middletown Formation at exit 9 in Haddam. View is to the northeast toward the median from the southbound lane. The upper layers of the fold have moved southeast (to the right) relative to the lower layers.

gneiss of the lower part of the Middletown Formation overlain by rusty-weathering gneiss and light-colored gneiss in the upper part of the Middletown Formation, above which occurs the gray, rusty-weathering Collins Hill Formation. CT 9 crosses rocks of the Killingworth Dome in the vicinity of exit 9, along with a small sliver of Middletown Formation in a spectacular fold at exit 9.

Veins of pegmatite, with its large mineral crystals, cut across the rocks in this region. Large pegmatite veins in Monson Gneiss occur on Hubbard Road northwest of exit 8. Dark green anthophyllite and the bluish gray crystals of iolite, the rare gem form of cordierite, have been identified in these veins on Hubbard Road. Iolite has the unusual property of dichroism, or showing two colors (blue and grayish brown), depending on the angle from which it is viewed. Anthophyllite is a clove brown to colorless iron-magnesium amphibole that typically occurs in ultramafic rocks. Ultramafic rocks may occur in or near major tectonic collision zones, in this case, probably the Bonemill Brook Fault, only 2 miles east of these pegmatites, which is potentially a major continental collision boundary.

Higganum Dike

The Higganum dike, a major feeder to the Jurassic basalt flows in the Hartford Basin, cuts northeast across Connecticut from North Branford to Stafford. CT 9 crosses the diabase dike at exit 9. The dike trends north here, forming the hill east of the Higganum Reservoir as it cuts through the gneiss of the Killingworth Dome. Brittle faults offset the dike along the western margin of the Killingworth Dome.

Millers Pond State Park

Millers Pond State Park, at the north end of the Killingworth Dome in Durham, is a good place to view the Bronson Hill rocks. The Collins Hill Formation crops out on the northwest side of the pond, and the Middletown Formation crops out on the southeast side. The blue-blazed Mattabesset Trail circles the lake, where bedrock forms some of the shore. The Eastern Border Fault of the Hartford Basin is about 1 mile west of the state park.

Beryl from pegmatite near Haddam Neck.
— Copyright © 2006 by Peabody Museum of Natural History, Yale University, New Haven, Connecticut. Photography

Pink pegmatite veins cut layered gneiss of the Killingworth Dome in outcrops along northbound CT 9 north of exit 9 in Haddam.

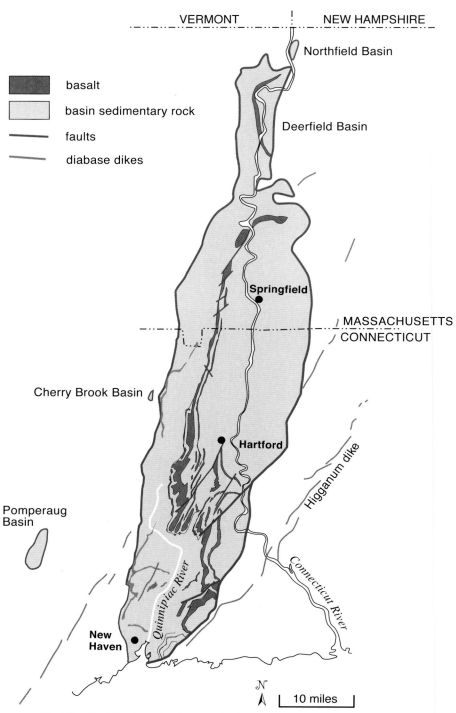

VERMONT | NEW HAMPSHIRE

Northfield Basin

Deerfield Basin

basalt

basin sedimentary rock

faults

diabase dikes

Springfield

MASSACHUSETTS
CONNECTICUT

Cherry Brook Basin

Hartford

Higganum dike

Pomperaug
Basin

Quinnipiac River

Connecticut River

New
Haven

N

10 miles

The Hartford Basin and other nearby basins contain linear ridges of basalt.
—Modified from McDonald, 1982

The Hartford Basin of Connecticut

The Hartford Basin, a prominent topographic feature that extends from Long Island Sound north to Northampton and Deerfield in Massachusetts, is one of several basins that formed when Pangea began to rift apart about 200 million years ago. Reddish to maroon sedimentary rocks and bold linear ridges of black basaltic lavas dominate the basin's landscape.

When a continent stretches and rifts apart, the crust thins to the point that hot magma reaches the surface of the earth. When magma reaches the surface as lava and solidifies quickly, the rock is called *basalt*; when the magma solidifies slowly at depth in a dike, the rock is called *diabase*. *Dolerite* is a synonym for diabase and is used on Rodgers's 1985 *Bedrock Map of Connecticut*. *Diabase* is used in this volume, however, as it is the accepted term in modern scientific literature.

Magma that flowed to the surface of Connecticut in Jurassic time is now one of the most valuable rocks in the state—basalt and diabase. Quarrymen use the term *traprock* for both of these dark, hard rocks. They are chemically stable, don't fracture easily, and don't powder on crushing. They are, therefore, ideal for use in roadbed construction, and the Hartford Basin hosts some large quarries. So exactly how and when did this precious resource arrive in Connecticut?

The earth's continents aggregated into a single supercontinent, Pangea, by 250 million years ago. Compressional forces associated with that aggregation formed the Appalachian Mountains in what is known as the Alleghanian mountain building event. Only 50 million years after the peak of the Alleghanian event, the supercontinent began to break apart.

Pangea began to split apart along deep-seated faults. The main zone of rifting developed in the North Atlantic Ocean basin, but major rifts also formed along the edge of the newly formed North American and African continents. Along the east coast of North America, many northerly trending basins formed, some onshore and some now submerged beneath the ocean. Basalt covered a large area, but much of it is now either eroded away or buried by younger sediments.

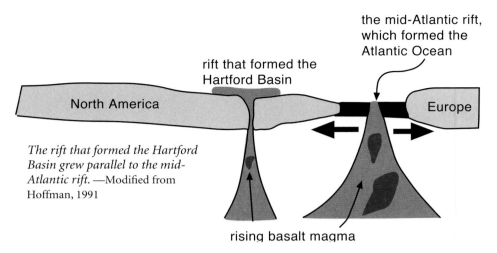

The rift that formed the Hartford Basin grew parallel to the mid-Atlantic rift. —Modified from Hoffman, 1991

The major rifting of the earth's crust in southern New England took place just east of the domes of the Shelburne Falls volcanic arc and just west of the Bronson Hill domes. This 80-mile-long rift valley reaches its maximum width of 35 miles near the Massachusetts-Connecticut state line. Mountains to the east and west of the basin began shedding sediments in Triassic time. In addition to coarse sediments of alluvial fans at the basin margins, finer sediments were deposited in lakes and streams in the central part of the basin.

Two smaller basins also formed in Connecticut: The 7-mile-long and 1.5-mile-wide Pomperaug Basin 20 miles to the west of the Hartford Basin in the towns of Southbury and Woodbury, and the tiny Cherry Brook Basin in Canton, 1.5 miles west of the Hartford Basin.

By the beginning of Jurassic time, deep faults reached the hot magma of the earth's interior. Magma rose to the surface along these faults, and lava flooded the continental margin for at least 60 to 100 miles inland. Magma along the faults solidified into rock over time and in some places is now visible on the land surface as a dike, specifically, a feeder dike. Much of the flood basalt has been eroded away, but we know it occupied areas outside the Hartford Basin because feeder dikes, such as the Higganum dike, continue for many miles beyond the basin.

Three major outpourings of lava, the Talcott, Holyoke, and Hampden Basalts, occurred in the Hartford Basin between about 195 and 185 million years ago. The first igneous activity in the basin began with the eruption of the Talcott Basalt and intrusion of the West Rock sill. A sill intrudes parallel to sedimentary rock layers, and this one intruded into the basin's Triassic sediments. As lava of the Talcott Basalt flooded over the land, it also flowed into the lakes in the basin, forming extensive pillow structures as it was quenched. Sediment was deposited on top of the basalt before the next outpouring of lava, the massive Holyoke Basalt. Hundreds

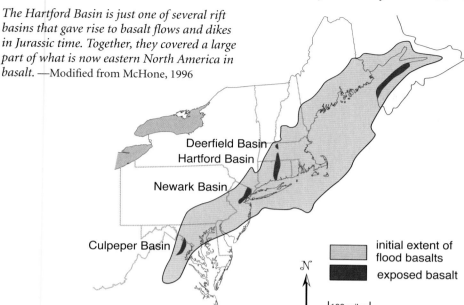

The Hartford Basin is just one of several rift basins that gave rise to basalt flows and dikes in Jurassic time. Together, they covered a large part of what is now eastern North America in basalt. —Modified from McHone, 1996

Deerfield Basin

Hartford Basin

Newark Basin

Culpeper Basin

initial extent of flood basalts

exposed basalt

N

|100 miles|

of thousands of years passed before the third and final outpouring, the Hampden Basalt. The sedimentary rocks between the basalt record evidence of climatic changes. Lakes grew and deepened in wetter climates and shrank in drier climates, leaving a record of alternating shallow-water deposits (red cracked mud, silt, and sand) and deep-water deposits (black, finely laminated shale).

The Talcott, Holyoke, and Hampden Basalts have distinctive chemical compositions that permit correlation with three major diabase dikes that cut across New England. The Talcott Basalt erupted from the 465-mile-long, northeast-trending Higganum dike. The dike runs from the eastern margin of the Hartford Basin in Guilford through the Bronson Hill upland and northeast through Massachusetts and Maine to New Brunswick, Canada. The Holyoke Basalt erupted from the Buttress dike, so named because of its topographic prominence in the cliff just north of the West Rock Tunnel on CT 15, where the dike cuts the West Rock sill. The Hampden Basalt erupted from the 8-mile-long Bridgeport dike near Orange, the most westerly of the three dikes, and intrudes Ordovician schists west of West Rock Tunnel. Each of these dikes is up to 165 feet thick, and extensive contact metamorphism and melting of the wall rock testify to the passage of large quantities of flowing magma. The only place where a dike can be seen connected to its volcanic products occurs beneath the Talcott Basalt on Warner Avenue in East Haven. Geologists have even found a place where the emerging lava of the dike changed directions, as you would expect if magma were coming up from below and then spilling out and flowing across the earth's surface.

Fault Blocks in the Hartford Basin

In northern Connecticut, the Hartford Basin is a flat lowland because the lava ridges are primarily in the westernmost part of the basin. From Hartford southward, however, the valley becomes an obstacle course of highly resistant fault block ridges. Movements along steeply west-dipping normal faults have shuffled the blocks progressively eastward with distance to the south, pushing the lava ridges up against the Bronson Hill upland. Additionally, in the southern part of the basin north of New Haven, several great dikes of intrusive basalt also form a mainly east-west series of hurdles to trip up travelers in the otherwise broad north-south corridor.

The normal faults are a product of tensional forces that stretched and thinned the continental crust as North America separated from Pangea. In normal faulting, rocks on one side of a fault move up relative to rocks on the other side. The fault blocks in the basin are like a series of stair steps, but not all of them step up or down systematically.

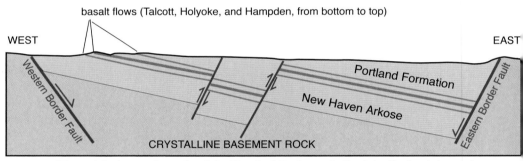

Normal faults cut the rocks of the Hartford Basin, and all originally flat-lying rocks now dip down to the east.

After the intense fault block movements in Early Jurassic time, the "basin" consisted of high, rugged mountains separated from adjacent blocks by steep faults. The blocks themselves must have consisted mainly of east-dipping layers and deep valleys filled with sediment eroded from the high mountain blocks. By Late Jurassic time these mountains were largely worn down to a nearly level plain. The Cretaceous coastal-plain sediments beneath Long Island Sound and Long Island likely extended across southern Connecticut and Rhode Island tens of miles north of where they are presently found.

Rocks of the Hartford Basin

At New Haven the eastward-thickening wedge of sedimentary basin rocks is only 7 miles wide, but it rapidly broadens northward to more than 20 miles near Hartford and the Massachusetts border. These Triassic-

View from Somers, Connecticut, toward highlands on the eastern side of the Hartford Basin.

and Jurassic-age rocks are the youngest exposed bedrock units on the mainland of southern New England. From Middletown, Rocky Hill, and New Britain northward, most bedrock at lower elevations has been blanketed by lake bottom sediments deposited in the short-lived Glacial Lake Middletown and the southern part of the long-lived, 220-mile-long Glacial Lake Hitchcock.

Rocks of the Hartford Basin

YOUNGEST	Portland Arkose
↑	Hampden Basalt (fed by Bridgeport Diabase)
	East Berlin Formation
	Holyoke Basalt (fed by Buttress Diabase)
	Shuttle Meadow Formation
	Talcott Basalt (fed by West Rock Diabase)
OLDEST	New Haven Arkose

New Haven Arkose. In Late Triassic time, alluvial fans spread into the newly forming basin from the adjacent mountains. The fans are now the 6,500-foot-thick, coarse- to fine-grained New Haven Arkose, a conglomeratic sandstone that contains weathered feldspars derived from nearby granitic highlands. The coarse sediments in particular were derived from mountains to the east. These coarse sediments were probably shades of brown and gray when deposited but became shades of red and brown after deposition when iron-rich groundwater circulated through the porous rock, depositing iron minerals such as hematite. The maroon to red mudstones, sandstones, and conglomerates of the New Haven Arkose contain caliche, a distinctive reddish brown or buff to white calcareous material that develops in stony soils in semiarid climates. The New Haven Arkose contains numerous sills of West Rock Diabase that are the same age as the overlying Talcott Basalt.

Talcott Basalt and West Rock Diabase. The Talcott Basalt is the oldest basalt in the Hartford Basin. Arcuate high ridges of the basalt's feeder, the intrusive West Rock Diabase, lie along or near the faulted, 17-mile-long west margin of the Hartford Basin from New Haven north to Southington.

Shuttle Meadow Formation. The Shuttle Meadow Formation consists of lakebeds composed of reddish brown silty shale.

Holyoke Basalt. The Holyoke Basalt flow of Early Jurassic age is named for the Massachusetts city of the same name north of Springfield. The single thick flow that comprises the approximately 650-foot-thick Holyoke flow has been traced for 260 miles through the Hartford and Deerfield Basins and 7 miles through the Pomperaug Basin. Its feeder dikes of **Buttress Diabase** commonly trend northeasterly nearly parallel with the northeasterly striking faults north of Meriden.

East Berlin Formation. The 550-foot-thick East Berlin Formation consists of gray mudstone, sandstone, and black shale. These sediments were deposited in lakes and streams that lapped onto alluvial fans along the eastern escarpment of the basin.

Hampden Basalt. The Hampden Basalt is greenish gray to bluish green on fresh surfaces and gray to rusty tan on weathered surfaces. This unit ranges from 150 to 200 feet thick. Layers up to 1 foot thick that are full of gas vesicles or bubbles mark the tops of flows, grading down into massive dense basalt. The presence of many vesicular zones within the Hampden Basalt in certain locations suggests it is composed of relatively thin flows compared to the Holyoke Basalt.

Portland Arkose. The eastern highlands escarpment was the site of river-deposited alluvial fans that merged laterally one into the other, forming the Portland Arkose. Below the coarse sandstone of the alluvial fans are floodplain deposits.

Jurassic Life

Widespread extinctions of a number of life-forms occurred during Triassic time, and no dinosaur footprints have been found in Triassic redbeds of the Hartford Basin. Fossils and footprints of dinosaurs, fishes, and other life-forms do, however, appear in the 200-million-year-old sediments of Jurassic time, when the lowland rift valley was characterized by a semiarid climate with temporary saline lakes, an environment hospitable to some new forms of life.

The study of dinosaur footprints in sediments of the Hartford Basin began in 1835 in Greenfield, Massachusetts, because curious townspeople noticed "turkey tracks" in sandy shale during a construction project. James Deane, a local physician and amateur paleontologist, studied the footprints in Jurassic rocks from a quarry in neighboring Turners Falls. He sent plaster casts of the footprints to Edward Hitchcock, who later wrote, "No facts in my life are more vividly impressed upon my memory than those relating to the footmarks. . . . As soon as I saw the specimens, I perceived the phenomena worthy of careful research." This correspondence initiated a new phase in Hitchcock's career, during which he described 154 species of animals based on carefully measured and sketched impressions in shale. His collection of ten thousand footprints is housed in the Pratt Museum at Amherst College, Massachusetts. A wide-ranging exhibit of dinosaurs from many parts of the world is housed in the Peabody Museum of Natural History at Yale University in New Haven, Connecticut.

In 1884 a partial dinosaur skeleton was discovered in a Manchester quarry. The companion block that had been removed was discovered to have been incorporated in a bridge abutment. When the bridge was dismantled in August of 1969, the block was rescued, and the long-separated bones were reunited, giving rise to a nearly complete *Ammosaurus*, a tiny dinosaur about the size of a cat with a 2-foot-long tail.

In 1966 a bulldozer operator, Edward McCarthy, exposed a spectacular series of dinosaur footprints at a construction site for a state building in Rocky Hill, Connecticut. The trackway has been preserved at Dinosaur State Park and is discussed in greater depth in **Interstate 91: New Haven— Massachusetts State Line.**

In addition to dinosaurs, many other animals inhabited the Hartford Basin. In Triassic time, the basin was located in the interior of the supercontinent Pangea and was characterized by a semiarid climate. In Jurassic time, the opening of the North Atlantic Ocean basin led to increasing rainfall, and dry periods oscillated with wet periods, each lasting some 20,000 years. Skeletons of four genera of fishes ranging from 6 to 30 inches long have been preserved in dark shales formed in oxygen-poor lakes. Thousands of fish species evolved during high stands of various Jurassic lakes, only to become extinct as the dry phase of the climate evaporated the lakes. The sediments of the basin also contain fossils of mussels, ostracodes, and "clam shrimp." Numerous trails and burrows in shale and sandstone provide evidence of insects, crustaceans, worms, and snails.

Glacial Lakes Middletown and Hitchcock

As the Wisconsinan continental ice sheet receded northward from Glacial Lake Connecticut in the Long Island Sound basin, meltwater drained southward into the Connecticut River Valley. Deltaic sediments were deposited in the river valley in a series of sediment-dammed ponds. This long mass of sediment fills the valley from South Cove in Essex northward through the Straits, the narrow bedrock canyon east of Middletown. The meltwater impounded behind this long plug of glacial sediment became what is known as Glacial Lake Middletown, the precursor to the long-lived, 220-mile-long Glacial Lake Hitchcock.

Much of what is known about these lakes has been discovered through study of delta deposits, which accumulated where meltwater entered the lakes. The elevation of the contact between the topset and foreset beds in a delta can be used to define the water level in a former lake. When meltwater flows into a lake, its velocity decreases and sediment is deposited below the water level in dipping foreset beds. As the delta grows into the lake, the meltwater stream has to flow across the foreset beds before reaching the lake. The stream deposits flat-lying topset beds that overlie the dipping foreset beds. Because the elevation of the contact between dipping foreset beds and overlying flat-lying beds marks the level of lake water, it also records the elevation of the lake spillway.

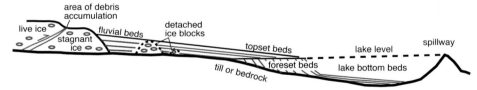

The contact between topset and foreset beds in a delta marks the surface of the lake and therefore the elevation of its spillway.

Glacial Lake Middletown occupied the Middletown area in the lower Mattabesset River valley and inundated the Berlin area in the upper valley. Deltas are present in Cromwell, Newington, and New Britain, and topset-foreset contacts in the delta sediments indicate that the lake surface was about 115 feet elevation when these deltas formed. Deltas built into the northeastern part of the lake at Cromwell and Rocky Hill formed the future dam for Glacial Lake Hitchcock.

As the ice lobe that filled the Connecticut Valley melted north of Windsor and Windsorville, further erosion at the Straits lowered the level of Glacial Lake Middletown below 110 to 115 feet. This allowed the drainage divide in New Britain between the Hartford area and the Middletown-Berlin area to emerge from beneath lake level. The level of a separate lake,

Glacial Lake Hitchcock in the Hartford area, was controlled by a spillway across this divide. Its waters spilled through the New Britain spillway into Glacial Lake Middletown and the two lakes coexisted for a while.

In the early stages of Glacial Lake Hitchcock, the New Britain spillway was eroded down more than 30 feet into glacial deposits until bedrock was reached, resulting in a stable water level. Deltas formed at the ice margin in Windsor and East Windsor record 110- to 115-foot lake levels, so we know the New Britain spillway was at that level early in the lake's formation. Still farther north, deltas in Suffield and Enfield, on the Massachusetts border, tell us that lake levels at the New Britain spillway were below 100 feet when they formed. Subsequent deltas in southern Massachusetts tell us that lake levels at the New Britain spillway were later between 85 and

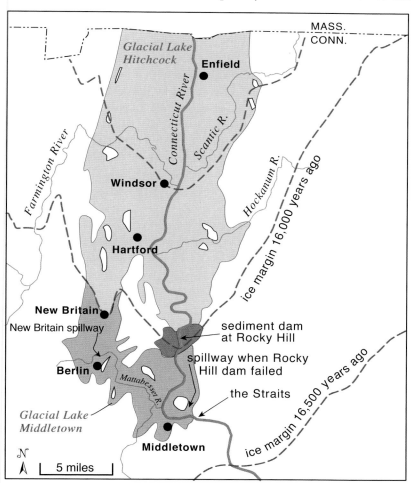

Glacial Lakes Middletown and Hitchcock formed in the Connecticut River Valley as the ice sheet melted north. —Modified from Stone and others, 2005

95 feet. For a time, Glacial Lake Hitchcock reached a stable level at 82 feet in elevation by the time the ice margin had retreated to just north of the Chicopee River valley in south-central Massachusetts 15,000 years ago. Because the bedrock elevation of the spillway is about 58 feet, the 82-foot lake level indicates that the water flowing through the spillway was about 24 feet deep!

Downcutting at the New Britain spillway was not merely a local affair. It was controlled by conditions of downcutting in the lower Connecticut River and by the lowering of water levels some 35 miles to the south in Glacial Lake Connecticut.

The stable level lasted until about 13,500 years ago when the sediment dam along the lake's southeastern shore at Rocky Hill was breached. The Rocky Hill dam of Glacial Lake Hitchcock extended for about 3 miles along both sides of the Connecticut River from just north of Wangunk Meadows in Portland and Cromwell Meadows to about the ferry crossing between Rocky Hill and Glastonbury. The sand and gravel now form a 2-mile-wide zone of kettled terrain. Glacial rebound, as well as erosion by small streams on the south side of the dam, may have contributed to the breach. Once water began flowing over the dam, it rapidly eroded the sediment, carving into the bedrock at the Rocky Hill narrows.

When the Rocky Hill dam failed, Glacial Lake Hitchcock was completely drained over the 50-mile stretch south of the Holyoke Range in Massachusetts, while the northern portion of the lake continued to exist for another 2,000 years. Then the postglacial Connecticut River cut down into the lake floor.

The modern elevations of topset-foreset contacts in Glacial Lake Hitchcock increase to the north. Like all lakes, the surface of Glacial Lake Hitchcock was flat, so topset-foreset contacts that formed at the same time were at the same elevation when the lake existed. After the weight of the ice was removed, the earth's crust rebounded more in the north than in the south, essentially tilting the imaginery horizontal plane that connects the topset-foreset contacts. By using the topset-foreset contact elevations, geologists have discovered that the crust has rebounded to the north-northwest at a rate of 4.74 feet per mile. When the North American continental ice cap covered the New England region, its weight depressed the earth's crust—but not uniformly because the ice cap tapered from very thick in Canada to very thin at its southern edge. The crust didn't begin to rebound until between 14,000 and 13,500 years ago.

—Road Guides in the Hartford Basin—

Interstate 91
New Haven—Massachusetts State Line
60 MILES

For the uninitiated traveler, the Hartford Basin may seem to be misnamed unless the trip begins at the Massachusetts state line and heads south. Between New Haven and Hartford, normal faults have raised ridges of basalt, which resisted glacial erosion. The ridges, collectively called the Metacomet Ridge, rise up to 700 feet above the valley floor. Near New Haven, the ridge system is on the east side of the valley; it crosses to the west side near Meriden. South of Meriden, the New Haven Arkose, the oldest sedimentary rock in the Hartford Basin, predominates in the valley, and north of Meriden, the Portland Arkose, the youngest rock in the basin, predominates near the surface, though it is generally covered by sediments deposited in Glacial Lake Hitchcock.

Yale University and the Peabody Museum of Natural History

Yale University, officially founded at Saybrook in 1701, and the Peabody Museum of Natural History, formally established in 1866, have been for the better part of two centuries a unique and broadly based source of geoscience information. They also publish the *American Journal of Science*. The Department of Geology and Geophysics and the museum lie 0.5 mile to the west of I-91 on Whitney Avenue in New Haven.

The Hall of Dinosaurs in the Peabody Museum is a world-class exhibit assembled amid the infamous "bone wars" that raged from 1866 to 1897 between the pioneer vertebrate paleontologists Edward D. Cope and Othniel C. Marsh. These scholarly rivals searched for large Mesozoic reptiles in the northern Rocky Mountains and Great Plains states. Dinosaurs also populated the volcanically active, semiarid lowlands of southern New England in Jurassic time. The dinosaurs that lived in southern New England left numerous footprints, and the bones of a few dinosaurs and Jurassic fish fossils up to 30 inches long have been preserved here. The Peabody Museum also has permanent exhibits on mammalian evolution, minerals, and earth science.

West Rock Ridge State Park

At West Rock Ridge State Park, you can see a sill of West Rock Diabase and younger diabase dikes cutting it. The massive, arcuate sill is penetrated by the West Rock Tunnel on CT 15, the Wilbur Cross Turnpike. The sill

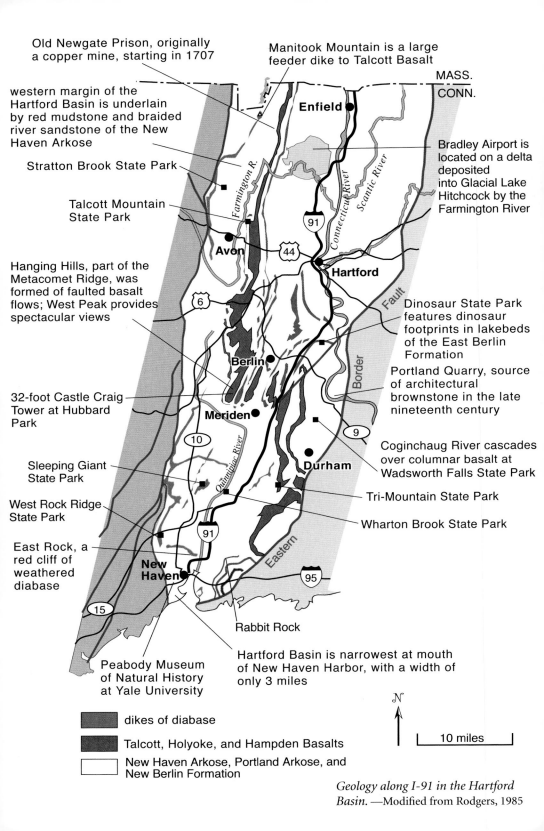

Old Newgate Prison, originally a copper mine, starting in 1707

Manitook Mountain is a large feeder dike to Talcott Basalt

MASS.
CONN.

Enfield

western margin of the Hartford Basin is underlain by red mudstone and braided river sandstone of the New Haven Arkose

Bradley Airport is located on a delta deposited into Glacial Lake Hitchcock by the Farmington River

Stratton Brook State Park

Farmington R.

Connecticut River

Scantic River

Talcott Mountain State Park

91

44

Avon

Hartford

Hanging Hills, part of the Metacomet Ridge, was formed of faulted basalt flows; West Peak provides spectacular views

Fault

Dinosaur State Park features dinosaur footprints in lakebeds of the East Berlin Formation

6

Berlin

Border

Portland Quarry, source of architectural brownstone in the late nineteenth century

32-foot Castle Craig Tower at Hubbard Park

Meriden

10

Quinnipiac River

9

Coginchaug River cascades over columnar basalt at Wadsworth Falls State Park

Sleeping Giant State Park

Durham

Tri-Mountain State Park

West Rock Ridge State Park

Wharton Brook State Park

91

East Rock, a red cliff of weathered diabase

New Haven

Eastern

95

15

Rabbit Rock

Peabody Museum of Natural History at Yale University

Hartford Basin is narrowest at mouth of New Haven Harbor, with a width of only 3 miles

N

dikes of diabase

Talcott, Holyoke, and Hampden Basalts

New Haven Arkose, Portland Arkose, and New Berlin Formation

10 miles

Geology along I-91 in the Hartford Basin. —Modified from Rodgers, 1985

served as a reservoir for the Talcott lava flow. About 1,000 feet north of the West Rock Tunnel, the northeast-trending dike of Buttress Diabase, which was derived from a different magma, crosscuts the West Rock sill. The Buttress dike and its segments have been traced from Orange, southwest of West Rock, to Cheshire, near Broad Brook Reservoir.

West Rock Ridge bathed in late-day sunlight. View from the west on CT 10, near Westville.

West Rock Ridge State Park is located near Southern Connecticut State University in the village of Westville in western New Haven. It is accessible from the intersection of CT 10 and CT 63. If you take the main approach to West Rock Ridge State Park from CT 10, you'll climb a steep road to a splendid viewpoint that looks to the south over New Haven and its harbor and to the lava ridges along the eastern margin of the Hartford Basin. To the north-northeast, the resistant form of Mt. Carmel in Sleeping Giant State Park is also made of the West Rock Diabase.

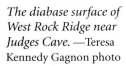

The diabase surface of West Rock Ridge near Judges Cave. —Teresa Kennedy Gagnon photo

Judges Cave, a glacial boulder on the summit of West Rock Ridge.

On the summit of West Rock Ridge is a glacial boulder called Judges Cave. In 1661, two of the judges who signed the death warrant for King Charles I in 1649 successfully eluded capture by the British by hiding in a crack between broken blocks of this glacial boulder. It is made of basalt and may have been plucked from the south-facing cliffs of the Hanging Hills of Meriden.

Just southwest of West Rock Ridge you can see patches of New Haven Arkose of Triassic age resting in depressions on an eroded surface of Maltby Lakes Metavolcanics of Ordovician age. Take exit 59 from CT 15 (the Wilbur Cross Parkway) and head north on CT 63 a few blocks to the Amity Shopping Center. A 300-foot-long outcrop on June Street behind the shopping center exposes this unconformity, which marks the western margin of the Hartford Basin. A dike of Buttress Diabase of Jurassic age cuts the outcrop. All three rock types exposed here have been polished by glacial ice.

East Rock Park

East Rock Park, a hilly area between the Mill River and the Quinnip-iac River, forms the eastern portal to the "lava gateway," the entrance to New Haven. The highest parts of the three northerly peaks—Whitney

Peak, East Rock, and Indian Head, are the continuation of the West Rock Diabase sill, here breached by glacial erosion that carved out the valley of the Mill River. The southern peak, Snake Rock, consists of diabase on its lower slopes and arkosic sandstone on the crest. The park has several access points, either two blocks east of the intersection of Cold Spring and Orange Streets near the location of the Ranger Station and Trowbridge Center (via Whitney Avenue), or north from I-91 on CT 5 to the Davis Street entrance.

Glacial Lake Quinnipiac

When the ice sheet receded north of Long Island Sound, meltwater surging down the Mill River deposited a large delta into Glacial Lake Connecticut at what is now Fair Haven. As the ice receded farther north, the delta sediments blocked the flow of the meltwater in the Quinnipiac River valley, impounding Glacial Lake Quinnipiac. The lake extended as far north as South Meriden. Deltas and varved lake sediments, called the New Haven clay, were deposited in it and fill the Quinnipiac River valley as far north as the bedrock gorge at South Meriden. These sediments are red, being derived from the underlying reddish brown sedimentary rock of Triassic age over which the ice in the valley moved. Even after the glacial lake drained, meltwater continued to flow southward from the upper Farmington River region. This meltwater incised the glacial lake deposits and deposited light-colored sediments derived from the metamorphic bedrock of the western highlands.

New Haven clay was used to make bricks in the Quinnipiac Valley. Several important clay pits lay to the east of State Street in Hamden and North Haven, north to its intersection with Sackett Point Road. You can see interbedded varved clays of Glacial Lake Quinnipiac beneath sediments deposited by Wharton Brook in the cutbank of an abandoned meander just south of the confluence of the Quinnipiac River and Wharton Brook. This area has been used for research by geology faculty and students of Yale University, who documented changes in the course of both streams between 1934 and 1986. The state acquired the land for Wharton Brook State Park, at the intersection of CT 5 and I-91, around 1918–1920 for use as a wayside rest. Just west of the park, toward Toelles Road, a number of ceremonial cremation pits, dated to about 4,000 years ago, were an important spiritual site for the Quinnipiac Indians.

The Quinnipiac River marsh, Connecticut's largest salt marsh, extends from New Haven Harbor northward on the west side of I-91 almost to its junction with CT 40 at exit 10. The valley beneath the marsh is filled with varved clays of Glacial Lake Quinnipiac overlain by fluvial terrace deposits. The tidal marsh developed on these low-lying terrace surfaces as sea level rose during the last 4,000 years.

Rabbit Rock

Rabbit Rock, an old Indian lookout, can be seen about 1 mile to the east of I-91, 1 mile north of exit 8. Although only about 375 feet above sea level, its summit commands a 360-degree view of the surrounding countryside. The hill is a segment of the north-trending Buttress dike, which fed the Holyoke Basalt.

Sleeping Giant State Park

The gigantic, prone, broad-shouldered, reclining figure occupying Sleeping Giant State Park in the Quinnipiac Valley is a laccolith—a bulbous mass of magma that domed up overlying sedimentary layers and crystallized into a thick mass of igneous rock. This magma, which crystallized into the West Rock Diabase, intruded between layers of the New Haven Arkose and resisted erosion more than the arkose that enclosed it.

Tri-Mountain State Park

Tri-Mountain State Park, located in Durham and Wallingford directly east of exit 14 on I-91, is only accessible via the Mattabesset hiking trail. Its three mountains are Pistapaug Mountain, Fowler Mountain, and Beseck Mountain, all part of a faulted linear ridge of Holyoke Basalt, known as Metacomet Ridge. A prominent northeast-trending normal fault with some left-lateral movement runs along the northwest side of Pistapaug Mountain, lifting it up on the southeast side.

An unusually large roadcut through the New Haven Arkose exposes southeast-dipping sandstone beds with white to buff layers marking old soil levels. The roadcut is along CT 40 in North Haven, 100 feet southeast of the Hamden town line. The head of Sleeping Giant is visible at the far left.

The same basalt ridge curves closer to I-91 in the northern part of Wallingford. Steep cliffs of Talcott lava flows and younger volcanic rocks and sediments loom up just 1 mile east of the interstate. The bedrock underlying the 10-mile-wide expanse of the Hartford Basin west of these mountains is composed of Triassic-age maroon sedimentary layers of the New Haven Arkose. In highway cuts you can see the east-dipping redbeds overlain by black lava flows and interbedded sedimentary rocks.

Barite in Cheshire

The Jinny Hill mines in Cheshire were the first barite mines in the United States. Three veins of barite in the New Haven Arkose were mined between 1838 and 1878. Little evidence of the mines remains today. Barite, a generally white, yellow, or colorless mineral, is the principal ore of barium. It's used in paint and drilling mud, and as filler in paper and textiles.

Hanging Hills of Meriden

The basin between Meriden and Hartford has undergone a spectacular transformation due to an abundance of parallel north-northeasterly striking faults. The Talcott Basalt, the Shuttle Meadow Formation, the thick Holyoke Basalt, and younger strata have been broken into fault blocks that have been shuffled like a deck of cards. The blocks, once a continuous series of south-trending ridges of the Metacomet Ridge system, were progressively offset in a northeasterly direction. The blocks are called the Hanging Hills because their steep, southern ends, visible to the north of I-691, are overhanging cliffs. As the ice sheet moved south during the most recent glacial stage, the ice rounded the north sides of the ridges but plucked basalt from their southern edge. The caprock—the basalt at the top of the ridges—is the massive Holyoke Basalt. The Shuttle Mountain redbeds and the Talcott Basalt are near the base of the ridges.

The fault blocks form West Peak, East Peak, South Mountain, and Cathole Mountain, Lamentation Mountain, Chauncey Peak, and Higby

Barite from Cheshire.
— Copyright © 2006 by Peabody Museum of Natural History, Yale University, New Haven, Connecticut. Photography by Claire Bucholz

View to the southeast from East Peak toward the basalt flow and talus slopes of South Mountain, with Merimere Reservoir at its base and Higby Mountain in the distance.

Joints trend northwest in the basalt of East Peak at the flagpole.

Mountain. The view from the lookout tower on West Peak extends west across the Hartford Basin to the western Connecticut uplands, south to Long Island Sound, and southeast to Higby Mountain and the eastern Connecticut highlands beyond.

Higby Mountain

North of exit 18 and the I-691 interchange, I-91 veers close to the base of Higby Mountain. The Cromwell Fault, a normal fault, runs along the western side of the mountain, near the interstate. The thick Holyoke Basalt that forms the crest of the mountain was lifted up along this fault. This particular fault continues northeast for 7 miles to South Glastonbury, where it

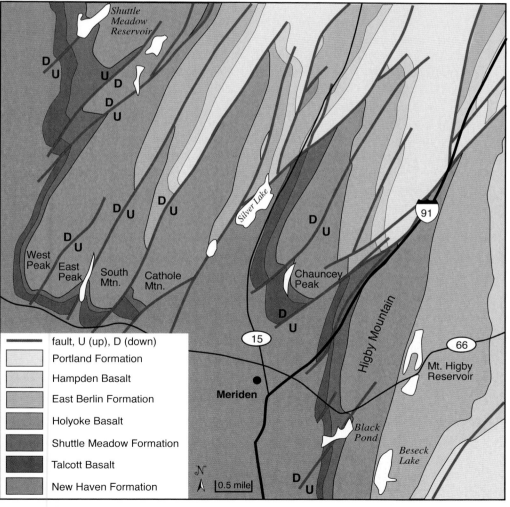

The Hanging Hills of Meriden are large fault blocks of mainly Holyoke Basalt. Rocks on the southeast side of normal faults moved up (U) and rocks on the northwest side moved down (D).

becomes the Eastern Border Fault. The north end of Black Pond, south of Higby Mountain, is cut by another northeast-trending normal fault whose downthrown side is to the northwest. The East Berlin Formation, which hosts some impressive dinosaur trackways, underlies Mt. Higby Reservoir on the north side of CT 66 almost to the Middletown line.

Dinosaur State Park

Dinosaur State Park is in Rocky Hill, 8 miles south of Hartford on I-91 and 1 mile east of exit 23. In 1966, bulldozer operator Edward McCarthy uncovered about 2,000 dinosaur tracks while excavating the site for a state building. The tracks, which are preserved on a single bedding plane of the East Berlin Formation, were made approximately 200 million years ago. Some geologists have suggested that all of the prints may have been made within a 24-hour period. The tracks, ranging from 10 to 16 inches long, were named *Eubrontes*, but no *Eubrontes* remains have been found in the Connecticut Valley. The only known dinosaur that matches the dominant track is *Dilophosaurus*, a three-toed meat-eating dinosaur that walked upright on hind legs measuring 20 feet long.

Five hundred of the tracks are sheltered under the park's geodesic dome, which features life-size Triassic and Jurassic dioramas and highlights of the discovery of the tracks. This educationally delightful park also features a professional-quality setting for do-it-yourself casting of dinosaur tracks. Visitors to the museum who wish to take home a dinosaur track must bring 10 pounds of plaster of paris, cooking oil, a plastic bucket, and rags. The park's "Arboretum of Evolution" encompasses 60 acres of living representatives of trees and shrubs typical of those that grew during the age of dinosaurs.

Glacial Lakes Middletown and Hitchcock

Glacial Lake Middletown, an early stage in the formation of Glacial Lake Hitchcock, formed along the Connecticut River at Middletown and in the Mattabesset River basin. About 16,000 years ago, glacial meltwater was impounded north of a great mass of sands and gravels deposited at the edge of the ice in the Connecticut River Valley near the Straits. See the introduction to this chapter for a further discussion of Glacial Lakes Middletown and Hitchcock.

Farmington River Delta at Bradley International Airport

East of Talcott Mountain in Windsor, the Farmington River heads northeast across a delta that formed where the Farmington River emptied into Glacial Lake Hitchcock. Bradley International Airport is perched atop sands and gravels of the delta. The delta deposits have a complex history. Only one part of them was graded to the stable 82-foot water level of the New Britain spillway of Glacial Lake Hitchcock. Most of the sediment in

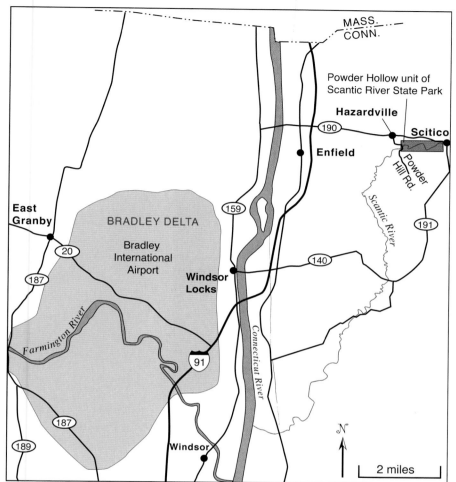

Bradley International Airport is located on a 20-square-mile glacial delta deposited in Glacial Lake Hitchcock by the Farmington River.

the delta was derived from the ice or from reworking of glacial meltwater deposits in the Farmington River valley west of Talcott Mountain.

Scantic River State Park

Scantic River State Park consists of nine disjointed units along the Scantic River southeast of the village of Hazardville in Enfield. The Powder Hollow unit, from the South Maple Street Bridge in Hazardville to the Broadbrook Road (CT 191) Bridge in Scitico, holds the most interest. It contains the ruins of a dam and mill foundation east of the Maple Street Bridge. The foundation lies in a location known as Powder Hollow, named for the Hazard Powder Company, which made gunpowder. The company was named for

East-dipping beds of the Portland Arkose in the streambed of the Scantic River. View looking upstream from the South Maple Street bridge near Hazardville.

its founder, Augustus Hazard, not for the explosive potential of its product. The broad, flat Scantic Valley, with its small, meandering stream, is a classic example of what geologists call an *underfit river,* one much too small to have cut the valley it occupies. This is one reason why geologists think the course of the Scantic River in Enfield and East Windsor marks the position of the preglacial Connecticut River. The Connecticut River flows on bedrock west of here in Suffield and Windsor Locks, but the bedrock valley below the sediments in the Scantic River valley is much deeper.

Enfield Rapids and Windsor Locks
A 6-mile-long stretch of rapids, originating upstream at Enfield Falls, marks a place in the valley where the glacier encountered a spur of more resistant Portland Arkose. The ice scoured out a new channel for the Connecticut River over these rocks, creating rapids that hampered travel along the Connecticut River north of East Windsor. A set of locks, completed in 1829, facilitated upstream navigation, first by steamboat and later by barges.

Newgate Copper Mine
The Newgate copper mine, west of Newgate Road in East Granby, is low on the western slope of Peak Mountain, which is capped by Holyoke Basalt.

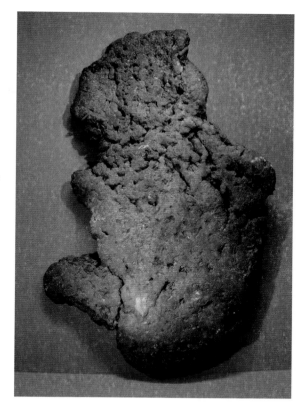

A copper nugget found in glacial drift in Hamden. —Copyright © 2006 by Peabody Museum of Natural History, Yale University, New Haven, Connecticut. Photography by Claire Bucholz

The Old Newgate Prison made use of an old copper mine.

The mineralization was discovered in 1705, and mining operations first began here in 1707. By 1741, little more than 100 tons of chalcocite, prepared for smelting, was recovered. The mines were worked intermittently up to 1900 but were unprofitable. In 1773 the Colony of Connecticut purchased the site and used the mine for a prison during the Revolutionary War and early statehood. It was named Old Newgate Prison after the notorious English prison, which it apparently surpassed in the barbaric treatment of prisoners.

The copper is located at an unconformity between the Talcott Basalt and the Shuttle Meadow Formation, which was deposited on an eroded surface of the basalt. Just below the unconformity, disseminated copper mineralization has been traced for over 1 mile in prospects. The copper ores bornite and chalcopyrite and their alteration products occupy spaces between detrital grains in the gray and black sandstones of the Shuttle Meadow Formation above the basalt. However, the interbedded red sandstones and shales are barren. A small amount of uraninite is present, associated with nodular copper sulfides. Gray sandstones within 65 feet of the unconformity that truncates the Talcott Basalt are the most intensely mineralized. Thermal solutions percolating through the rock may have deposited chalcocite, a copper sulfide mineral, in zones in the sandstone originally cemented with ankerite, an iron-rich carbonate mineral.

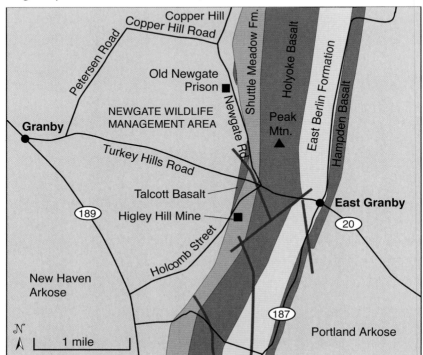

Geologic map of the region around Old Newgate Prison and the Higley Hill Mine.

Interstate 95
Branford—West Haven
6 MILES

I-95 crosses the Eastern Border Fault of the Hartford Basin at exit 54. The fault zone is complex here, with several faults placing rocks of different ages against each other. Basically, however, the crystalline rocks to the east of the fault zone have moved up relative to the Hartford Basin rocks to the west. South of I-95 at exit 54, a fault block consisting of several hundred feet of gray siltstone of the Shuttle Meadow Formation is situated against a block of Talcott Basalt. Several hundred feet northeast of exit 54 the fault zone consists of a broad, 1-mile-long silicified and mylonitized zone near Pisgah Brook and the pond into which it drains.

Branford's Shaky Ground

In 1999 a team of geoscientists discovered evidence of an active fault while researching long-term sea level rise in marshes along the Farm River in Branford. This fault, a segment of the Eastern Border Fault, may have caused a rhythmic series of quakes over the past 1,200 years. Using radiocarbon dating of organic material, the geoscientists dated former sea levels in a marsh along the Farm River and in a marsh on Kelsey Island, in Long Island Sound. They determined that the level of the island marsh has dropped more than 3 feet relative to the Farm River marsh since 815 BC.

The work indicates that a series of earthquakes occurs in the area about every 200 years, on average. Sediment analysis suggests uplift comparable to that before previous quakes is now occurring. A series of minor earthquakes has been recorded along the fault in recent decades.

The most recent quake of any significance in Connecticut, of magnitude 4.5 to 5, occurred in East Haddam on May 16, 1791. An eyewitness reported that stone walls and chimney tops were shaken down. The East Haddam quake has long been thought to have been associated with an area in East Haddam near Moodus, where in a two-month period in the 1980s, Weston Observatory recorded some seven hundred tiny quakes, calling them the "Moodus Noises." In fact, rumblings have been heard in Moodus for centuries, and the town's name is actually derived from an Indian word for "place of noises." However, some scientists now wonder if the earthquake felt in East Haddam in 1791 was associated with the fault in Branford instead.

Fortunately, geologists think that earthquakes in this region probably wouldn't exceed magnitude 5. At most, the area might experience shaking strong enough to topple items off shelves and crack foundations and chimneys.

In the 3 miles between exit 54 in Branford and exit 51 in East Haven, I-95 crosses the entire sequence of east-dipping basalt flows and interlayered

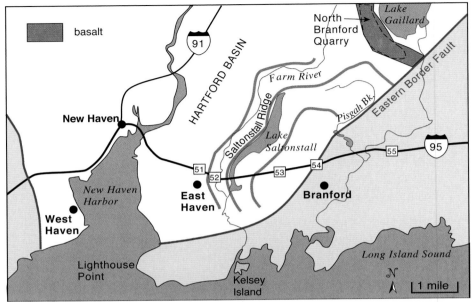

Geology along I-95 between Branford and West Haven. —Modified from Rodgers, 1985

sediments that filled the Hartford Basin from Late Triassic to Jurassic time. Between exit 53 and Lake Saltonstall, the interstate cuts through a low pine-covered ridge formed by the Hampden Basalt, the highest of the lava flows. Saltonstall Ridge, on the western shore of Lake Saltonstall, is composed of the Holyoke Basalt, the thickest of the flows. Finally, just east of exit 51, the road cuts through a low, weathered ridge of Talcott Basalt as it completes its descent to the lowland that lies on the New Haven Arkose.

North Branford Quarry in Holyoke Basalt

The Holyoke Basalt, the largest and most massive of the three flows of Jurassic age, extends into East Haven just south of Lake Saltonstall. North of the lake, the basalt is quarried at the North Branford Quarry, the largest traprock quarry in the world. An enormous lake of lava ponded to a depth of 300 feet against the escarpment formed by the Eastern Border Fault. It solidified into the great thickness of Holyoke Basalt here. The 8-mile-long eastern face of the North Branford quarry offers an unparalleled opportunity to study a basalt flow.

New Haven

The Hartford Basin is narrowest at the mouth of New Haven Harbor, with a breadth of only 3 miles. Along I-95, the Triassic-age New Haven Arkose underlies the lowland between exit 51 in East Haven and the western

I-95 roadcut through east-dipping Holyoke Basalt west of Lake Saltonstall.

margin of the basin at exit 44 in West Haven. The ridges that mainly occur in the lowland east of I-91 in East Haven and New Haven are upheld by intrusive dikes of diabase that served as feeders to the basalt flows. The Quinnipiac Bridge affords an excellent view of East and West Rocks to the north and the Quinnipiac estuary.

See **Interstate 91: New Haven—Massachusetts State Line** for the geology of New Haven.

US 44
Manchester—Avon
18 MILES

The Eastern Border Fault, a normal fault, forms the eastern margin of the Hartford Basin near Manchester Green and Highland Park. The Mesozoic-age sediments in the basin have been downfaulted in relation to the Glastonbury Gneiss of Ordovician age. The sediments of the northern part of Glacial Lake Manchester lie snugly against the fault. They extend west and south through the village of Oakland and Center Springs Park, north of Center Street (US 44A) in the center of Manchester. The small lake formed between the upland on the east and the lobe of ice in the Connecticut River Valley on the west about 16,000 years ago, prior to the formation of Glacial Lake Hitchcock.

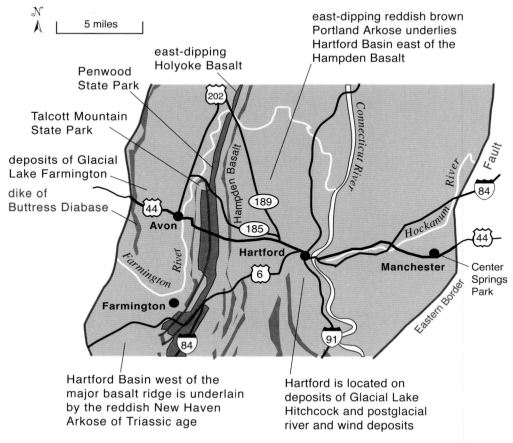

Geology along US 44 across the Hartford Basin. —Modified from Rodgers, 1985

Sediments deposited in deltas built into Glacial Lakes Middletown and Hitchcock occupy a broad swath in northwestern Manchester along the Hockanum River. On the Manchester–East Hartford line, the Hockanum River flows between two drumlin fields (nine drumlins in all) and has eroded down through delta deposits. West of Burnside, the Hockanum River meanders across a 2-mile-wide stream terrace deposited by the postglacial Connecticut River after Glacial Lake Hitchcock drained. In westernmost East Hartford, US 44 traverses 0.7 mile of the modern floodplain before crossing the Connecticut River into Hartford via the Bulkeley Bridge.

West Hartford

The Portland Arkose, a reddish brown, coarse-grained sandstone, underlies US 44 to the middle of West Hartford, 1.5 miles west of St. Joseph's College. Thick layers of poorly sorted and somewhat weathered sands and gravels of the Portland Arkose east of Hartford contain evidence of streams flowing down from the Bronson Hill Terrane. These stream sediments, stained bright red with iron oxide, were laid down in alluvial fans and deltas and contain numerous crosscutting channels. They are present in roadcuts and natural outcrops, especially along I-84 between exits 63 and 59 and along nearby highway on-ramps and off-ramps. Groundwater readily flows through these porous sediments, and in winter, tonguelike sheets of ice extend from porous levels where water emerges from the outcrops.

In West Hartford, US 44 crosses the Hampden Basalt about 0.6 mile west of CT 218 (Main Street). The shales of the East Berlin Formation, which are older and therefore stratigraphically below the Hampden Basalt, occur east and west of Mountain Road.

Holyoke Basalt of Talcott Mountain

West of Mountain Road, the terrain rises steeply toward Talcott Mountain, formed of two parallel ridges of Holyoke Basalt. A north-trending fault runs between the two ridges in the valley that contains the Hartford reservoirs. The fault lifted the basalt to the east relative to the basalt to the west, creating the double thickness of Holyoke Basalt. The beds of the western, downfaulted-block dip about 5 to 10 degrees east, whereas the block east of the Hartford reservoirs dips 15 degrees east. Outcrops of the Holyoke Basalt lava sequence are abundant along the highway, but keep your eyes on the road—this section of US 44 is notoriously dangerous to drive. The fault that divides the Holyoke Basalt continues north, curving through the notch in Talcott Mountain that's traversed by CT 185. To the south, the fault passes the southern Hartford reservoirs and curves southwest through Farmington and beyond.

As you head west on US 44, you'll cross onto the rocks below the Holyoke Basalt. The western contact of the Holyoke Basalt with the thin but conspicuous shales of the Shuttle Meadow Formation runs through Ely Pond, on the town line between Avon and West Hartford. The contact of the Shuttle Meadow Formation with the Talcott Basalt grazes the northwestern tip of Ely Pond.

Talcott Mountain and Penwood State Parks

Talcott Mountain State Park occupies the northern end of the western ridge of Talcott Mountain where it abuts CT 185. The Heublein Tower is said to have been designed by its owner between 1911 and 1914 to resemble a German castle perched over the Rhine. It rises 165 feet above the top of Talcott Mountain and 1,000 feet above the Farmington River. From the parking lot near CT 185, a steep trail ascends the ridge to the tower. The Metacomet Trail runs through this state park and the adjacent Penwood State Park, to the north of CT 185. The trail is named after the chief of the

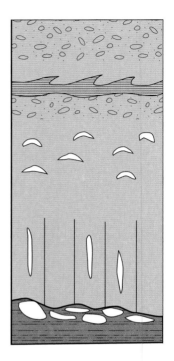

vesicular basalt

flow breccia

vesicular basalt

basalt with half-moon vesicles

The Talcott Basalt contains many vesicles, places where gas formed in the lava. Sometimes small mineral crystals occur inside vesicles.

massive basalt

columnar basalt with cylindrical vesicles

New Haven Arkose with siltstone

The mineral prehnite often lines cavities in basalt. This specimen is from Farmington. — Copyright © 2006 by Peabody Museum of Natural History, Yale University, New Haven, Connecticut. Photography by Claire Bucholz

Wampanoag Indians. Also known as King Philip, Metacomet led his warriors against the colonists in King Philip's War from 1675 to 1676, when he was killed. King Philip's Cave is a deep overhang on the sheer west face of the Talcott Basalt in Talcott Mountain State Park.

Farmington River and Glacial Lake Farmington

The Farmington River begins in the Berkshire Hills of Massachusetts and flows southeasterly to Farmington along the same trend the glaciers traveled. At Farmington the river makes a U-turn and heads straight north. Prior to the Pleistocene ice age, the river continued south toward Long Island Sound. Debris left by the melting glacier plugged the river's preglacial course, so now the river flows north along the west side of Talcott Mountain.

While the melting continental glacier receded northward about 16,000 years ago, Glacial Lake Farmington occupied the west side of Talcott Mountain south of the ice. The south end was dammed by the same sediment that plugged the preglacial course of the Farmington River. The lake extended up the valley of the Farmington River from Plainville through Farmington, Avon, and southernmost Simsbury. When the ice margin retreated north of the village of Tariffville, the lake water escaped through a preexisting gap in the basalt ridge there. Water levels lowered significantly in the valley to the level of what is called Glacial Lake Tariffville.

The modern Farmington River follows this narrow gorge through the basalt ridge at Tariffville. The gorge exposes the entire sequence of Hartford Basin rocks, from the Talcott Basalt up through the Shuttle Meadow sediments, the thick Holyoke Basalt, the East Berlin sedimentary rocks, the Hampden Basalt, and the Portland Arkose. All units are best viewed along the north bank of the Farmington River and along the Tariffville Road, but good exposures of the basalts and the interleaved sedimentary formations also are present in roadcuts along on CT 189.

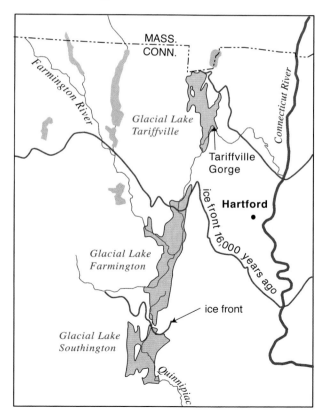

Glacial Lakes Farmington and Tariffville. —Modified from Stone and others, 2005

Avon

The 5-mile-wide lowland west of Talcott Mountain is underlain by the east-dipping, reddish, poorly sorted New Haven Arkose of Triassic age, a sandstone characterized by weathered feldspars. Just west of the Farmington River in the center of Avon is the picturesque Avon Park North, in which the town hall and the Avon Historical Society are located. Many of the older buildings were constructed of red and maroon sandstone of the New Haven Arkose in the 1920s by the Ensign-Bickford Company as a dynamite factory. Although no longer in business at those sites, the company is still operating in Simsbury, Avon, and Ellington, and at Powder Hollow on the Scantic River in Enfield.

Buttress Dike on the Western Border of the Hartford Basin

A prominent vertical dike of Buttress Diabase is located near the western margin of the Hartford Basin. Its massive appearance and medium-grained crystals give the dike a different appearance from the stratified, east-dipping lava ridges to the east. This is the result of the diabase having solidified within the earth's crust, not on the surface. The dike is exposed along US 44 in a 40-foot-high roadcut several hundred feet west of CT 167. The dike is offset to the west by a northwest-trending fault, so US 44 passes diagonally through about a 1,200-foot thickness of basalt. The western faulted margin of the Hartford Basin is a little over 0.1 mile west of the dike. This geological contact brings the New Haven redbeds of Late Triassic time in contact with Ordovician metamorphic rocks of the Collinsville Dome.

Roadcut on US 44 west of CT 167 through a diabase dike of Jurassic age along the Western Border Fault.

Connecticut 9
Middletown—New Britain
15 MILES

Eastern Border Fault

CT 9 crosses the boundary between the crystalline rock uplands of the Bronson Hill Terrane and the Hartford Basin at exit 11. The Eastern Border Fault trends north-south here, crossing the Connecticut River at the Straits and then paralleling CT 17 north to Chestnut Hill Road in Glastonbury. North of this intersection, the northeast-trending Cromwell Fault marks the eastern border of the Hartford Basin. South of the junction, the Cromwell Fault continues southwest on a straight course through the Hartford Basin to Meriden, along the west margin of Higby Mountain.

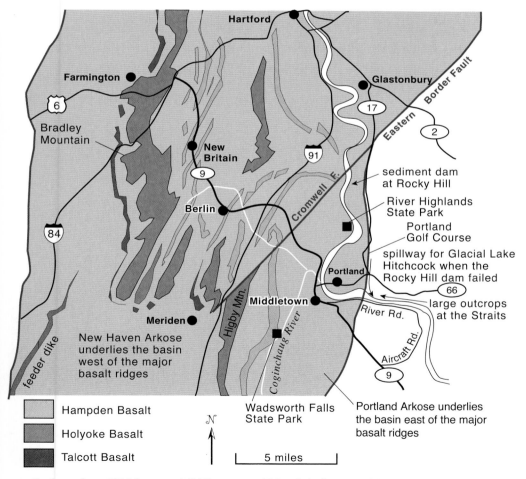

Geology along CT 9 between Middletown and New Britain. —Modified from Rodgers, 1985

East of Middletown and across the Connecticut River in Portland, CT 66 crosses the Eastern Border Fault. On the east side of the fault, you can see large outcrops of schist of the Collins Hill Formation of Ordovician age on the north side of the road. Collins Hill, the namesake for this rock, is just east of the Portland Golf Course.

Portland Brownstone

The reddish brown Portland Arkose, or brownstone as it's commonly called, underlies CT 9 from where it traverses the Eastern Border Fault to its junction with I-91. The arkose, which is the youngest Jurassic sediment in the Hartford Basin, was quarried on the east bank of the Connecticut River in Portland and used as building stone, most notably in old buildings at Wesleyan University in Middletown. Commercial quarrying began in 1783 and was an important industry in the latter half of the 1800s. Dinosaur footprints have been found in the quarries in Portland.

The Portland Golf Course, which lies 0.75 mile east of CT 17 in Portland, contains coarse conglomerates of the Portland Arkose. This mixture of cobbles and boulders was carried downslope from the margin of the basin in a stream that cut down into the eastern highlands of the Bronson Hill Terrane. The mixture is called a *fanglomerate* because its sediment is

St. Andrew's Episcopal Church in Meriden was constructed in 1867 with brownstone from the Portland Quarry. —Teresa Kennedy Gagnon photo

dominated by gravel and boulders deposited in a radial pattern from the center of an old alluvial fan.

Wadsworth Falls State Park

Wadsworth Falls State Park is southwest of Middletown on the Coginchaug River. To see the waterfalls, head south of the park entrance on CT 157. Turn left (southeast) on Cherry Hill Road and follow the Coginchaug River downstream from the bridge. Wadsworth Falls is near the former site of Simeon North's gun factory, which made military pistols in the 1800s. The Coginchaug River begins near Durham Meadows Wildlife Management Area and flows north through Wadsworth Falls State Park before joining the Mattabesset River in Cromwell Meadows Wildlife Management Area.

Wadsworth Falls cascades over columnar pillars of Hampden Basalt exposed along the upthrown east side of the northeast-striking reverse Coginchaug Fault. As hot lava cools, it shrinks and cracks. The cracks form perpendicular to the quickly cooling surfaces, which are usually the top and bottom of the lava flow. The columns formed by the cracks generally have five or six sides.

The north side of the falls is massive basalt containing holes produced by gas escaping from the molten lava as it cooled on the earth's surface. Farther to the north are a series of much smaller columns in the upper part of the outcrop and larger columns below. On the south side of the Coginchaug, the riverbank below the falls consists of a wall of miniature basalt columns.

Wadsworth Falls cascades over columnar basalt columns in Wadsworth Falls State Park east of Cherry Hill Road.

Reddish brown Portland Arkose, the sedimentary rock deposited on top of the Hampden Basalt, outcrops along trails in the park. Clarence C. Wadsworth, the park's namesake, gave this property to the state of Connecticut in 1942.

River Highlands State Park

River Highlands State Park, a wooded property in Cromwell, features a 150-foot-high bluff on the west bank of the Connecticut River. To get there, take Field Road north from North Cromwell. Turn east on a dirt road just south of where Field Street crosses the railroad. After several hundred feet, take a trail that goes straight up the hill from the dirt road. The park sits on the surface of a glacial delta built into Glacial Lake Middletown. This delta later formed part of the Rocky Hill dam for Glacial Lake Hitchcock. When Glacial Lake Hitchcock breached this sediment dam, the floodwater eroded the river bluff here. For more discussion about Glacial Lakes Middletown and Hitchcock, see the introduction to this chapter. The River Highlands trail system includes a hike along the edge of the bluff. You can also walk along the water's edge near the "Blowhole," where you can hear the wind whistling.

Fault Blocks of Hampden Basalt

A series of north-northeast-trending, steeply west-dipping normal faults has sliced up the Hartford Basin like a loaf of bread and shuffled the uplifted blocks into an obstacle course of at least four ridges of Hampden Basalt along CT 9. From its intersection with I-91 to the end of CT 9 in Farmington, just north of New Britain, there are eleven northeast-trending faults large enough to be shown on the 1985 *Bedrock Map of Connecticut*. These faults represent a collapse of the basin south of Hartford such that some blocks moved upward or downward relative to the block on the other side of the fault. Raised up along the east side of each fault is a ridge of Hampden Basalt underlain by the reddish brown, silty strata of the East Berlin Formation.

East-dipping East Berlin Formation with reddish brown silty shale and gray to white silty sandstone on the exit 22 on-ramp to eastbound CT 9 from CT 15 (the Berlin Turnpike).
—Teresa Kennedy Gagnon photo

domes of
Shelburne Falls
volcanic arc

Berkshire
Massif

MASS.
CONN.

Everett
thrust
sheet

NEW YORK

Housatonic
Massif

Canaan
Mtn.
thrust
sheets

Manhattan
thrust
sheet

Hoosac thrust sheet

Cameron's Line

New Milford
Massif

metamorphosed
volcanic rocks of
accretionary wedge

HARTFORD BASIN

Pomperaug
Basin

Hudson
Massif

Waterbury
Dome

East Derby Fault

N

New Haven

10 miles

Long Island Sound

LAURENTIA CONTINENT

carbonate shelf

Middle Proterozoic
gneiss of Laurentia

UNMETAMORPHOSED ROCKS

rift valleys of
Mesozoic age

METAMORPHIC REGIONS

volcanic arc and accretionary
wedge rocks metamorphosed
during Acadian mountain
building event

thrust sheets of Cambrian rocks
metamorphosed during
Taconic mountain building event

*Major geologic features in western Connecticut. Cameron's Line, a thrust fault,
separates rock deposited on the Laurentian continental shelf from sediments
deposited in deep waters of the Iapetus Ocean.*

Western Connecticut

Western Connecticut is a maze of folds, faults, and tiny slivers of different rock types. Many of the rocks formed on or near the Laurentian continent from Late Proterozoic to Ordovician time and then endured several episodes of tectonic deformation. The geology is very complex, and many aspects have not been clearly resolved.

The oldest rocks in western Connecticut are Grenville gneisses that formed 1.2 to 1.1 billion years ago during the Grenville mountain building event. The tectonic collision responsible for this event culminated in the formation of the supercontinent Rodinia. When Rodinia rifted apart about 750 million years ago, these gneisses formed the east coast of a new continent called Laurentia. That coastline lay roughly where the border of New York and Connecticut is today, and to the east lay the Iapetus Ocean. The Grenville gneisses, which still form the bulk of the earth's crust here, are visible in western Connecticut in large mountain blocks called *massifs*. These hard rocks are more resistant to erosion than the surrounding rocks, so they stand as mountains today. From north to south, they are the Berkshire Massif, Housatonic Massif, New Milford Massif, and Hudson Massif.

About 500 million years ago, in Cambrian time, sediments eroding from the mountains on the east coast of Laurentia were deposited in the sea on the continental shelf on top of Grenville gneisses. Beach sands accumulated along the coast, and in the shallow nearshore waters carbonates formed, rich with the calcium carbonate remains of life. Farther out to sea, clastic sediments were deposited on the continental slope and rise. Laurentia was close to the equator, so the environmental setting was somewhat similar to the modern Bahama Banks, southeast of Florida. With time, the carbonates would become the Stockbridge Marble and the beach sands would become the Cheshire Quartzite. Sediments on the continental slope and rise are now the Everett, Manhattan, Canaan Mountain, and Hoosac Schists.

In Early Ordovician time, a volcanic island chain developed on the deep ocean floor off the coast of Laurentia, similar to the modern volcanic chain

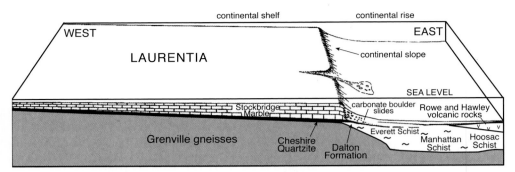

The continental shelf of Laurentia in Late Cambrian and Early Ordovician time before the Taconic mountain building event. —Modified from Bird and Dewey, 1970

of Japan. Magma poured out of volcanoes onto the seafloor. The arc, which is called the Shelburne Falls volcanic arc, developed above an east-dipping subduction zone. A belt of highly deformed domes in western Connecticut and Massachusetts is the remains of the volcanoes. In Connecticut the zone of domes includes, from north to south, the Granville, Granby, North Canton, Collinsville, Bristol, Waterbury, and Seymour Domes. The eastern margin of the belt is formed by the western faulted margin of the Hartford Basin. The volcanic terrane east and south of the Waterbury Dome consists of the Bridgeport, Stratford, and Milford blocks, north-northeast-trending fault-bound blocks containing remnants of volcanic rocks. The domes range from about 4 miles wide near the Collinsville Dome on the Massachusetts border to nearly 12 miles wide at the Waterbury Dome. The size of the domes probably increases with depth.

Granitic gneiss forms the cores of the larger domes. The Collinsville Formation and schist of the Taine Mountain Formation, both Ordovician in age, are present at the surface in the cores of the other domes. The domes are mantled, or partially encircled along their eastern margin, by silvery to gray, coarse-grained Straits Schist, a rock deposited in Silurian and Devonian time. The configuration of the Straits Schist accentuates the interpreted volcanic shape of the domes.

To the west of the arc, an accretionary wedge formed above the subduction zone. The wedge contains ocean floor sediments scraped off the down-going slab of ocean crust. The Rowe Schist, a widespread rock west of the volcanic domes, is recognized as one of the main rocks in the accretionary wedge. The distinctive green chloritic or epidote-rich schists of the Rowe represent deposits on or near the ocean's deep abyssal plain. Another rock from the deep sea, the Ratlum Mountain Schist, contains medium-grained schist and granular quartz and feldspar schist, as well as black or mottled, massive amphibolite and hornblende gneiss. Other rocks associated with the volcanic arc include the Hawley and Cobble Mountain Formations.

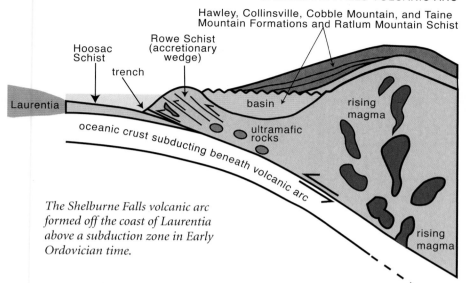

WEST

EAST

SHELBURNE FALLS VOLCANIC ARC

Hawley, Collinsville, Cobble Mountain, and Taine
Mountain Formations and Ratlum Mountain Schist

Rowe Schist
(accretionary
wedge)

Hoosac
Schist

trench

Laurentia

basin

rising
magma

oceanic crust subducting beneath volcanic arc

ultramafic
rocks

*The Shelburne Falls volcanic arc
formed off the coast of Laurentia
above a subduction zone in Early
Ordovician time.*

rising
magma

Taconic Mountain Building Event

Between 485 and 440 million years ago, rocks on the east coast of Laurentia were metamorphosed and transported along large thrust faults.
Great masses of metamorphosed clastic ocean sediments of Cambrian and
Ordovician age in western New England rest atop a sequence of metamorphosed limestone of the same age. Before the theory of plate tectonics was
developed in the mid-1960s, geologists couldn't figure out how this happened. These large-scale features—sheets of rock sitting on top of other
sheets—became known as Taconic overthrusts, named for the Taconic
Range of eastern New York, westernmost Massachusetts, and northwestern
Connecticut, where the overthrust sheets were first recognized.

It was not until the late 1960s and 1970s that geologists, armed with the
theory of plate tectonics, recognized that a collision of Laurentia with an
offshore volcanic chain was a plausible mechanism for the overthrusting.
The volcanic chain could act like a gigantic bulldozer, scraping up large
sheets of clastic sediments from the ocean floor and pushing them upslope
along fault planes onto the continental shelf. This collision is called the
Taconic mountain building event.

For many years, geologists inferred that the volcanic arc that caused
the collision was the Bronson Hill arc, which lies east of the Hartford
Basin. However, age dates obtained from the Shelburne Falls and Bronson Hill arcs in the 1980s and 1990s indicate that the Bronson Hill arc
formed at the very end of the Taconic mountain building event. Today,
some geologists think the Shelburne Falls arc was the first arc to collide

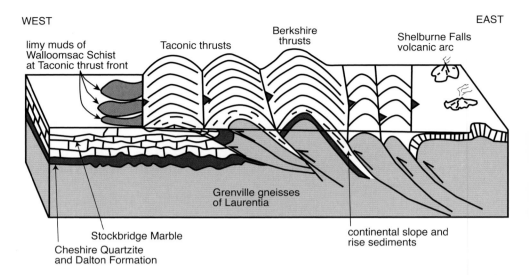

WEST

EAST

limy muds of
Walloomsac Schist
at Taconic thrust front

Taconic thrusts

Berkshire
thrusts

Shelburne Falls
volcanic arc

Grenville gneisses
of Laurentia

Stockbridge Marble

Cheshire Quartzite
and Dalton Formation

continental slope and
rise sediments

Schematic diagram of the eastern margin of the Laurentian continent showing Taconic thrust sheets moving west over continental shelf deposits.

with Laurentia. The east-dipping subduction zone may have then reversed directions, with the Bronson Hill arc forming over a west-dipping subduction zone between 454 and 442 million years ago, toward the end of the Taconic event. Other geologists think that both the Shelburne Falls and Bronson Hill volcanic rocks were part of one long-lived arc.

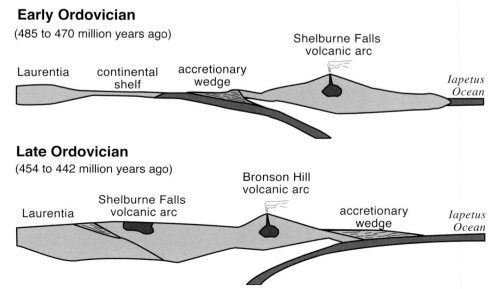

Early Ordovician

(485 to 470 million years ago)

Shelburne Falls
volcanic arc

Laurentia   continental
                  shelf

accretionary
wedge

*Iapetus
Ocean*

Late Ordovician

(454 to 442 million years ago)

Bronson Hill
volcanic arc

Shelburne Falls
volcanic arc

Laurentia

accretionary
wedge

*Iapetus
Ocean*

One volcanic arc formed above a subduction zone in Early Ordovician time, and another formed above a subduction zone in Late Ordovician time. —Modified from Karabinos and others, 1998

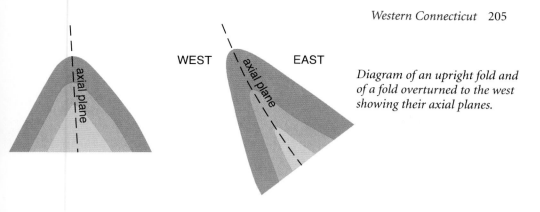

WEST EAST

Diagram of an upright fold and of a fold overturned to the west showing their axial planes.

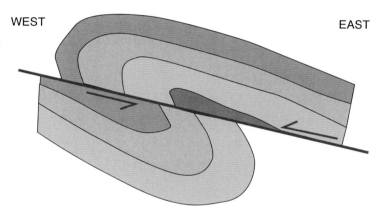

WEST

EAST

Diagram of fold broken by a thrust fault along which the upper plate has been shoved westward.

When rocks formed of sediment deposited on the continental shelf, such as the Stockbridge Marble, were compressed during the collision with the westward-moving volcanic arc, they were compressed into folds with axial planes dipping to the east. When the rocks were no longer strong enough to deform simply by folding, they broke and slid along low-angle faults or thrust faults that typically dip to the east like the axial planes of the folds. These easterly dips mean that the folds and faults developed as a result of rock masses having been shoved from the east upward toward the west.

In the early 1950s, Eugene Cameron mapped a conspicuous geological boundary separating the predominantly carbonate strata to the west and the ocean bottom and volcanic rocks to the east. Cameron was interested in the distribution of the carbonate reef strata, including the Stockbridge Marble, deposited in shallow water on the continental shelf of Laurentia relative to the volcanic-rich sequence east of it, including the Ratlum Mountain and Rowe Schists, which were deposited in the deep sea beyond the edge of the continental shelf. We now know that Cameron's Line is a mylonitized thrust fault along which a thrust sheet moved. It basically separates rocks that formed on the Laurentian shelf, slope, and rise from the accretionary wedge and volcanic arc rocks that formed farther out to sea. In other words, it is the suture between Laurentia and the volcanic arc that collided with it in Ordovician time. In Connecticut, the fault extends from the Massachusetts border in north-central Connecticut south to northwestern Greenwich.

South of I-84 and in the Danbury area, the Rowe and Ratlum Mountain Schists are less prevalent. They are often replaced by Harrison Gneiss, which is, in part, a migmatitic gneiss. They are also intruded by Ordovician igneous rocks, including the 453-million-year-old, coarse-grained, dark Brookfield Gneiss. Between 448 and 436 million years ago, several members of the Newtown Complex also intruded the Rowe and Ratlum Mountain Schists in the form of hot magma.

These rocks in southwestern Connecticut have puzzled geologists for years and given rise to several interpretations. They may be part of the same accretionary wedge but have undergone deeper burial here than farther north, giving rise to migmatites and plutons. Or they may be part of a later magmatic arc generated above a subduction zone.

Acadian Mountain Building Event

The Acadian mountain building event took place over a lengthy time interval from about 420 to 375 million years ago, and its several phases are so varied that it's hard to imagine them as one colossal event. Microcontinents associated with Gondwana rammed into Laurentia, sandwiching the Bronson Hill volcanic arc in between. The Acadian mountain building event caused compressional folds, thrust faults, high-grade metamorphism tapering off to the west, and widespread intrusion of granitic magmas. The event appears to have swept across southern New England from southeast to northwest. One of the structures formed at this time in western Connecticut was the East Derby Fault, the west side of which moved northeast relative to the southeast side.

In western Connecticut the zone affected by Acadian mountain building overlaps the zone of Taconic deformation. Only Acadian metamorphism is recognized between the western margin of the Hartford Basin and Cameron's Line except in the center of the Waterbury Dome, which exposes rocks metamorphosed by the Taconic mountain building event. The Straits Schist, which was deposited after the Taconic event ended, was metamorphosed in the Acadian event.

Mount Prospect and Hodges Complexes

Two mafic and ultramafic bodies of rock have long been of interest to geologists because they intruded along Cameron's Line, the thrust fault separating thrust sheets capped by rocks deposited on the Laurentian continental shelf from accretionary wedge rocks deposited in the Iapetus Ocean. One ultramafic body is the 14-square-mile Mount Prospect

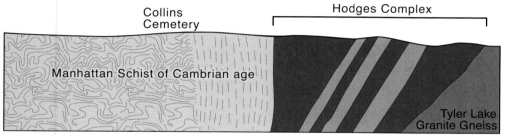

WEST   EAST

East-west geologic cross section of the Hodges Complex and the 466-million-year-old Tyler Lake Granite Gneiss. —Modified from Gates and Christensen, 1965

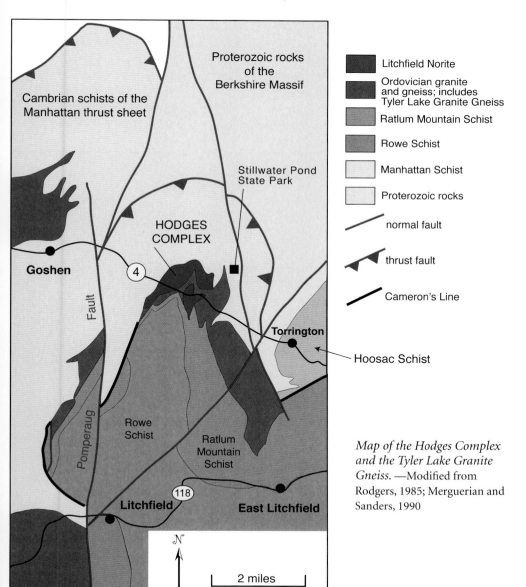

Map of the Hodges Complex and the Tyler Lake Granite Gneiss. —Modified from Rodgers, 1985; Merguerian and Sanders, 1990

Complex, located in Litchfield near Bantam Lake; the other is the smaller Hodges Complex, located in West Torrington southwest of Stillwater Pond State Park. Eugene Cameron mapped and described the complexes in 1951 when he delineated the boundary. Because the complexes intruded along the line but were not sheared by it, we know they are younger than the thrust fault.

A distinctive rock unit of both complexes is the Ordovician Litchfield Norite, a dark, coarse- to medium-grained, uniform rock containing orthopyroxenes, such as hypersthene, and labradorite, a calcium-rich plagioclase. Hypersthene is grayish, greenish, black, or dark brown and often has a bronze or greenish brown play of color on the cleavage surface. Labradorite is a dark mineral of the plagioclase feldspar group common in igneous rocks with an intermediate to low silica content. It shows a rich, beautiful play of colors, commonly blue or green, and is much used for ornamental purposes.

In the Mount Prospect Complex, the sulfide ore minerals pyrite, pyrrhotite, pentlandite, and chalcopyrite are concentrated mainly in olivine

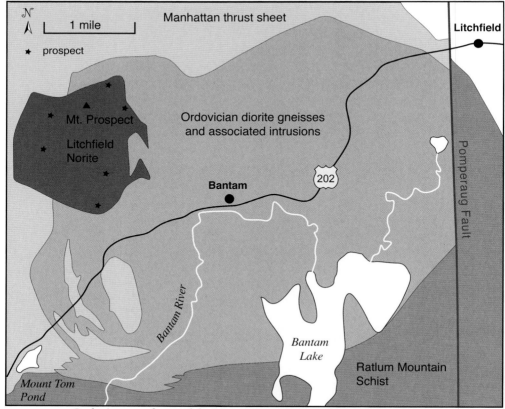

Geologic map of part of the Mount Prospect Complex. —Modified from Cameron, 1943; 1951

norite, quartz norite, and hypersthene pyroxenite, which were intruded in that order. Some sulfide minerals are also present in wall rocks and xenoliths. The sulfides filled fractures and replaced the original silicate minerals after a series of dikes cut the ore-bearing rocks. Although the sulfides appear to be related to the dikes, they were formed by the action of circulating hot water, not magma.

The intrusion of the Hodges Complex and Tyler Lake Granite Gneiss may be related to the migration of the subduction zone toward the ocean to the east and development of the Bronson Hill volcanic arc. Mount Tom State Park is west of Bantam Lake along US 202 on the Litchfield-Washington line.

Jurassic Rifting

About 200 million years ago, the supercontinent Pangea split apart, and the Atlantic Ocean soon entered the rift. The Hartford Basin, a failed rift, formed at the same time, dropping down along normal faults. The Western Border Fault cut off the eastern edges of several domes of the Shelburne Falls volcanic arc. In several places along the western border of the Hartford Basin, geologists have found places where basin sediments were deposited directly on an eroded surface of the crystalline rocks of the domes. The Pomperaug Basin, a much smaller rift basin, formed in western Connecticut. The Pomperaug Fault, which forms its eastern border, cuts north-south across western Connecticut.

Glaciation

The Hudson Valley lobe of the Wisconsinan continental glacier moved down the Hudson River. As it made its way southward, it also spread to the southeast over the Taconic Mountains and the uplands of western Connecticut. The orientation of glacial scratches and grooves, as well as the long axes of drumlins in the region, tell us that the ice rose up and over the mountains as it headed for Long Island. The position of meltwater features, such as recessional moraines, tells the story of where the ice front was during the northwestward retreat of the glacier. More than ten glacial lakes developed in western Connecticut as the glacial front receded northwestward.

In western Connecticut, narrow valleys are deeply eroded into the bedrock of the broad upland region. The Housatonic River, one of the two major drainage systems in western Connecticut, flows south from Massachusetts to Bulls Bridge in Kent, where it abruptly turns southeast and flows toward Derby. There, the Housatonic joins a tributary, the southeast-flowing Naugatuck River, which follows a deeply incised preglacial valley on its way to Long Island Sound. The Farmington River, the other major drainage system in western Connecticut, originates in southern Massachusetts and flows south to Farmington, where glacial sediments blocked its pre-glacial path, diverting it back north. The river then cuts east, joining the Connecticut River north of Hartford.

The Naugatuck River cut its deep valley prior to the Pleistocene glaciation. View to the north along CT 8 at Tobys Rock Mountain in Beacon Falls. —Teresa Kennedy Gagnon photo

— Road Guides in Western Connecticut —

Interstate 84
Southington—Danbury
30 MILES

Unconformity at Southington Mountain

I-84 crosses the Western Border Fault of the Hartford Basin at exit 27. Southington Mountain, on the north side of the interstate here, has been raised up along this fault relative to the basin to the east. Although this fault forms the western margin of the basin from the Massachusetts border to the Hamden-Bethany line, several angular unconformities have been preserved. An unconformity is where sedimentary rock is deposited on an erosional surface of a much older rock such that a gap is missing from the rock record. An angular unconformity is where the angle of bedding differs between the older and younger rock, indicating a period of uplift or mountain building prior to deposition of the younger rock. One angular unconformity is in Southington, east of Mount Vernon Road near the base of Southington Mountain at Roaring Brook. Here the New Haven Arkose was deposited on an eroded surface of the Ordovician Pumpkin Ground Member of the Harrison Gneiss. Unfortunately, this unique site is on private property and accessible only by special permission.

Waterbury Dome

Waterbury is centered on the Waterbury Dome, the heart of a volcano in the Shelburne Falls volcanic island arc about 480 million years ago. The south-flowing Naugatuck River has cut deep through the core of the dome, which is gray Waterbury Gneiss of Cambrian age. Spectacular outcrops of this gneiss occur along the south side of I-84 between exits 23 and 22 on the mountainside that features "Holy Land," a former tourist attraction.

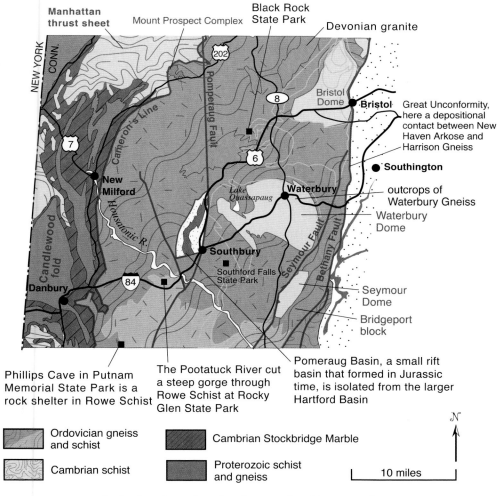

Bedrock geology along I-84 between Southington and Danbury. —Modified from Rodgers, 1985

Large outcrops of Waterbury Gneiss in "Holy Land," a former tourist attraction, rise above I-84 between exits 23 and 22 in Waterbury. —Teresa Kennedy Gagnon photo

Closeup of Waterbury Gneiss. —Teresa Kennedy Gagnon photo

Though truncated by faults on the east and west, the Waterbury Dome has a diameter of 11 miles at the surface. The eastern margin of the dome has been cut off along the Seymour Fault, which passes 0.25 mile east of Old Naugatuck Reservoir and through the town of Prospect. The Pomperaug Fault bounds the western margin of the Waterbury Dome. The dome has moved up along both faults relative to the Bridgeport block to the east and the Pomperaug Basin to the west.

Overlying the Waterbury Gneiss is a narrow band of the felsic granular basal member of the Taine Mountain Formation of Ordovician age interleaved with the silvery schist of the Collinsville Formation. Circling it is the Straits Schist, deposited over the top of the volcanic domes in Devonian time. The dominant metamorphism recorded in the core of the Waterbury Dome is of Middle to Late Ordovician age and therefore dates from the Taconic mountain building event. Ordovician strata surrounding the core record Devonian metamorphism from the Acadian mountain building event. A good place to see Taine Mountain and Collinsville Formations is along trails in Southford Falls State Park, south of I-84 on the Southbury-Oxford line. Many roadcuts in these formations occur on CT 8 north and south of I-84.

Eightmile Brook cascades over Collinsville Formation at Southford Falls State Park. —Teresa Kennedy Gagnon photo

Black Rock State Park

Black Rock State Park, west of Reynolds Bridge off US 6 in Mattatuck State Forest, seems to be misnamed because the park contains a prominent, light-colored cliff-forming rock. Around 1657, the Paugusset Indians gave mineral rights in this area to residents of Farmington, who were looking for graphite, which is found in black rocks. Even though no graphite was found, the name Black Rock stuck. Both Collinsville Formation and Straits Schist occur in the park. The generally gray and silvery schist of the

Collinsville Formation contains a medium-grained amphibolite and horn-blende gneiss, which are black rocks that may have misled those searching for graphite. Black Rock State Park is located within the Reynolds Bridge Dome, a small dome associated with the Shelburne Falls volcanic arc.

Middlebury Stone Wall

The Wisconsinan continental ice sheet picked up loose rocks of various sizes in its icy clutches and carried them along until the ice melted. Once free of the ice, the rock fragments blanketed the land, forming a deposit called *till* or *ground moraine*. It generally remained undisturbed until unsuspecting farmers tried to cultivate the land. If you're trying to iden-tify land covered with till, look for stone walls. Farmers constructed these walls on pasture or property boundaries, mainly between 1750 and 1850, by clearing boulders and cobbles from fields underlain by till. They also dumped the stones in piles. If you draw a line on a map around regions with stone walls, you'll have a pretty good generalized map of land for-merly covered by a blanket of till.

A 3.5-mile-long stone wall, finished in 1907 on the former Whittemore Farm, was constructed by forty-five men working for eight years. This wall, near the east shore of Lake Quassapaug in Middlebury, was constructed to survive the rigors of frost heaves. Its base begins in a 6-foot-deep and 6-foot-wide trench.

Pomperaug Basin

I-84 skirts to the south of Pomperaug Basin, a small, elongate Mesozoic basin between exits 15 and 14. US 6 and the Pomperaug River cut south through the basin. The extensively faulted rocks in the basin consist of east-dipping redbeds and basaltic lavas of Triassic and Jurassic age. Though the Pomperaug Basin formed at approximately the same time as the much larger Hartford Basin, its rocks are distinct from those of the Hartford Basin. When Pangea began to split apart, the Pomperaug and Hartford rift basins formed parallel to the large rift that became the Atlantic Ocean.

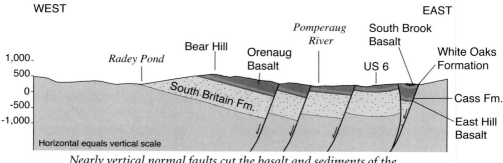

Nearly vertical normal faults cut the basalt and sediments of the Pomperaug Basin. —Modified from Burton and others, 2005

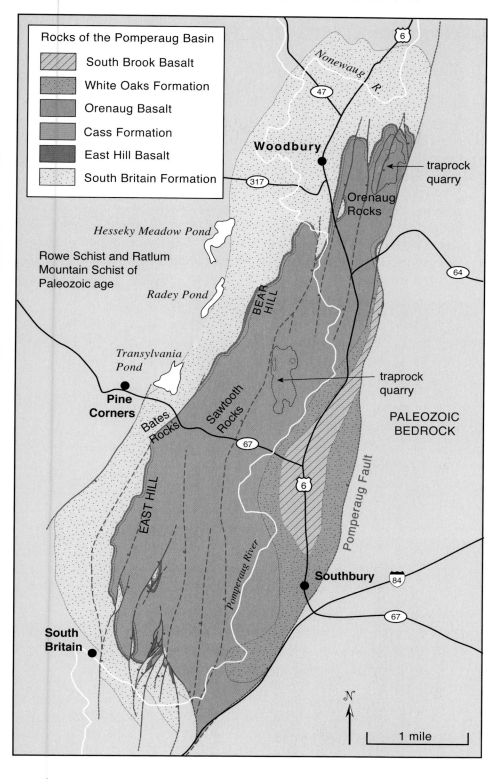

The Pomperaug Basin, with basalt and sedimentary rocks, is a small version of the Hartford Basin. —Modified from Burton and others, 2005

Eruptions of basalt filled the Pomperaug Basin, just as in the Hartford Basin, and sand and silt were deposited between eruptions. The basalt now forms ridges in the basin. Good exposures of the Orenaug Basalt occur in a quarry east of US 6 and south of Woodbury and in a quarry north of CT 67 at Sawtooth Rocks. The East Hill Basalt and the Orenaug Basalt crop out in the hills east of South Britain. The Pomperaug Fault, which forms the basin's eastern margin, extends north through much of western Connecticut, cutting Ordovician schists.

Roxbury Minerals

Rocks west and north of the Pomperaug Basin consist predominantly of Ratlum Mountain and Rowe Schists intruded by small bodies of Ordovician granite. The schists were deposited on the ocean floor as volcanic sediments in Cambrian and Ordovician time and then were metamorphosed during

Kyanite, a metamorphic mineral, from the Rowe Schist in Roxbury. Kyanite forms at medium temperatures and high pressures in regionally metamorphosed rocks.
—Copyright © 2006 by Peabody Museum of Natural History, Yale University, New Haven, Connecticut. Photography by Claire Bucholz

the Acadian mountain building event. Many museum-quality specimens of metamorphic minerals have been collected in Roxbury, and garnets were mined for abrasives from small prospect pits near Roxbury Falls. Brown, tabular staurolite crystals occur with the garnets in some rocks.

In the 1860s and 1870s, a furnace smelted siderite, an iron carbonate mineral, at the Roxbury Iron Mine. The property, now protected by the Roxbury Land Trust as Mine Hill Park, has some of the most extensive furnace remains in Connecticut. The ore occurs in a vein cutting the Ratlum Mountain and Rowe Schists near the contact with granite gneiss of Ordovician age. The granite gneiss was quarried here and used to construct the furnace. To reach the park, follow CT 67 northwest from Southbury to Roxbury Station along the Shepaug River. Take Mine Hill Road on the west side of the river. Mineral collecting is not permitted.

Rocky Glen State Park

At Rocky Glen State Park, the north-flowing Pootatuck River has cut a narrow gorge through Rowe Schist just upstream from its confluence with the Housatonic River. The park is north of I-84 at exit 10 in Sandy Hook. Along Glen Road, which runs the length of the gorge, you can see calc-silicate beds of Cambrian age. An iron bridge, originally built in 1890, may be visited on foot by parking on Dayton Street or may be seen from the top of Glen Road.

The village of Sandy Hook is located on the northern edge of a large area of unconsolidated sediments deposited in deltas in Glacial Lake Pootatuck. The glacial lake was formed when the north-flowing Pootatuck River was dammed by ice to the north. The deposits extend south along the river valley to Huntingtown.

Putnam Memorial State Park

Putnam Memorial State Park, located south of I-84 on CT 58 in Redding, is a good place to see garnets in the Rowe Schist. Garnet is the Connecticut state mineral, an apt choice for a state with so many metamorphic rocks. Garnet crystals, shaped like multisided globes, come in many colors and

Almandine, a dark, iron-bearing garnet, from Redding.
— Copyright © 2006 by Peabody Museum of Natural History, Yale University, New Haven, Connecticut. Photography by Claire Bucholz

chemical variations. Almandine, a reddish brown garnet with iron in its chemical composition, is the type most common in Connecticut. Garnets grow when clayey or silty sedimentary rocks are metamorphosed. The silvery Rowe Schist, originally deposited during Cambrian and Ordovician time as an alumina-rich mud on the ocean floor, contains many garnets that grew when the rock was metamorphosed.

A Revolutionary War memorial, a statue of Israel Putnam astride his horse, stands on a large outcrop of Rowe Schist near the park entrance. Phillips Cave, a rock shelter along one of the park's trails, is made of large boulders of Rowe Schist that a continental glacier plucked from the bedrock and piled here.

Interstate 95
West Haven—Greenwich
50 MILES

Glacial Features along the Coast

The Wisconsinan continental ice sheet formed drumlins as it pushed south toward its most southerly position, at Long Island, transporting and depositing huge quantities of glacial till in the process. Marsh Hill in Orange, north of I-95 exit 41, is a drumlin. In West Haven, about 1 mile southwest of Allington, is a 304-foot-high drumlin. The highest bedrock outcrop is at 174 feet in elevation—130 feet below the crest of the drumlin! A well drilled at the summit penetrated 107 feet of till without hitting bedrock. A well drilled at the crest of a drumlin near Pond Point in Milford penetrated 56 feet of till without hitting bedrock. Tashua Hill in Trumbull and Round Hill in Easton are also drumlins. A cluster of drumlins, Clark Hill, Burwell Hill, Eels Hill, Bryan Hill, and Merwin Hill, occurs in Milford. Glacial outwash sediments bury the base of these drumlins, so they are actually larger than they appear to be.

Charles Island, visible from Silver Sands State Park, is probably part of the Hammonasset-Ledyard moraine. A broad marsh separates the beach at Silver Sands from the city of Milford, but a boardwalk across the marsh allows visitors to see this biologically rich area. At low tide a ridge of sand and gravel connecting the beach to Charles Island is exposed. The island, a state natural area preserve, provides nesting habitat for herons, egrets, and bitterns. Legend has it that Captain Kidd buried treasure on Charles Island in 1699.

Stratford-Milford Block

A fault forms the border between the western uplands and the Hartford Basin throughout most of Connecticut, but unconformities between the

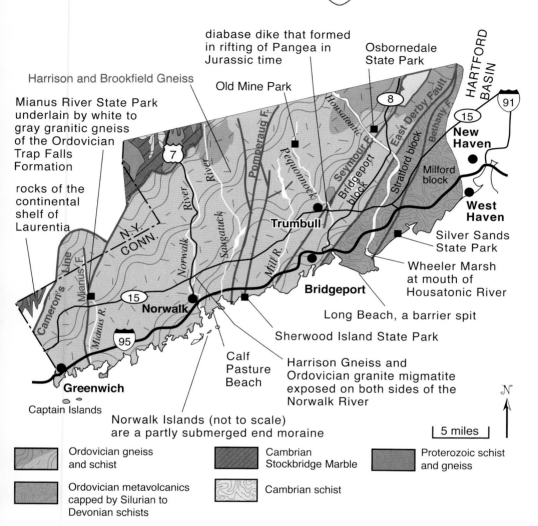

Ordovician gneiss and schist

Ordovician metavolcanics capped by Silurian to Devonian schists

Cambrian Stockbridge Marble

Cambrian schist

Proterozoic schist and gneiss

Bedrock geology along I-95 between West Haven and Greenwich. —Modified from Rodgers, 1985

New Haven Arkose of Triassic age and the Paleozoic rocks to the west have been preserved in places. In Woodbridge, Triassic New Haven redbeds were deposited on top of an eastward-dipping eroded surface of Maltby Lakes Metavolcanics, part of the Stratford and Milford blocks of rocks of Ordovician age. The angular unconformity is exposed in a 300-foot-long outcrop at June Street behind the Amity Shopping Center on the west side of CT 63, just west of CT 15 (the Wilbur Cross Parkway) near exit 59. A dike of Buttress Diabase of Jurassic age cuts the outcrop. All three rock types exposed here have been polished by glacial ice.

Between West Haven and Bridgeport, I-95 crosses gray to silvery Oronoque Schist and greenstone and schist of the Maltby Lakes and Allingtown Metavolcanics of Ordovician age capped by the Wepawaug gray schist and phyllite of Silurian to Devonian age. The western boundary of this belt is the northeast-trending East Derby Fault, which extends northeastward from Bridgeport to Lake Chamberlain in southern Bethany, where it strikes into and merges with the north-trending Western Border Fault of the Hartford Basin. The northeast-trending Bethany Fault divides the Milford block from the Stratford block, but both blocks contain similar rocks.

I-95 follows the southwest strike of the silvery gray Oronoque Schist for 3 miles from West Haven to exit 41 in Orange. It then travels over the Allingtown Metavolcanics, a massive greenstone, for nearly 2 miles across the marshland of Milford Harbor. For 0.5 mile west of exit 39, I-95 traverses a region underlain by the Maltby Lakes Metavolcanics, and between CT 121 and exit 38 it traverses the distinctive Wepawaug Schist. The western margin of the schist is the north-northeast-trending Bethany Fault, which parallels I-95 between exits 38 and 36. Between exit 34 in Devon and the southward projection of the East Derby Fault at Bridgeport Harbor, the interstate traverses land underlain by the Oronoque Schist.

Bridgeport Block and the Seymour Fault

The Bridgeport block is a well-defined, northeast-trending, fault-bounded block 33 miles long by 2 to 5 miles wide. The rocks within it, including the Seymour Dome, are part of the Shelburne Falls volcanic arc. The Bridgeport block extends from Long Island Sound northeast to Bethany, where it is truncated by the Bethany Fault, which forms the western, down-faulted margin of the Hartford Basin all the way to the Massachusetts border and beyond. The East Derby Fault bounds the Bridgeport block on the east and is also truncated by the Bethany Fault along the southeastern margin of Lake Chamberlain in southern Bethany.

Along most of its length, the western margin of the Bridgeport block is the Seymour Fault, which is sufficiently deep-seated to have reached magma. More than 38 miles of diabase dikes occur in and near the Seymour Fault from Fairfield to Hitchcock Lake on the Waterbury-Wolcott line. The magma fed the basalt flows in the Hartford Basin in Jurassic time. From Huntington in Shelton to Southport in Fairfield, the fault isn't visible, but the border of the Bridgeport block is the alignment of these northeast-trending segments of diabase dikes. The Red Trail at Osbornedale State Park in Derby crosses a 100-foot-wide diabase dike.

The rock formations of the Bridgeport block form an anticlinal fold overturned to the southeast. They are mainly stratified, gray to spotted, medium- to coarse-grained foliated Pumpkin Ground Member of the

Harrison Gneiss of Ordovician age and lesser amounts of silvery to gray, coarse-grained Straits Schist of Silurian to Devonian age. A narrow band of Straits Schist is preserved along the western margin of the East Derby Fault. The southern part of the Bridgeport block has a central core of white to light gray Shelton granitic gneiss, a member of the Trap Falls Formation of Ordovician age. The core gneiss is strongly elongate, having been compressed by tectonic forces during Ordovician time.

Charles E. Wheeler Marsh

Where the Housatonic River empties into Long Island Sound, the extensive Charles E. Wheeler marsh reaches as far west as the Bridgeport-Fairfield line, west of exit 25. Salt marsh deposits, formed during the last 4,000 years as sea level rose, overlie former floodplain deposits of the river. This salt marsh has numerous arteries that distribute nutritious river muds to the ecosystem. In Devon and Stratford, the Housatonic River has cut down through delta deposits of Glacial Lake Connecticut.

Long Beach and Lordship Outwash Fan

Long Beach in Stratford, a sandy barrier spit that ties Pleasure Beach to the mainland, protects the marshland of the Stewart B. McKinney National Wildlife Refuge. Prevailing ocean currents that flow westward transport sand from Lordship toward Pleasure Beach via Long Beach.

Extending east-southeast offshore from Lordship is the Lordship fan, a linear mound of sediment deposited underwater by meltwater issuing from the base of the ice as it stood in Glacial Lake Connecticut. This linear fan was deposited deep in the lake and subsequently buried by thick glacial lake varves. The ice margin stood along this linear array of sediment

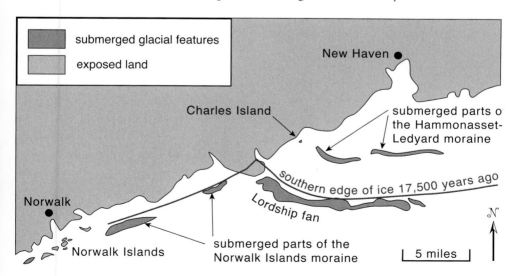

The Lordship fan was deposited by meltwater issuing from the base of the ice as it stood in Glacial Lake Connecticut. —Modified from Stone and others, 2005

about 17,500 years ago, at the same time the Norwalk Islands moraine was being formed to the west. The Lordship section of Stratford occupies the surface of a delta built into Glacial Lake Connecticut along the margin of the Wisconsinan ice sheet.

Old Mine Park

Old Mine Park, just east of the junction of CT 25 and CT 111 in north-central Trumbull, contains the remains of a tungsten mine. Nonresident visitors to this 62-acre, wooded recreational area must obtain a one-day permit at the police headquarters on Edison Road in Trumbull. The basal layers of Straits Schist, exposed here in Shaganawamps Hill, contain the valuable tungsten ore, here in the form of the mineral wolframite. Other minerals occurring here include pyrite, fluorite, quartz, scheelite, and topaz.

The first record of minerals at Shaganawamps is in a lease for obtaining mineral substances in 1757. In 1803, Elnathan Sherman of Trumbull leased

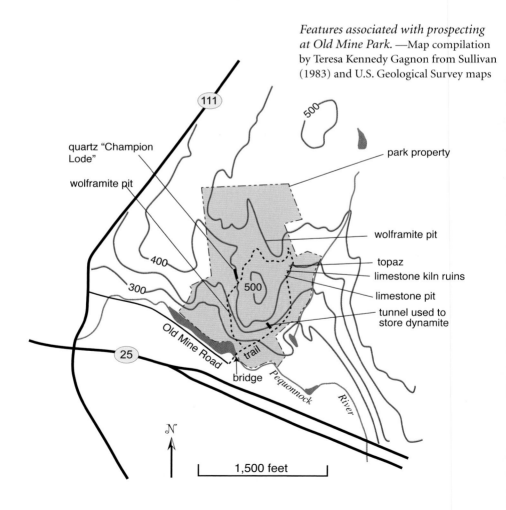

Features associated with prospecting at Old Mine Park. —Map compilation by Teresa Kennedy Gagnon from Sullivan (1983) and U.S. Geological Survey maps

111

quartz "Champion Lode"

wolframite pit

park property

wolframite pit

topaz

limestone kiln ruins

limestone pit

tunnel used to store dynamite

400

300

500

25

Old Mine Road

trail

bridge

Pequonnock River

500

N

1,500 feet

Black crystal of the tungsten ore wolframite from Old Mine Park in Trumbull. —Copyright © 2006 by Peabody Museum of Natural History, Yale University, New Haven, Connecticut. Photography by Claire Bucholz

Topaz crystal from Old Mine Park in Trumbull. —Copyright © 2006 by Peabody Museum of Natural History, Yale University, New Haven, Connecticut. Photography by Claire Bucholz

Roadcut in Straits Schist along CT 25 south of the Whitney Avenue overpass and about 1 mile south of Old Mine Park in Trumbull. —Teresa Kennedy Gagnon photo

the right for Philo and George Sherman to transport lime from Shaga-nawamps to a kiln, which may be either the one whose vandalized remains are near the topaz vein, or a now-buried kiln in the riverbank west of the footbridge at Old Mine Park. In the early 1800s, Benjamin Silliman of Yale University determined that samples of rocks brought to him from the location of Old Mine Park contained tungsten and tellurium. Silliman, the first professor of chemistry and natural history at Yale, founded the renowned *American Journal of Science* in 1818. He was born in Trumbull less than 4 miles from the site of the tungsten that he was later to identify.

Beginning in 1855, the discovery of hitherto unknown properties of tungsten-steel alloys breathed new life into previously on-again, off-again prospecting of the tungsten minerals. In 1902, the American Tungsten Mining and Milling Company of West Virginia constructed extensive buildings at the mine, but the plant soon shut down because pyrite could not be removed from the tungsten ore.

Sherwood Island State Park

In 1914, a salt marsh known as Sherwood Island, in Westport, became the first property acquired by the Connecticut State Park Commission. Located at exit 18, the park features beaches with alternating layers of red, black, and white sand. The red garnet, black magnetite, and white quartz are sorted by the waves because they are different densities and have distinct shapes. Jetties and a drumlin divide the shore into two beaches. At Sherwood Point, the southeastward extension of the drumlin, a granite monument is dedicated to the Connecticut residents who perished on September 11, 2001.

Harrison Gneiss

The bedrock formations near I-95 between Westport, near exit 18, and the New York border, are light gray, medium-grained foliated gneisses of the Harrison Gneiss of Ordovician age and a migmatized sequence of silvery to rusty-weathering schist and foliated gray to white granitic gneiss of the Trap Falls Formation of Ordovician age. This block of rocks has been metamorphosed to a high grade and is intimately mixed with granitic intrusive rocks. Between CT 15 (Merritt Parkway) and Long Island Sound in Stamford and Greenwich, glacial processes and erosion have washed the Harrison Gneiss relatively clean of unconsolidated deposits. A good place to see outcrops is along CT 15 east of Rockwood and Putnam Lakes in Greenwich. The Nodular Member of the Harrison Gneiss, with outcrops along Cos Cob Harbor in Greenwich, has prominent quartz-sillimanite nodules. The Ordovician plutonic igneous rocks resemble in both age and composition the rocks of the Bronson Hill volcanic arc, found east of the Hartford Basin. Whether they were once part of the same arc has yet to be determined.

Norwalk Harbor, Norwalk Islands, and Tidal Marshes

The Norwalk River, crossed by I-95 between exits 16 and 15, opens into Norwalk Harbor, which is one of many drowned river valleys along the Connecticut coast, flooded as sea level rose at the end of the ice age. The bedrock geology underlying Norwalk Harbor, including the Harborview district and Calf Pasture Park, consist of interlayered Ordovician Trap Falls gneisses and Harrison Gneiss, a foliated gray to black gneiss containing

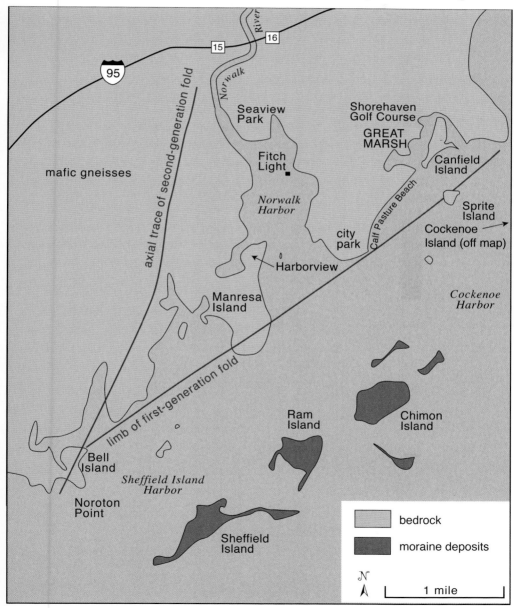

The Norwalk Islands are the remains of a moraine. The mainland is folded bedrock.

The linear chain of Norwalk Islands in Long Island Sound, as viewed from Calf Pasture Beach, is an end moraine. —Teresa Kennedy Gagnon photo

the dark minerals hornblende, biotite, and some garnet. The bedrock has been folded twice. The southern limb of the first-generation fold, created during the Taconic mountain building event, passes from Bell Island through Manresa Island to Sprite Island. The axial trace of the second-generation fold, created during the Acadian event, trends northward from Noroton Point on Sheffield Island Harbor toward exit 15.

The Norwalk Islands, a linear cluster of islands south of Norwalk Harbor, are the remains of an end moraine that have been partially reshaped by the restless waves of Long Island Sound. The moraine parallels the shore. About 17,500 years ago, the receding ice front paused offshore along the line of the Norwalk Islands, depositing the moraine. Deposition of the Lordship fan, a line of sediment deposited underwater in Glacial Lake Connecticut, probably occurred at the same time. The Fish Islands of Darien, just west of the Norwalk Islands, are made of bedrock, resistant knobs of massive granite gneiss, and blanketed with glacial sediment. Farther southwest, the Captain Islands in Greenwich are another moraine segment along the same line as the Norwalk Islands.

Tidal marshes, a distinctive sedimentary environment of the Connecticut shore, develop in areas sheltered from wave action. They usually occur in areas protected by rocky headlands, often on top of glacial deltas that built into Glacial Lake Connecticut as the shoreline emerged from under the ice. The northern part of Manresa Island, now the site of a power plant, is one of the nearshore salt marshes. Between the South Norwalk mainland and north of Manresa Island lies a large salt marsh. Seaview Park, on the east side of the river, overlooks the mudflats north and south of Fitch Light.

The largest marsh in the Norwalk area is the 0.3-square-mile Great Marsh, on the mainland northwest of Sprite Island in East Norwalk. Cores in Great Marsh indicate that the marsh grew over deposits of glacial sand and gravel protected by islands of bedrock on which Canfield Island and Shorehaven Island have developed. Salt marshes were once more extensive along the mainland behind the islands, but many were destroyed by

human activity. Today, an increased rate of sea level rise is leading to erosion and submersion of the marshes. Under natural conditions, they could expand inland over low-lying areas as sea level rises, but modern human development will restrict this.

Mianus River State Park

The two tracts of Mianus River State Park are in westernmost Stamford and north of CT 15 (Merritt Parkway). The very long, linear valley filled by Mianus Reservoir, which forms the east side of the northern tract of Mianus River State Park, was eroded along the north-trending Mianus Fault, a normal fault with rocks on the east moved down relative to those on the west. The northern tract of the park is mainly underlain by white to gray granitic gneiss, the Shelton Member of the Trap Falls Formation of Ordovician age. The western part of the park is underlain by interlayered rusty-weathering schist and light gray gneiss.

The southern tract of parkland, north of Stanwich and mainly west of the Mianus River, is divided not only by the north-trending Mianus Fault but also by a north-northeast-trending fault that joins the Mianus Fault near the south end of the park. The southern tract is mainly underlain by gray to silvery schist interlayered with granular quartz and feldspar schist, as well as a small area each of Harrison Gneiss, consisting of interlayered dark and light gray, foliated gneiss, and gneiss of the Shelton Member of the Trap Falls Formation.

Continental Shelf Remnant in Western Greenwich

The westernmost corner of Greenwich, west of Round Hill (a drumlin) and southwest of Converse Lake, contains a "vest-pocket-sized" sample of the Laurentian continental shelf. Cameron's Line, the eastern margin of the continental shelf strata, makes a turn into and then out of northwest Greenwich before going southwest into New York City. Just west of Cameron's Line, the Late Proterozoic to Cambrian Manhattan Schist has been thrust over Ordovician Walloomsac Schist, Cambrian to Ordovician Stockbridge Marble, and Cambrian Dalton Formation of the continental shelf. You can see these rock formations along trails at the 500-acre Audubon Center in Greenwich. Take exit 28 from CT 15 (Merritt Parkway), head north on Round Hill Road, and then turn left on John Street and go west toward Riversville Road.

US 7
Canaan—Norwalk
75 MILES

You can get a good idea of the kinds of sediments deposited on the ancient Laurentian continental shelf of eastern North America by traveling along US 7 between Canaan in northern Connecticut and Danbury in the south. Following the Housatonic River, US 7 traverses scenic and fertile valley bottoms underlain mainly by the Stockbridge Marble of Cambrian to Ordovician age. The marble, a beautiful rock used for building stone, was originally deposited in carbonate banks similar to those that make up today's Bahama Banks, southeast of Florida. The carbonate was then transformed into marble by heat and pressure during the Taconic mountain building event between 485 and 440 million years ago. Marble deposits in western Connecticut consist of calcium carbonate and calcium-magnesium carbonate with a small amount of quartz and feldspar.

The breadth of the Stockbridge Marble in Connecticut becomes progressively narrower as you follow US 7 south to Danbury. Southwest of Danbury, the Stockbridge Marble exposures shift westward into New York, and in southern Connecticut it is found only in northwesternmost Greenwich. The large massifs made of Grenville gneisses also shift progressively westward.

Canaan Mountain

Between Canaan and South Canaan, US 7 passes just west of Canaan Mountain, the namesake of the Canaan Mountain Schist of Cambrian age. This schist, which makes up the mass of the mountain, occurs in two thrust sheets that were transported in a west to northwesterly direction during the Taconic mountain building event in Ordovician time.

Great Falls and the Housatonic River

Great Falls, located 0.5 mile north of the bridge over the Housatonic River northwest of Falls Village, is an impressive waterfall over a series of ledges of Stockbridge Marble. The cascade above the falls gives way rapidly to the waterfall, which drops steeply about 40 to 50 feet. During the wet spring season, the cascading section above the falls develops into noisy rapids, forming a cloud of mist rising above the plunging Great Falls.

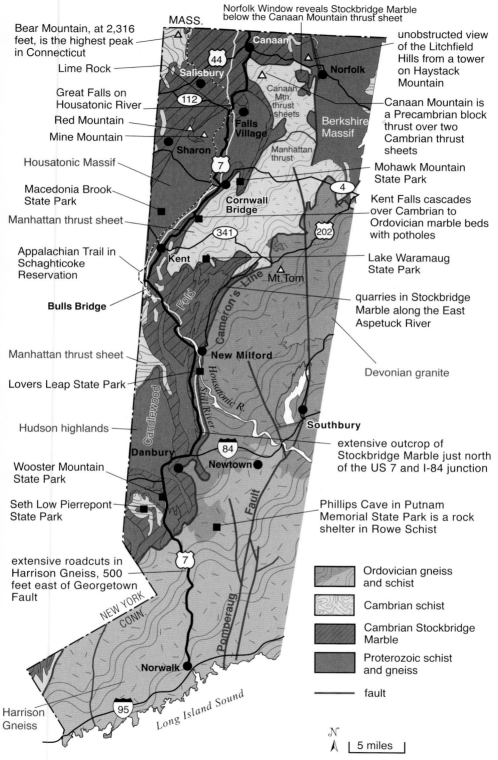

Bear Mountain, at 2,316 feet, is the highest peak in Connecticut

Lime Rock

Great Falls on Housatonic River

Red Mountain

Mine Mountain

Housatonic Massif

Macedonia Brook State Park

Manhattan thrust sheet

Appalachian Trail in Schaghticoke Reservation

Bulls Bridge

Manhattan thrust sheet

Lovers Leap State Park

Hudson highlands

Wooster Mountain State Park

Seth Low Pierrepont State Park

extensive roadcuts in Harrison Gneiss, 500 feet east of Georgetown Fault

Harrison Gneiss

Norfolk Window reveals Stockbridge Marble below the Canaan Mountain thrust sheet

MASS.

Canaan

44

Salisbury

112

Falls Village

Sharon

7

Cornwall Bridge

341

Kent

Fold

Mt. Tom

Cameron's Line

New Milford

Housatonic R.

Still River

Candlewood

Danbury

84

Newtown

7

Fault

Pomperaug

Norwalk

NEW YORK
CONN.

95

Long Island Sound

Canaan Mtn. thrust sheets

Manhattan thrust

Berkshire Massif

4

202

Norfolk

Southbury

unobstructed view of the Litchfield Hills from a tower on Haystack Mountain

Canaan Mountain is a Precambrian block thrust over two Cambrian thrust sheets

Mohawk Mountain State Park

Kent Falls cascades over Cambrian to Ordovician marble beds with potholes

Lake Waramaug State Park

quarries in Stockbridge Marble along the East Aspetuck River

Devonian granite

extensive outcrop of Stockbridge Marble just north of the US 7 and I-84 junction

Phillips Cave in Putnam Memorial State Park is a rock shelter in Rowe Schist

Ordovician gneiss and schist

Cambrian schist

Cambrian Stockbridge Marble

Proterozoic schist and gneiss

fault

N

5 miles

Bedrock geology along US 7 between Canaan and Norwalk. —Modified from Rodgers, 1985

View to the north of Canaan Mountain from just east of US 7 near South Canaan. The hump on the west (left) side of the mountain is a part of the upper thrust sheet of Cambrian age.

Great Falls, on the Housatonic River, tumbles over Cambrian and Ordovician marble at Falls Village.

Water power was necessary for the region's iron production. The Housatonic River, with its large volume of water and drop in elevation, was an especially attractive source of hydropower. It has been harnessed on both banks near Great Falls and also at Little Falls, a small drop that existed upstream from Great Falls before it was inundated by the present-day dam. Iron from Ore Hill in Salisbury was hauled to the furnace at Lime Rock, 2 miles west of US 7 on CT 112. Like all furnaces, its location was chosen because of its proximity to water.

Appalachian Trail

Connecticut maintains a 53-mile section of the Appalachian Trail over mountains such as 1,475-foot Mount Prospect northwest of Falls Village and along relatively flat ground near the bank of the Housatonic River. US 7 lies east of the trail except just briefly near the junction with CT 112. The 2,200-mile-long Appalachian Trail was completed in 1937. By an act of Congress in 1968, it became the first national scenic trail. The Mohawk Trail, a blue-blazed trail in the mountains to the east of the Housatonic River, joins the Appalachian Trail in Falls Village.

Housatonic Highlands

Between the junction with CT 112 and Cornwall Bridge, US 7 runs along a gorge cut through Middle Proterozoic gneiss and granite gneiss of the

Cambrian dolomite of the Stockbridge Marble at the overlook on the west bank of the Housatonic River just above Great Falls.

View to the northwest of the Housatonic Highlands from US 7, 0.1 mile south of its junction with CT 45.

Housatonic Highlands. You can see Middle Proterozoic granite gneiss at Macedonia Brook State Park, north of Kent. The brook has eroded a gorge through the hard rock of the highlands.

Between Cornwall Bridge and Bulls Bridge, US 7 runs along a valley floored with Stockbridge Marble. The Housatonic Highlands rise to the west of the river. To the east, the hills are made of the Manhattan thrust sheet. US 7 is just west of the thrust fault that places the Manhattan thrust sheet over the top of the marble. Brilliant white outcrops of Stockbridge Marble are visible along and from US 7, especially along the west bank of the Housatonic River between 1 and 2 miles north of Bulls Bridge. Folds and thrust faults can be seen in the carbonate shelf strata a few hundred feet upstream from Bulls Bridge.

Kent Falls State Park

Kent Falls is a 1,000-foot-long series of several cascading falls on Kent Falls Brook, which enters the Housatonic River from the east. The combined vertical drop is about 400 feet. You can hike up the hill beside the falls along a path and boardwalk stairs. The lower two falls cascade over resistant layers of well-exposed Stockbridge Marble. Look for potholes and folds in the marble.

Kent Falls State Park is perfectly situated to expose the thrust fault that places Manhattan Schist over Stockbridge Marble. The basal part of the Manhattan thrust sheet is at the top of the upper falls. The Manhattan thrust sheet is mainly composed of a single block of rock 22 miles long and 6 miles wide, which extends without interruption from northern Goshen to Bulls Bridge. The rock is formed of micaceous feldspar schists and gneisses similar to the Hoosac Schist, except that the Manhattan

Stockbridge Marble forms the bank of the Housatonic River north of Bulls Bridge.

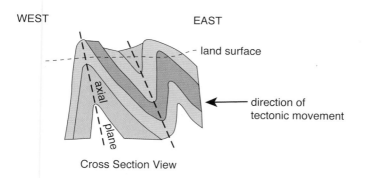

WEST

EAST

land surface

axial plane

direction of
tectonic movement

Cross Section View

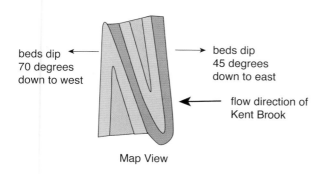

beds dip
70 degrees
down to west

beds dip
45 degrees
down to east

flow direction of
Kent Brook

Map View

The compressional forces that
folded the Stockbridge Marble
moved east to west, creating
overturned folds. The western
limb of each fold dips more
steeply than the eastern limb.
You can recognize these folds
in outcrops in places like Kent
Falls State Park, where you
can trace a bed from one side
of the fold to the other.

The uppermost falls at Kent Falls State Park. —Teresa Kennedy Gagnon photo

The lowermost waterfall at Kent Falls State Park cascades over folded layers of Stockbridge Marble.

Schist is intruded by light-colored stocks of Ordovician felsic gneiss. Unlike the Hoosac Schist, there is little or no evidence that the Manhattan Schist was deposited directly on Middle Proterozoic gneisses.

Iron Ore at Kent

The iron ore deposits in the Walloomsac Schist at Ore Hill in Kent, isolated some distance from the Salisbury District proper, were limonite, as in the Salisbury District. However, the Kent deposits differ somewhat from the Salisbury ore. Lying in a faulted area and bordered by carbonate rock, schist, and quartzite, the Kent ore is higher in phosphorus and therefore somewhat lower in quality than the Salisbury ore. Nevertheless, thousands of tons of ore were mined here, first for many of the area forges and later for production of pig iron at the Kent Furnace and other ironworks. The Connecticut Mining Museum in Kent features the region's mining history and minerals.

Lake Waramaug State Park

Lake Waramaug State Park, east of Kent off CT 341, is located along the western shore of the northwest cove of Lake Waramaug, which is nestled in a lake basin almost exclusively underlain by the Stockbridge Marble. However, a single finger of land, Golf Course Hill on the northwest cove west of Lake Waramaug Road, calls attention to the fact that the lake is on the southern margin of the Manhattan thrust sheet. The summit of this south-southeast jutting hill consists of Manhattan Schist.

Marble near New Milford

The broad valley at New Milford is underlain by Stockbridge Marble, which is well exposed in quarries northeast of Boardman Bridge. Tory's Cave, an unmarked but nonetheless well-known cave, occurs in the Stockbridge Marble in Boardman Mountain south of Gaylordsville and north of Boardman Bridge. The marble is a large xenolith enclosed in Ordovician granite gneiss.

About 9 miles upstream from New Milford along the East Aspetuck River is a belt of marble that was suitable for use as building stone. The town of Marble Dale in Washington was established around this industry in the early 1800s. The old quarries are no longer visible.

Lake Candlewood

Lake Candlewood is a reservoir created for hydroelectric power in 1929. Water from the Housatonic River is pumped into the reservoir when demand for electricity is low and then released to generate power when demand is high. The pump and power station are on US 7. The lake curves around the mountainous region of the Lake Candlewood fold, which is convex to the west. This 30-mile-long, arched structure extends from east of Kent on the north to Danbury on the south. The arch has Grenville gneisses at its core and is mantled by quartzite and schist of the Dalton Formation and Stockbridge Marble and intruded by Ordovician granite.

Still River Valley and Lovers Leap

US 7 follows the flat valley of the north-flowing, meandering Still River between its confluence with the Housatonic River, near Lovers Leap State Park, and Danbury. The valley, floored by Stockbridge Marble, lies just west of Cameron's Line, the thrust fault that separates rocks formed on the Laurentian continent from those formed in the Iapetus Ocean and its volcanic arcs. Just east of Cameron's Line is Lovers Leap State Park, the famous bluff above the narrows of the Housatonic River just downstream from the Still River confluence. The bluff is made of biotite schist and amphibolite of the Ratlum Mountain Schist. Wolf Pit Mountain, on the east side of the Housatonic River, is made of 453-million-year-old Brookfield Gneiss. The gneiss contains xenoliths of Ratlum Mountain Schist. Extensive roadcuts through the Stockbridge Marble are visible on US 7 just north of the I-84 junction.

The sediments on the flat valley floor of the Still River were deposited in Glacial Lake Danbury, a lake impounded by the continental glacier as it retreated northward. The lake existed in three different stages, each

Ratlum Mountain Schist below the old iron bridge over the Housatonic River gorge at Lovers Leap State Park. —Teresa Kennedy Gagnon photo

View looking east at Stockbridge Marble in roadcut along Picket District Road across the Still River valley with bluff of Lovers Leap State Park in distance. Here, the Still River flows along Cameron's Line, a fault zone. —Teresa Kennedy Gagnon photo

View of white Stockbridge Marble outcrops northeast of Danbury on the Danbury-Brookfield line near the southern junction of US 7 and US 202.

controlled by a different spillway, or overflow channel. New spillways emerged from beneath the ice as it retreated northward.

Ordovician Gneisses between Topstone and Norwalk

US 7 crosses Cameron's Line, a northeast-trending fault, near Topstone in westernmost Redding. A large part of southwestern Connecticut southeast of Cameron's Line is underlain by a variety of gneisses of Ordovician age. Near Branchville, US 7 passes through extensive roadcuts of Harrison Gneiss, a light gray, medium-grained foliated gneiss. It has been metamorphosed to a high grade and is mixed with intrusive granitic gneiss of Ordovician age.

A 40-foot-wide zoned pegmatite intrudes the Ordovician gneiss at Branchville. The pegmatite has been mined for manganese phosphates, as well as minerals such as mica, feldspar, and quartz. The mine is about 500 feet east of the Branchville railroad station east of US 7.

Quarry Head Preserve in Wilton

Quarrying of granite gneiss of Ordovician age began in Wilton in the 1700s. The town's most notable quarry is now set aside as the Quarry Head Preserve. Its rock was used for house foundations, the steps of the town hall, St. Mary's Church in Norwalk, and the Ridgefield Congregational Church. The quarry is located east of CT 33, 0.5 mile north of Keelers Ridge Road. Many discarded blocks at the quarry preserve tool marks of

A carved inscription featuring a compass on a rock near the Quarry Head Preserve. The paper map on the rock portrays the shape of the property.

Numerous discarded blocks of fine-grained granite gneiss remain scattered along the slope of the former processing area at the top of the Quarry Head Preserve. Note the size of the trees that have grown up near the southeast, downstepping face of the quarry site since it was abandoned.

instruments in use in the past, such as drill holes and chisel markings. Aligned drill holes have long been used to break blocks of granite gneiss along straight, relatively planar surfaces, though the discarded blocks at the site attest that many did not break as intended.

US 44
Canton—New York State Line
42 MILES

Collinsville Dome

US 44 crosses the north-trending Western Border Fault of the Hartford rift basin about 0.8 mile west of its intersection with CT 167 in Canton, 200 feet west of the Simsbury-Canton line. In the US 44 roadcut, you see the location of the vertical fault where New Haven redbeds of Triassic age to the east are in contact with Ordovician rocks of the Collinsville Dome, one of the volcanoes of the Shelburne Falls arc. This dome is one in a series of large folded structures that lie, on average, in a 3- to 5-mile-wide linear belt just west of the Hartford Basin from New Hampshire to Long Island Sound. The eastern quarter of the Collinsville Dome has been cut off by the Western Border Fault.

Like other related domes, the Collinsville Dome has an onionlike structure with progressively older rock layers exposed toward the center of the eroded dome. About 0.25 mile west of Canton, US 44 grazes the northern contact between the core Bristol Gneiss and the next younger layer, the Collinsville Formation, both of Ordovician age. The Bristol Gneiss

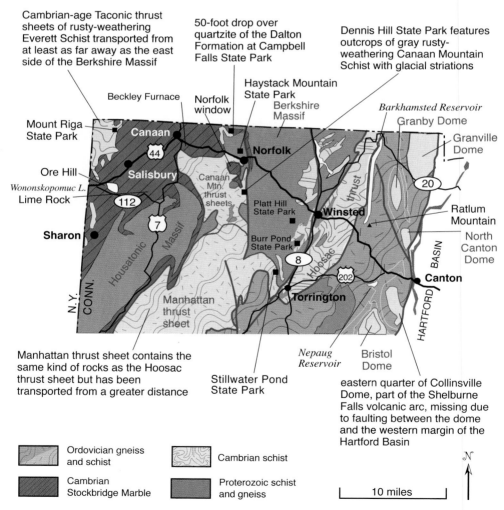

Bedrock geology along US 44 between Canton and the New York state line.
—Modified from Rodgers, 1985

consists of light gray, medium-grained granite gneiss. The younger Collinsville Formation consists of fine- to medium-grained amphibolite and hornblende gneiss. The latter, a metamorphosed volcanic rock formation, forms the northern part of the inner dome for a distance of 2.5 miles along US 44. A few hundred feet of the distinctive gray and silvery, medium- to coarse-grained mica schist of the Collinsville Formation encircle the darker rocks of the formation. The equally distinctive silvery, coarse-grained Straits Schist of Silurian and Devonian age lies to the west of the Collinsville Formation. US 44 crosses the 1-mile-wide band of Straits Schist east and west of Cherry Brook, where it contains graded beds. Graded beds result from vertical variation in grain size because coarse grains settle out of water faster than finer grains. In the Straits Schist, coarse, quartz-rich beds grade up into fine-grained micaceous layers, indicating these beds are right side up.

The Cherry Brook Basin, a very small fault-bound structure, contains a tiny wedge of New Haven Arkose of Triassic age. The eastern fault boundary runs parallel to CT 179 along Cherry Brook in Canton, about 1 mile west of the much larger Hartford Basin. The wedge of Triassic sediments is about halfway between Canton Center and North Canton.

Rowe Schist in New Hartford

Nepaug State Forest, in New Hartford, straddles the boundary between the belt of domes to the east and the ocean floor rocks to the west, which include the Cambrian to Ordovician Rowe Schist and the Ordovician Ratlum Mountain Schist, Hawley Formation, and Cobble Mountain Formation. These schists were originally deposited as sedimentary and volcanic rocks in the Iapetus Ocean to the east of the Laurentian continental shelf. The formations grade into one another where depositional environments changed on the ocean floor. The foliation of the schists dips steeply to the west, for the most part, dipping away from the crest of the Collinsville Dome. The Silurian to Devonian Straits Schist of the dome belt has been deposited atop the eastern part of these ocean floor rocks. The light gray to silvery Rowe Schist encloses pods and lenses of dark ultramafic rock that are especially abundant southwest of Puddle Town in New Hartford.

A conspicuous unconformity between the overlying Straits Schist and the Ordovician Cobble Mountain Formation occurs at the northernmost point of Nepaug Reservoir, just a few hundred feet east of the Nepaug Dam.

Ratlum Mountain Schist

Ratlum Mountain, which rises to the east of Lake McDonough, is the namesake of the Ratlum Mountain Schist. One place you can see this rock is at Satan's Kingdom State Recreation Area, a kayak and white-water area near the US 44 crossing of the Farmington River. Steep cliff faces of Ratlum

Mountain Schist rise precipitously above the swift-flowing river. This gorge has been designated as part of the National Wild and Scenic River System.

Hoosac Thrust Sheet

Between New Hartford and Winsted, US 44 crosses the Hoosac thrust sheet, formed of gneisses capped by Hoosac Schist and separated from the main Berkshire Massif by steep thrust faults and normal faults. The leading, western edge of the Hoosac thrust sheet is near Hartland, Riverton, and Winsted. Some remnants of Hoosac Schist decorate the crest of the Grenvillian gneissic blocks of the Berkshire Massif as much as 4 miles west of the leading edge. It's unclear whether these were deposited on the gneiss or thrust over it.

What we do know is that the Hoosac Schist was deposited on an eroded surface of Middle Proterozoic Grenville gneisses in Late Proterozoic to Early Cambrian time. This coarse-grained, rusty-weathering micaceous schist contains abundant quartz-rich lenses and associated feldspars, which are typically oligoclase crystals in higher grades of metamorphism and albite in lower metamorphic grades.

Peoples State Forest and American Legion State Forest, along the Farmington River in Barkhamsted, are located on the Hoosac thrust sheet. Two forest trails provide good views and magnificent exposures of Grenville gneisses and the Hoosac Schist, hard rocks that resist erosion and form mountainous terrain: the Henry Buck Trail, a 2.3-mile loop trail in the north end of the Peoples State Forest, and the Turkey Vulture Ledges Trail, which is off Legion Road at the south end of the American Legion State Forest. The Stone Museum in Peoples State Forest includes iron ores and a reproduction of a charcoal hearth. The East River Road, which runs along the border between the two state forests, was important for transporting iron during early colonial times.

Torrington Fault

At Winsted, US 44 crosses the north-northeast-trending Torrington Fault, a normal fault that separates the main mass of the Berkshire Massif to the west from a smaller chunk to the east overlain by Hoosac Schist. CT 8 runs along the upthrown side of the fault for 6 miles south of Winsted. The Still River also follows the trace of the fault, probably because the fault created a zone of persistent weakness in the rocks that allowed the river to cut down here. The Torrington Fault branches from the north-trending Pomperaug Fault. Between the Winchester line and Nelsons Corner, CT 8 lies in or nearly on the Torrington Fault.

Berkshire Massif

Between Winsted and Norfolk, US 44 crosses the Middle Proterozoic gneiss of the Berkshire Massif. Where the highway straddles a tract of the

Algonquin State Forest 4 miles northwest of Winsted, 20- to 40-foot-high roadcuts expose Middle Proterozoic gneisses with steeply dipping foliation and pegmatites.

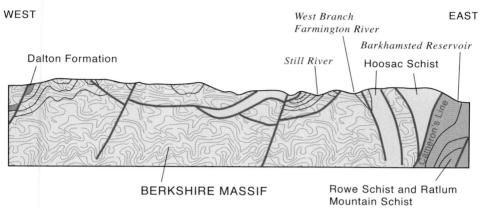

Cross section through the Berkshire Massif. —Modified from Rodgers, 1985

Roadcut through Grenville gneisses near Winsted.

Middle Proterozoic granitic gneiss in the Berkshire Massif on CT 44 just east of Laurel Way. Gray feldspar crystals are prominently aligned in nearly vertical gneissic layering.

Middle Proterozoic gray, medium-grained, well-layered gneiss intruded by dikes of pink granitic gneiss on US 44 in Algonquin State Forest 0.5 mile west of the Mad River Dam.

Two state parks south and west of Winsted expose the Middle Proterozoic rocks of the Berkshire Massif. The western shore of Burr Pond in Burr Pond State Park is underlain by Grenville granitic gneisses; from the eastern shore to Pond Road is underlain by Hoosac Schist; and the belt between Pond Road and the Torrington Fault near Burrville is again underlain by Grenville granitic gneisses. A small area of rusty-weathering Hoosac Schist crops out at the northeast end of Burr Pond.

At 1,457 feet, Platt Hill in Platt Hill State Park overlooks Highland Lake and is one of Connecticut's oldest picnic spots. The hill is almost entirely underlain by pink Grenville granitic gneisses of Middle Proterozoic age, with the northwest corner and adjacent areas underlain by well-layered gray gneiss, also Middle Proterozoic, intruded by the pink to gray granitic gneiss.

An amazingly diverse collection of Grenvillian granite and gneiss, as well as Paleozoic specimens of museum quality, armor the dam on the West Branch of the Naugatuck River at Stillwater Pond State Park, west of CT 8 in a scenic ravine just east of CT 272. The Berkshire Massif appears to have contributed generously to this archival collection.

Norfolk's Tectonic Window

The Norfolk tectonic window is one of the most enlightening geologic features in northwestern Connecticut. During the Taconic mountain building event in Ordovician time, sheets of rock were thrust westward over the top of Stockbridge Marble on the Laurentian continental shelf. At Norfolk, the overthrust sheets were arched upward in such a way that erosion removed them and exposed the marble. Such a feature is called a

View to the northeast, with Haystack Mountain on the right and the thrust window on the left.

"window" because it allows you to look completely through the sequence of overlying rocks.

A 1.5-square-mile area in the center of the window reveals the Stockbridge Marble and the Dalton Formation. Partially surrounding these carbonate rocks is the rusty-weathering schist of the lower Canaan

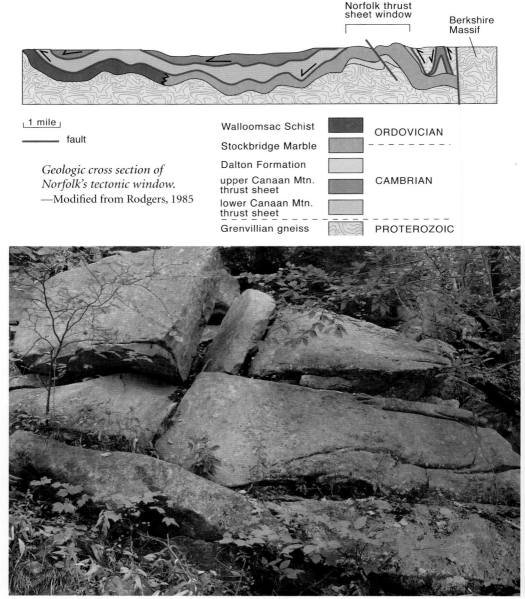

WEST · EAST

Norfolk thrust sheet window

Berkshire Massif

1 mile

——— fault

Geologic cross section of Norfolk's tectonic window.
—Modified from Rodgers, 1985

Walloomsac Schist		ORDOVICIAN
Stockbridge Marble		- - - - - - - -
Dalton Formation		
upper Canaan Mtn. thrust sheet		CAMBRIAN
lower Canaan Mtn. thrust sheet		
Grenvillian gneiss		PROTEROZOIC

Middle Proterozoic gneiss of the Berkshire Massif at the trailhead parking lot at Haystack Mountain State Park.

Mountain thrust slice, and surrounding that, schist of the upper Canaan Mountain thrust slice. The highest thrust slice surrounding the Norfolk window is Grenvillian gneiss. This hard, resistant rock, which caps the mountains, is exposed north of US 44 in Haystack Mountain State Park and south of US 44 in Dennis Hill State Park.

Marble Valley

The valley of the Housatonic River from Danbury north through Massachusetts is known as the "Marble Valley," and between Norfolk and Salisbury, US 44 runs almost entirely over carbonate rocks of the Stockbridge Marble of Cambrian and Ordovician age. The exception is limited outcrops of clastic rocks of the Dalton Formation of Cambrian age halfway between East Canaan and Canaan. The carbonate rocks were deposited on Grenville gneisses, which formed the Laurentian continental shelf in Cambrian time. Iron deposits have been found near the contact of the Stockbridge Marble and the Walloomsac Schist, the largest near Lakeville, in Salisbury.

Beckley Furnace in North Canaan

The first iron forge in North Canaan was built on the Blackberry River in 1739. More than one hundred years later, in 1847, the Beckley Furnace was built upstream. The Beckley Furnace is located along Lower Road, which follows the Blackberry River between East Canaan and US 7.

This monument in East Canaan, located at the junction of the east end of Lower Road and US 44, is constructed of boulders of glassy Cheshire Quartzite, a rock rarely seen in outcrops.

The Beckley Furnace, on the north side of the Blackberry River.

A dam just upstream of the Beckley Furnace provided water power for forcing air into the furnace. Water was also used to power the great helve hammers that rang up and down the valley, beating impurities out of the iron. The forge is a 40-foot-high smokestack constructed of blocks of marble where workers heated and cast iron. The four Gothic arches, one on each side, furnished hot air to the furnace. A mass of waste iron that accumulated inside the furnace rests in front of it today. In 1880, a fire nearly destroyed the factory, but the stack was rebuilt in 1896, about 8 feet taller than the original. You can see the changes made at that time by a discontinuity in the stonework near the top of the furnace. The Beckley Furnace closed in 1918 or 1919.

Twin Lakes Cave

In eastern Salisbury, US 44 passes just south of Cave Hill, which contains Twin Lakes Cave. Commercial tours of this cave began in 1870, but now it is only explored by adventurous spelunkers. It has several lengthy passageways, rooms, and alcoves, all in the Stockbridge Marble. Caves in limestone, dolomite, and marble form when water and air dissolve the calcium carbonate along cracks in the rock.

A dam on the Blackberry River upstream from the Beckley iron furnace. It is constructed against marble, which is visible on south bank (right). *A 30-inch-diameter pipe on the north bank* (left) *carried water to the forge.*

Iron Ore of the Salisbury District

In 1731, while exploring the western part of Salisbury, John Pell and Ezekiel Ashley discovered the largest and richest deposit of the Salisbury Iron District at a place that became known as Ore Hill. The deposit is west of Wononskopomuc Lake near the junction of US 44 and CT 112. The Salisbury Iron District became the foremost producer of iron in North America at that time, triggering Connecticut's "Iron Age." Mines and forges sprang up across northwestern Connecticut and supported a thriving industry in Salisbury, North Canaan, Falls Village, Norfolk, Sharon, Cornwall, and Kent. This region was an important source of iron for cannons used in the Revolutionary War. Echoes of the iron industry still reverberate in the names of local places, such as Furnace Road, Forge Lane, Hammertown, Mine Mountain.

In 1732, Thomas Lamb from Springfield, Massachusetts, set about buying land and water rights on key rivers and outlets to Wononskopomuc Lake, or Lakeville Lake as it is sometimes called, until he controlled 5,000 acres, along with their water rights. Lamb mined ore from what was initially called "Lamb's Three Acre Grant." The mine, which operated for

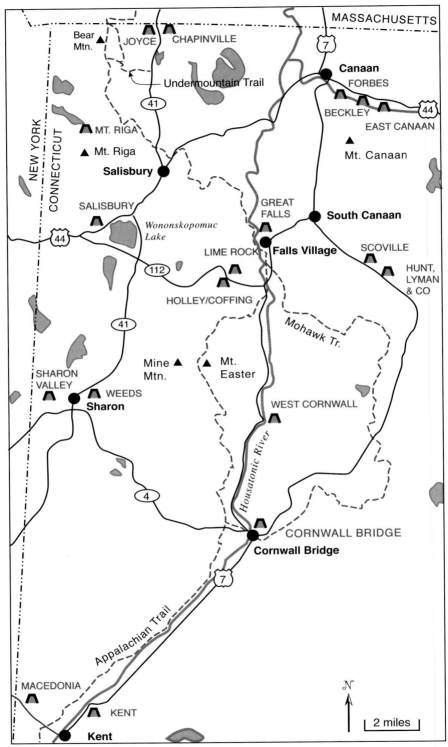

Map of northwestern Connecticut showing the location of eighteen iron furnaces in the Salisbury Iron District. Three other furnaces (Bull Bridge, Waramaug, and Roxbury) are not shown. —Modified from Kirby, 1998

more than fifty years, was later known by names such as Hendrick's Ore Bed, Davis Ore Bed, and Davis Mine, successively. In 1735, Lamb built his forge in Lime Rock's Furnace Hollow, located near what is now referred to as Lime Rock Park. The ore was carried by horseback to Lime Rock along the route now followed by CT 112.

As the demand for iron grew, so did the need for greater understanding of the geological occurrence of the ore. The "iron men," as the miners were known, were aware that the ore occurred as a relatively thin layer or lens near the contact between two distinctly different kinds of rock, the gray to white Stockbridge Marble, which was deposited on the continental shelf of Laurentia, and the dark Walloomsac Schist, formerly a limy mudstone that initially interfingered with and then was deposited on top of the marble. While finding the contact between two flat-lying sedimentary rocks is fairly straightforward, it is tricky to find it between two units that

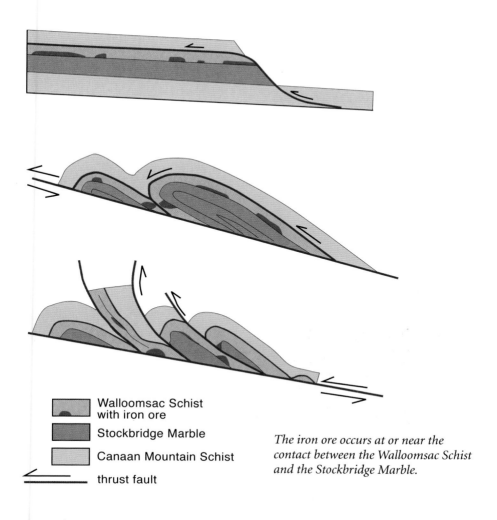

Walloomsac Schist with iron ore

Stockbridge Marble

Canaan Mountain Schist

thrust fault

The iron ore occurs at or near the contact between the Walloomsac Schist and the Stockbridge Marble.

have been contorted not only by large and small folds but also by thrust faulting. Moreover, the iron ore did not consistently form along the contact. And finally, glacial deposits cover the rock units in many places. The ore is in the form of limonite and goethite (hydrous forms of iron) and siderite (iron carbonate). Called *bog iron*, these forms of iron precipitated out of the seawater, which was likely elevated in iron because of the weathering of iron-rich rocks of offshore volcanic islands.

Limonite, goethite, and siderite were not the only sources of iron in the Housatonic watershed. Magnetite was mined from the basement gneiss of the Housatonic Massif between Sharon and Kent. The content of iron in magnetite ranges from 69.0 percent to 72.4 percent, which is higher than the amount in the limonite ores. However, the concentration of magnetite in the gneiss proved to be relatively low, and only limited amounts of the mineral were used in local iron production.

Taconic Range and Mount Riga State Park

The Taconic Range extends along the eastern border of New York between northern Connecticut and Vermont. This range, which includes Round Mountain, Bear Mountain, Gridley Mountain, Bald Peak, Lions Head, and Mount Riga in Connecticut, is part of the Taconic thrust sheet and rests directly on rocks of the carbonate shelf. This thrust sheet, which extends as far west as the Hudson River, moved westward tectonically, possibly hundreds of miles, from its original location on the continental slope and rise. The Everett Schist of Cambrian age, which makes up this thrust sheet, resembles the Canaan Mountain Schist. Indian Mountain, south of US 44 on the Salisbury-Sharon line, is also capped with Everett Schist that has been thrust over the Walloomsac Schist.

Limonite, a hydrous form of iron, from the Walloomsac Schist. —Copyright © 2006 by Peabody Museum of Natural History, Yale University, New Haven, Connecticut. Photography by Claire Bucholz

The 1.9-mile-long Undermountain Trail in Mount Riga State Park begins off CT 41, 3 miles north of Salisbury, and joins the Appalachian Trail just south of 2,316-foot Bear Mountain, the highest *peak* in Connecticut; the highest *point* is northwest of there on the slopes of Mount Frissell, whose peak is in Massachusetts. The trees in this mountainous region were used to make charcoal to heat the iron furnaces. Along the trails in Mount Riga State Park, you can see charcoal pits, roads, and hearths associated with the charcoal industry.

WEST   EAST

Everett Schist Taconic overthrust fault   Canaan Mountain Schist   Berkshire Massif
        Walloomsac Schist   *Housatonic River*

Stockbridge Marble

Dalton Formation
Proterozoic gneiss

Walloomsac Schist	▆	ORDOVICIAN
Stockbridge Marble	▨	– – – – – – – –
Dalton Formation	▢	
Canaan Mtn. and Everett Schists	▢	CAMBRIAN
Grenvillian gneiss	▨	PROTEROZOIC
fault	▬▬	

Cambrian schists cap the mountains in northwestern Connecticut, thrust to the west over the top of the younger Walloomsac Schist of Ordovician age.

Glossary

accretionary wedge. A triangular mass of sediment on the landward side of an oceanic trench composed of debris scraped off the upper surface of the subducting, or down-going, plate.

actinolite. A greenish amphibole mineral that grows as needle or fibrous crystals in metamorphic schists and altered mafic and ultramafic igneous rocks.

alaskite. A very pale granite with few or no dark minerals.

albite. A sodium-rich plagioclase feldspar mineral that is colorless to white and occurs in metamorphic and igneous rocks.

alluvial fan. A relatively flat to gently dipping, fan-shaped wedge of loose rock material deposited by streams where they flow out of narrow valleys onto broad valleys or plains, especially in semiarid regions.

amphibole. A group of dark, iron- and magnesium-rich minerals commonly present in igneous and metamorphic rocks. Hornblende, the most common amphibole, crystallizes into black needles.

amphibolite. A medium- to coarse-grained metamorphic rock composed of hornblende and plagioclase. An **amphibolite schist** is a strongly foliated amphibolite that can be readily split.

andalusite. A metamorphic silicate mineral that occurs in alumina-rich schist and gneiss. It has the same chemical composition as kyanite and sillimanite.

andesite. A grayish volcanic rock that consists mostly of plagioclase and one or more of the dark minerals biotite, hornblende, and pyroxene. It is intermediate in composition between basalt and rhyolite.

anticline. In layered rocks, a folded arch with the oldest rocks in the center.

arkose. A sandstone composed mainly of quartz and orthoclase feldspar, derived from weathering granite.

ash. Small shreds of lava that escape in the air during a volcanic eruption. Ash consolidates into tuff.

barrier beach. A long, narrow, coastal sandy island extending parallel to the shore but separated from it by a lagoon or marsh.

basalt. A black or very dark gray volcanic rock that consists mainly of microscopic crystals of plagioclase feldspar, pyroxene, and perhaps olivine.

basement. The fundamental rocks of the continental crust, mainly granite, schist, and gneiss.

batholith. A mass of coarsely granular igneous rock, generally granite, that is exposed over an area greater than about 40 square miles.

bedrock. Solid rock exposed in place or that underlies unconsolidated superficial sediments.

biotite. Dark mica, a platy mineral. It is a minor but common mineral in igneous and metamorphic rocks.

boudinage. A structure in strongly deformed metamorphic rocks in which a layer, vein, or sill is stretched, thinned, and broken into bodies resembling boudins, or sausages.

boulder train. A linear or fan-shaped distribution of boulders and other rock fragments from the same bedrock source, transported by a glacier.

breccia. A rock broken into angular to rounded fragments held together by a fine-grained matrix. Produced by any one of a variety of processes.

calc-silicate rock. A metamorphic rock consisting of calcium-bearing silicate minerals formed by metamorphism of limy sedimentary rock.

calcareous. Rock consisting of more than 50 percent calcium carbonate.

carbonaceous. Materials rich in carbon, such as coal.

carbonate rock. A sedimentary rock composed of carbonate minerals such as calcite and dolomite.

chert. A sedimentary rock composed mainly of microscopic crystals of quartz, usually occurring as concretionary nodules in limestone.

chiastolite. A form of the mineral andalusite.

chlorite. A green, platy, micaceous mineral characteristic of low-grade metamorphic mafic rocks—rocks with iron and magnesium.

clast. A grain or fragment of a rock produced by disintegration of a larger rock mass. A **clastic rock** is composed of broken fragments derived from preexisting rocks.

clay. A sedimentary material composed of weathered minerals with grain sizes less than $1/256$ millimeter in diameter.

cleavage. A planar fabric in an unmetamorphosed or weakly metamorphosed, fine-grained rock.

coarse-grained. A relative term used to describe the size of constituents in a rock. Said of igneous rocks with minerals larger than 0.2 inch in diameter. Said of sedimentary rocks with particles larger than 0.08 inch in diameter.

coastal plain. A low, gently sloping region on the margin of an ocean.

conglomerate. A coarse-grained sedimentary rock composed of pebbles, cobbles, or boulders set in a fine-grained matrix of silt or sand.

continent. A large landmass that is, or was, comparable in size to a modern continent. Laurentia, a Precambrian continent, evolved into the larger North American continent.

continental rise. The gently sloping edge of the continent that is adjacent to the abyssal region of the ocean.

continental shelf. The gently dipping part of the continental landmass between the shoreline and the more steeply dipping continental slope.

continental slope. The most steeply sloped part of the continental margin, between the shelf and the rise.

crossbed/crossbedding. A sedimentary bed, usually in sand or silt, that is at an angle to the main bedding.

crust. The upper surface of the lithosphere. **Continental crust** consists mainly of granite, gneiss, and schist; **oceanic crust** consists of basalt.

crystalline. Said of a rock formed of interlocking mineral crystals, usually igneous or metamorphic.

cumberlandite. A coarse-grained ultramafic rock with a high percentage of olivine.

delta. A nearly flat accumulation of clay, sand, and gravel deposited in a lake or ocean at the mouth of a river.

diabase. An igneous rock with the composition of basalt but that cooled far enough beneath the surface to have visible crystals.

dike. A sheet of igneous rock that formed when molten magma filled a fracture in a solid rock. The magma in a **feeder dike** rose to the surface of the earth.

diorite. A plutonic igneous rock intermediate in composition between granite and gabbro.

dip. The sloping angle of a planar surface in rocks such as a sedimentary bed or metamorphic foliation.

dolomite. A sedimentary rock composed of calcium magnesium carbonate.

dome. A circular or elliptical uplift of rock, sometimes in the form of an anticline or a mass of igneous rock.

drift, glacial. All sediment deposited by a glacier, whether directly from the ice or from standing or flowing meltwater.

drumlin. A streamlined deposit of glacial till elongated in the direction of ice movement and having an elliptical profile.

epidote. A typically pistachio green mineral formed in low-grade metamorphic rocks derived from alumina- and iron-bearing limy sediments. Also, an alteration mineral in mafic igneous rocks.

erratic, glacial. A block of rock transported by glacial ice and deposited at a distance from the bedrock outcrop from which it was derived.

esker. A long, narrow, commonly sinuous ridge deposited by a stream flowing in a tunnel beneath an ice sheet.

extrusive igneous rocks. Rocks that solidify from magma on the surface of the earth.

fault. A fracture or zone of fractures in the earth's crust along which blocks of rock on either side have shifted. A **normal fault** forms under extensional forces, and one side drops relative to the other side. A **reverse fault** forms under compressional forces, and one side is pushed up and over the other side. In a **strike-slip fault**, rocks on one side move sideways relative to rocks on the other side.

feldspar. The most abundant rock-forming mineral group, making up 60 percent of the earth's crust and including calcium, sodium, or potassium with aluminum silicate. Includes plagioclase feldspars (albite and anorthite) and alkali feldspars (orthoclase and microcline).

felsic. An adjective used to describe an igneous rock composed of light-colored minerals, such as feldspar, quartz, and muscovite.

felsite. A light-colored extrusive igneous rock composed of feldspar and quartz.

fine-grained. A relative term used to describe the size of constituents in a rock. Said of igneous rocks with minerals too small to see with the unaided eye. Said of sedimentary rocks with silt-size or smaller particles.

fluvial. Refers to rivers or streams.

fold. A bend in a rock layer.

foliation. A textural term referring to planar arrangement of minerals or structures in any kind of rock.

foreset beds. Inclined sedimentary layers of sand or silt deposited on the margin of a delta.

formation. A body of sedimentary, igneous, or metamorphic rock that can be recognized over a large area. It is the basic stratigraphic unit in geologic mapping. A formation may be part of a larger **group** and may be broken into **members**.

gabbro. A dark igneous rock consisting mainly of plagioclase and pyroxene in crystals large enough to see with a simple magnifier. Gabbro has the same composition as basalt but contains much larger mineral grains.

garnet. A family of silicate minerals with widely varying chemical compositions. Garnets occur in metamorphic and igneous rocks and are usually reddish.

gneiss. A coarse-grained metamorphic rock with a streaky foliation due to parallel alignment of minerals, usually in bands of light- and dark-colored minerals.

Gondwana. A supercontinent that formed in late Precambrian time.

graded bed. A sedimentary bed in which particle size progressively changes, usually from coarse at the base to fine at the top.

granite. An igneous rock composed mostly of orthoclase feldspar and quartz in grains large enough to see without using a magnifier. Most granites also contain mica or amphibole.

granodiorite. A group of coarse-grained plutonic rocks intermediate in composition between granite and diorite.

greenstone. A dark green, altered or metamorphosed basalt or gabbro. The green comes from the minerals chlorite, actinolite, or epidote.

headland. Bedrock jutting out from the coast into the ocean.

hornblende. An iron and calcium silicate mineral, the most common of the amphibole group. It commonly crystallizes into blackish needles in igneous and meta-morphic rocks.

Iapetus Ocean. The ocean that existed in the general position of the Atlantic Ocean before the assembly of the continental masses that made up the Pangean supercontinent in Paleozoic time.

ice front. The edge of a glacier.

ice sheet. A thick glacier covering a large region.

igneous rock. Rock that solidified from the cooling of molten magma.

Illinoian. The second-to-last major glaciation during Pleistocene time.

interlobate. The region where two adjacent glacial lobes meet. An **interlobate angle** is the angle formed by the intersection of two adjacent lobes.

intrusive igneous rocks. Rocks that cool from magma beneath the surface of the earth. The body of rock is called an **intrusion**.

isotopic dating. Measure of the age of rocks using radioactive elements in minerals. **Radiocarbon dating** measures age using the decay of carbon-14 in plant material.

joint. A planar fracture or crack in a rock.

kame. A variety of stratified landforms deposited by meltwater streams in contact with the ice of a glacier.

kettle. A bowl-shaped depression or hole in glacial drift, such as Walden Pond, formed by burial of a block of ice by the drift. A depression forms when the ice melts.

kyanite. A blue or light green metamorphic mineral having the same chemical formula as andalusite and sillimanite, but formed at medium temperatures and high pressures.

Laurentia. The largest continental nuclei in the Rodinian supercontinent. It broke free of the supercontinent between 750 and 550 million years ago and eventually evolved into the North American continent.

lava. Molten rock erupted onto the surface of the earth.

limestone. A sedimentary rock composed of calcium carbonate.

lobe. The rounded, terminal edge of a continental glacier.

mafic. An adjective used to describe an igneous rock composed of dark minerals such as hornblende, biotite, and pyroxene.

magma. Molten rock within the earth.

magnetite. A strongly magnetic iron oxide mineral.

mantle. The part of the earth between the interior core and the outer crust.

marble. Metamorphosed limestone.

massive. Said of a rock that is relatively homogeneous.

metamorphic rock. Rock derived from preexisting rock that changes mineralogically and texturally in response to changes in temperature and/or pressure, usually deep within the earth.

metamorphism. Recrystallization of an existing rock. Metamorphism typically occurs at high temperatures and often high pressures.

metasedimentary rock. A sedimentary rock that has been metamorphosed.

metavolcanic rock. A volcanic rock that has been metamorphosed.

mica. A family of silicate minerals, including biotite and muscovite, that crystallize into thin flakes. Micas are common in many kinds of igneous and metamorphic rocks.

micaceous. Containing micas, such as muscovite, biotite, and chlorite.

microcline. A potassium-rich alkali feldspar, a common rock-forming mineral. It forms at higher temperatures than orthoclase.

microcontinent. A small, isolated fragment of continental crust.

migmatite. A composite of metamorphic rock, commonly gneissic, mixed with igneous rock crystallized from magma melted out of or injected into the gneiss.

moraine. A landform made of glacial till, typically a ridge deposited at the edge of a glacier.

mountain building event. An event in which rocks are folded, thrust faulted, metamorphosed, and/or uplifted. Intrusive and extrusive igneous activity often accompanies it.

mudstone. A sedimentary rock composed of mud.

muscovite. A common, colorless to light brown mineral of the mica group. It is present in many igneous, metamorphic, and sedimentary rocks.

mylonite. A metamorphic rock produced by shearing of rock masses past each other, resulting in brittle fracturing of certain minerals, such as feldspar and micas, and recrystallization of ductilely deformed quartz.

normal fault. A fault in which rocks on one side move down relative to rocks on the other side in response to extensional forces.

olistolith. An exotic block included in a debris flow or submarine flow.

olivine. An iron and magnesium silicate mineral that typically forms glassy green crystals. A common mineral in gabbro, basalt, and peridotite.

orthoclase. A potassium-rich alkali feldspar, a common rock-forming mineral. It forms at higher temperatures than microcline.

ostracode. A small bivalved crustacean, often preserved as a fossil.

outwash. Sand and gravel deposited by meltwater from a receding glacier.

overthrust. A low-angle thrust fault with considerable displacement (measured in miles). An **overthrust sheet** is the body of rock that moved over the top.

Pangea. A supercontinent that assembled about 300 million years ago. It broke into the modern continents beginning about 200 million years ago.

pegmatite. An igneous rock, generally granitic, composed of extremely large crystals.

peridotite. A coarse-grained ultramafic igneous rock consisting mainly of olivine. The earth's mantle consists mainly of peridotite.

phyllite. A metamorphic rock intermediate in grade (and grain size) between slate and schist. Very fine-grained mica typically imparts a lustrous sheen.

plagioclase. A feldspar mineral rich in sodium and calcium. One of the most common rock-forming minerals in igneous and metamorphic rocks.

pluton. An large intrusion of igneous rock.

porphyry. An igneous rock in which larger crystals exist in a fine-grained but completely crystalline matrix.

pyroxene. A family of silicate minerals that occur mostly in dark, mafic igneous and metamorphic rocks.

quartz. A mineral form of silica. Quartz is one of the most abundant and widely distributed minerals in rocks. It comes in a wide variety of forms, including clear crystals, sand grains, and chert.

quartzite. A metamorphic rock composed of mainly quartz and formed by the metamorphism of sandstone.

recessional moraine. A ridge of till deposited at the edge of a receding glacier.

red bed. Sandstone, siltstone, or shale that is predominantly red because of the presence of hematite, an iron oxide.

rhyolite. A felsic volcanic rock, the extrusive equivalent of granite. It contains quartz and feldspar in a very fine-grained matrix.

rift. A long, narrow rupture in the earth's crust. A **rift basin** or **rift valley** is the trough formed by the rift.

Rodinia. An early supercontinent consisting of a cluster of all major landmasses that existed by about 750 million years ago.

sand. Weathered mineral grains, most commonly quartz, between $\frac{1}{16}$ and 2 millimeters in diameter.

sandstone. A sedimentary rock made primarily of sand.

schist. A metamorphic rock that is strongly foliated due to an abundance of platy minerals.

sedimentary rock. A rock formed from the consolidation of loose sediment.

serpentine. A group of rock-forming minerals derived from the alteration of magnesium-rich silicate minerals and having a greasy or silky luster and soapy feel. A rock composed of serpentine is called *serpentinite*.

shale. A deposit of clay, silt, or mud solidified into more or less solid rock.

shear zone. The zone in which deformation occurs when two bodies of rock slide past each other.

sill. An igneous intrusion that parallels the planar structure of the surrounding rock.

sillimanite. A needle-shaped alumina silicate mineral with the same chemical composition as andalusite and kyanite. Sillimanite forms at very high temperatures and pressures of regional metamorphism and near the intrusive or contact border with igneous rocks.

silt. Weathered mineral grains larger than clay but smaller than sand (between $\frac{1}{256}$ and $\frac{1}{16}$ millimeter in diameter).

siltstone. A sedimentary rock made primarily of silt.

slate. Slightly metamorphosed shale or mudstone that breaks easily along parallel surfaces.

soapstone. A metamorphic rock composed mainly of talc, a mineral derived from the alteration of iron-magnesium silicate minerals common in mafic rocks such as gabbro.

spillway. The overflow channel from body of water, such as a glacial lake.

spit. A long, narrow body of sand extending into the water from the shore.

staurolite. A dark mineral in mica schists and gneisses formed during medium-grade metamorphism.

strata. Layers of sedimentary rock. A single layer is a **stratum**.

strike. The direction or trend of a feature as it intersects the horizontal.

subduction zone. A long, narrow zone where an oceanic plate descends into the mantle below a continental plate at a collision boundary.

supercontinent. A clustering of all of the earth's continental masses into one major landmass; this has occurred at least three times in geologic history.

syncline. In layered rocks, a folded trough with the youngest rocks in the center.

talus. An accumulation of rock fragments derived from and resting at the base of a cliff or rocky slope.

tectonics. A branch of geology dealing with the structure and forces within the outer part of the earth, including continental plate movements.

terminal moraine. The ridge of till deposited at the farthest extent of the glacier, marking the cessation of glacial advance.

terrane. An assemblage of rocks that share a more or less common origin and history.

thrust fault. A low-angle reverse fault. An **overthrust fault** is a thrust fault that transports large masses of rock many miles.

thrust sheet/thrust slice. A body of rock above a thrust fault.

till. Unsorted and unstratified sediment deposited directly from glacial ice. It is likely to contain rock fragments of all sizes.

topset beds. Horizontal sedimentary beds on the top surface of a delta. They usually cover foreset beds.

traprock. Any dark-colored, fine-grained igneous rock used for crushed stone.

trench, oceanic. A narrow, elongate depression that develops where the ocean floor begins its descent into a subduction zone at a collisional plate boundary.

trilobite. A three-lobed marine arthropod that lived from Cambrian to Permian time.

trondhjemite. A very light-colored granitic rock consisting mainly of sodic plagioclase and quartz.

tuff. Volcanic ash more or less consolidated into solid rock.

turbidite. A sediment or sedimentary rock deposited by a swift, bottom-flowing current laden with suspended sediment.

ultramafic. An adjective used to describe black to dark green rocks that are more mafic than basalt, consisting mainly of iron- and magnesium-rich minerals such as hypersthene, pyroxene, or olivine. They make up the oceanic crust and mantle.

unconformity. A break or gap in the geologic record where one rock unit is overlain by another that is not next in the stratigraphic succession. An **angular unconformity** exists when the bedding of the underlying, older rock dips at a different angle, usually steeper, than the bedding of the overlying, younger rock.

varves. From the Swedish *varv*, meaning "layer," referring to alternating layers of fine-grained sediment deposited annually in a standing body of glacial meltwater. The lighter, silt-size particles represent the summer layer and the darker, clay-size particles represent the winter layer.

vein. A deposit of minerals that fills a fracture in rock.

volcanic arc. A chain of volcanoes that formed above a subduction zone.

wall rock. The rock enclosing a vein, dike, or ore deposit.

weather. To soften, crumble, or discolor because of exposure to atmospheric agents such as rain.

Wisconsinan. The last stage of glaciation in Pleistocene time. It began about 80,000 years ago and ended about 10,000 years ago.

xenolith. A piece of rock from the surrounding bedrock contained within an igneous intrusion.

Bibliography

Acaster, M., and M. E. Bickford. 1999. Geochronology and geochemistry of Putnam-Nashoba Terrane metavolcanic and plutonic rocks, eastern Massachusetts: Constraints on the early Paleozoic evolution of eastern North America. *Geological Society of America Bulletin* 111:240–53.

Agassiz, L. 1840. *Etudes sur les glaciers.* Neuchatel, Jent et Gassmann.

Agassiz, L. 1866. *Geological Sketches.* London: Trübner Co.

Alden, W. C. 1925. *The Physical Features of Central Massachusetts.* U.S. Geological Survey Bulletin 760:13–105.

Aleinikoff, J. N., R. P. Wintsch, R. P. Tollo, D. M. Unruh, C. M. Fanning, and M. D. Schmitz. 2007. Ages and origins of rocks of the Killingworth Dome, south-central Connecticut: Implications for the tectonic evolution of southern New England. *American Journal of Science* 307:63–118.

Antevs, E. 1922. *The Recession of the Last Ice Sheet in New England.* New York: American Geographical Society.

Bell, M. 1985. *The Face of Connecticut: People, Geology, and the Land.* Hartford: Connecticut Geological and Natural History Survey.

Bertoni, R., J. Dowling, and L. Frankel. 1977. Freshwater-lake sediments beneath Block Island Sound. *Geology* 5:631–35.

Bird, J. M., and J. F. Dewey. 1970. Lithosphere plate–continental margin tectonics and the evolution of the Appalachian orogen. *Geological Society of America Bulletin* 81:1031–60.

Boothroyd, J. C., and O. D. Hermes, eds. 1981. *Guidebook for Field Studies in Rhode Island and Adjacent Areas.* New England Intercollegiate Geological Conference, 73rd annual meeting, University of Rhode Island, Kingston.

Burton, W. C. 2006. *Bedrock Geologic Map of the Early Mesozoic Pomperaug Basin and Surrounding Basement Rocks, Litchfield and New Haven Counties, Connecticut.* U.S. Geological Survey Open File Report 2006-1011.

Burton, W. C., P. Huber, J. G. McHone, and P. M. LeTourneau. 2005. A new look at the structure and stratigraphy of the Early Mesozoic Pomperaug Basin, southwestern Connecticut. In *Guidebook for Field Trips in Connecticut,* ed. N. W. McHone and M. J. Peterson, 1–44. New England Intercollegiate Geological Conference, 97th annual meeting, Yale University.

Cameron, E. N. 1943. Origin of sulphides in the nickel deposits of Mount Prospect, Connecticut. *Bulletin of the Geological Society of America* 54:651–86.

Cameron, E. N. 1951. Preliminary report on the geology of the Mt. Prospect Complex. Connecticut Geology and Natural History Survey Bulletin No. 76.

Carr, R. L., and J. O. Edwards. 1981. Selected mineral collecting sites in northeastern Rhode Island. In *Guidebook for Field Studies in Rhode Island and Adjacent Areas,* 201–7. Eds. J. C. Boothroyd and O. D. Hermes. New England Intercollegiate

Geological Conference, 73rd annual meeting, University of Rhode Island, Kingston.

Chase, H. B. Coal mines in Narragansett Basin. Unpublished manuscript completed in 1978. Archived in James Skehan's private collection

Dalziel, I. W. D. 1997. Neoproterozoic-Paleozoic geography and tectonics: Review, hypothesis, environmental speculation. *Geological Society of America Bulletin* 109(1):16–42.

Domonell, W. G. 1998. *Newgate: From Copper Mine to State Prison*. Litchfield, Conn.: Simsbury Historical Society.

Ellis, C. W. 1962. Marine sedimentary environments in the vicinity of the Norwalk Islands, Connecticut. Hartford: Connecticut State Geological and Natural History Survey.

Finch, R. 1996. *The Smithsonian Guides to Natural America: Southern New England, MA, CT, RI*. Washington, D.C.: Smithsonian Books.

Gates, R. M., and N. I. Christiansen. 1965. *The Bedrock Geology of the West Torrington Quadrangle*. Connecticut Geological and Natural History Survey Quadrangle Report 17.

Getty, S. R., and L. P. Gromet. 1992. Evidence for extension at the Willimantic Dome, Connecticut: Implications for the late Paleozoic tectonic evolution of the New England Appalachians. *American Journal of Science* 292:398–420.

Goldsmith, R. 1982. Recessional moraines and ice retreat in southeastern Connecticut. In *Late Wisconsinan Glaciation of New England*. ed. G. J. Larson and B. D. Stone, 61-76. Dubuque, Iowa, Kendall/Hunt Publishing Co.

Gray, N. H. 2005. The historic New-Gate and cobalt mines of Connecticut. In *Guidebook for Field Trips in Connecticut*, ed. N. W. McHone and M. J. Peterson. New England Intercollegiate Geological Conference, 97th annual meeting, Yale University.

Hames W. E., R. J. Tracy, and R. J. Bodnar. 1989. Postmetamorphic unroofing history deduced from petrology, fluid inclusions, thermochronometry, and thermal modeling: An example from southwestern New England. *Geology* 17(8):727–30

Hermes, O. D. 1987. Geologic relationships of Permian Narragansett Pier and Westerly Granites and Jurassic lamprophyric dike rocks, Westerly, Rhode Island. *Centennial Field Guide Volume 5*: 181–86. Northeastern Section of the Geological Society of America.

Hermes, O. D., L. P. Gromet, and D. P. Murray. 1994. *Bedrock Geologic Map of Rhode Island*. Rhode Island Map Series No. 1, University of Rhode Island, Kingston. Scale 1:100,000.

Hickey, L. J., and C. MacClintock. 2005. Reading the rock and landscape record of the New Haven Region. In *Guidebook for Field Trips in Connecticut*, ed. N. W. McHone and M. J. Peterson. New England Intercollegiate Geological Conference, 97th annual meeting, Yale University.

Hitchcock, E. 1858. *Ichnology of New England. A Report on the Sandstone of the Connecticut Valley, Especially its Fossil Footmarks*. Boston: William White, Printer of the State.

Hoffman, P. F. 1991. Did the breakout of Laurentia turn Gondwanaland inside-out? *Science* 252:1409–12.

Karabinos, P., S. D. Samson, J. C. Hepburn, and H. M. Stoll. 1998. Taconian orogeny in the New England Appalachians: Collision between Laurentia and the Shelburne Falls arc. *Geology* 26:215–18.

Karabinos, P., H. M. Stoll, and J. C. Hepburn. 2003. The Shelburne Falls arc—Lost arc of the Taconic orogeny. In *New England Intercollegiate Geologic Conference Guidebook*, ed. J. Brady and J. Cheney, B3-1–B3-17. Amherst, Massachusetts: New England Intercollegiate Geologic Conference.

Kirby, E. 1998. *Echoes of Iron in Connecticut's Northwest Corner, with a Field Guide to the Iron Heritage Trail*. Edited by E. G. Shapiro. Sharon, Conn.: Sharon Historical Society.

Koteff, C., and F. D. Larsen. 1989. Postglacial uplift in western New England: Geologic evidence for delayed rebound. In *Earthquakes at North-Atlantic Passive Margins: Neotectonics and Postglacial Rebound*, ed. S. Gregresen and P. W. Bashman, 105–23. Norwell, Mass.: Kluwer Academic Publishers.

Koteff, C., and F. Pessl, Jr. 1981. *Systematic Ice Retreat in New England*. U.S. Geological Survey Professional Paper 1179.

Leary, J. 2004. *A Shared Landscape: A Guide and History of Connecticut's State Parks and Forests*. Rockfall, Conn.: Friends of Connecticut State Parks.

Lewis, R. S., and J. R. Stone. 1991. Late Quaternary stratigraphy and depositional history of the Long Island Sound Basin: Connecticut and New York. *Journal of Coastal Research*, Special Issue 11:1–23.

Little, R. 2003. *Dinosaurs, Dunes, and Drifting Continents: The Geology of the Connecticut Valley*. 3rd ed. Easthampton, Mass.: Earth View.

Lyons, P. C., and H. B. Chase, Jr. 1976. Coal flora and stratigraphy of the northwestern Narragansett Basin. In *NEIGC Guidebook for Field Trips to the Boston Area and Vicinity*, ed. B. Cameron, 405–27. Princeton, N.J.: Science Press.

Mahoney, B. 1991. *Teaching Trails at Old Mine Park: A Fieldtrip in Geology*. North Salem, N.Y.: Learning Without Borders Publishing.

Maria, A., and O. D. Hermes. 2001. Volcanic rocks in the Narragansett Basin, southeastern New England: Petrology and significance to early basin formation. *American Journal of Science* 301:286–312.

McDonald, N. G. 1982. Paleontology of the Mesozoic rocks of the Connecticut Valley. In *NEIGC Guidebook for Field Trips in Connecticut and South-Central Massachusetts*, ed. R. Joesten and S. S. Quarrier, 143–72. Hartford: Connecticut Geological and Natural History Survey.

McDonald, N. G. 1996. *The Connecticut Valley in the Age of Dinosaurs: A Guide to the Geologic Literature, 1681–1995*. Hartford: Connecticut Geological and Natural History Survey Bulletin 116.

McHone, J. G. 1996. Broad-terrane Jurassic flood basalts across northeastern North America. *Geology* 24:319–22.

McHone, J. G. 2004. *Great Day Trips to Discover the Geology of Connecticut*. Wilton, Conn.: Perry Heights Press.

McHone, J. G. 2004. *Connecticut in the Mesozoic World*. Hartford: Connecticut Geological and Natural History Survey Misc. Paper No. 1.

Merguerian, C., and J. E. Sanders. 1990. *Cameron's Line and the Hodges Complex, West Torrington, Connecticut*. New York: New York Academy of Sciences, Section of Geological Sciences Trips on the Rocks Guidebook, 1990–91 Field Trips.

Mosher, S. 1976. Pressure solution as a deformation mechanism in Pennsylvanian conglomerates from Rhode Island. *Journal of Geology* 84:355–64.

Murray, D. P. 1987. *The Alleghanian Orogeny in the Narragansett Basin area, southern Rhode Island*. GSA Centennial Field Guide, Northeast Section.

Murray, D. P. 1988. *Rhode Island: The Last Billion Years*. Kingston: University of Rhode Island.

Murray, D. P., ed. 1998. *Guidebook to Field Trips in Rhode Island and Adjacent Regions of Connecticut and Massachusetts*. New England Intercollegiate Geological Conference, 90th annual meeting, University of Rhode Island, Kingston.

Murray, D. P., J. W. Skehan, and J. Raben. 2004. Tectonostratigraphic relationships and coalification trends in the Narragansett and Norfolk Basins, New England. *Journal of Geodynamics* 37:583–611.

Newman, W. S., D. L. Thurber, D. M. Krinsley, and L. A. Sirkin. 1968. The Pleistocene geology of the Montauk Peninsula. In *Guidebook to Field Excursions*, ed. R. M. Finks, 155–73. New York State Geological Association, 40th annual meeting, Queens College, New York.

Oldale, R. N. 1992. *Cape Cod and the Islands, the Geological Story.* East Orleans, Mass.: Parnassus Imprints.

Pease, M. H., Jr. 1982. The Bonemill Brook fault, eastern Connecticut. In *NEIGC Guidebook for Field Trips in Connecticut and South-Central Massachusetts*, ed. R. Joesten and S. S. Quarrier, 263–87. Connecticut Geological and Natural History Survey Guidebook Number 5.

Philpotts, A. R., and P. M. Asher. 1993. Wallrock melting and reaction effects along the Higganum diabase dike in Connecticut: Contamination of a continental flood basalt feeder. *Journal of Petrology* 34(5):1029–58.

Philpotts, A. R., and A. Martello. 1986. Diabase feeder dikes for the Mesozoic basalts in southern New England. *American Journal of Science* 286:105–126.

Philpotts, A. R., B. J. Skinner, and F. T. Lane. 2005. A visit to the North Branford traprock quarry operated by Tilcon Connecticut, Inc. In *Guidebook for Field Trips in Connecticut*, ed. N. W. McHone and M. J. Peterson, 235–49. New England Intercollegiate Geological Conference, 97th annual meeting, Yale University.

Press, F. and Siever, R. 1974. *Planet Earth.* W. H. Freeman.

Quinn, A. W., and G. W. Springer. 1954. *Bedrock Geology of the Bristol Quadrangle and Vicinity, Rhode Island–Massachusetts.* U.S. Geological Survey. Geological Quadrangle Map GQ-42. Scale 1:24,000.

Quinn, A. W. 1971. *Bedrock Geology of Rhode Island.* U.S. Geological Survey (in cooperation with the State of Rhode Island Development Council). Bulletin 1295. Washington.

Rast, N., and J. W. Skehan. 1981. The geology of the Precambrian rocks of Newport and Middletown, Rhode Island. In *Guidebook to Geologic Field Studies in Rhode Island and Adjacent Areas*, ed. J. C. Boothroyd and O. D. Hermes. New England Intercollegiate Geological Conference, 73rd annual meeting, University of Rhode Island, Kingston.

Rast, N., and J. W. Skehan. 1993. Changing tectonic environments of the Avalon Superterrane and the Nashoba Terrane in Massachusetts. *Journal of Geodynamics* 17:1–20.

Rast, N., J. W. Skehan, and S. Mosher. 1986. Paleoenvironmental and tectonic controls of sedimentation in coal-forming basins of southeastern New England. In *Paleoenvironmental and Tectonic Controls in Coal-Forming Basins of the United States*, ed. P. C. Lyons and C. L. Rice, 9–30. Geological Society of America Special Paper 210.

Raymo, C., and M. E. Raymo. 1989. *Written in Stone: A Geological History of the Northeastern United States.* Old Saybrook, Conn.: Globe Pequot Press.

Richardson, C. 1928. *A History of the Simsbury Copper Mines.* M.S. thesis at Trinity College, Hartford, Conn.

Rodgers, J., compiler. 1985. *Bedrock Map of Connecticut.* Connecticut Geological and Natural History Survey in cooperation with the U.S. Geological Survey.

Rutherford, M. J., and O. D. Hermes. 1984. Melatroctolite-anorthositic gabbro complex, Cumberland, Rhode Island: Petrology, origin, and regional setting. *Geological Society of America Bulletin* 95:844–54.

Seidemann, D. E., W. D. Masterson, M. P. Dowing, and K. K. Turekian. 1984. K-Ar dates and ^{40}Ar/^{39}Ar age spectra for Mesozoic basalt flows in the Hartford Basin, Connecticut, and the Newark Basin, New Jersey. *Geologic Society of America Bulletin* 95:594–98.

Sevigny, J. H., and G. N. Hanson. 1995. Late-Taconian and pre-Acadian history of the New England Appalachians of southwestern Connecticut. *Geological Society of America Bulletin* 107:487–98.

Shaler, N. S., J. B. Woodworth, and A. F. Foerste. 1899. *Geology of the Narragansett Basin.* United States Geological Survey Monograph XXXII.

Sirkin, L. A. 1974. Palynology and stratigraphy of Cretaceous strata in Long Island, New York, and Block Island, Rhode Island. *U.S. Geological Survey Journal Research* 2:431–40.

Sirkin, L. A. 1976. Block Island, Rhode Island: Evidence of fluctuations of the late Pleistocene ice margin. *Geological Society of America Bulletin* 87:574–80.

Sirkin, L. A. 1982. Wisconsinan glaciation of Long Island, New York, to Block Island, Rhode Island. In *Late Wisconsinan Glaciation in New England*, ed. G. J. Larson and B. D. Stone, 35–59. Dubuque, Iowa: Kendall Hunt Publishing.

Sirkin, L. A. 1996. *Block Island Geology: History, Processes and Field Excursions.* Watch Hill, R.I.: Book and Tackle Shop.

Sirkin, L. A., and A. Veeger. 1998. Glacial geology and hydrogeology of Block Island. In *Guidebook to Field Trips in Rhode Island and Adjacent Regions of Connecticut and Massachusetts*, ed. D. P. Murray. New England Intercollegiate Geological Conference, 90th annual meeting, University of Rhode Island, Kingston.

Skehan, J. W. 1983. Geological profiles through the Avalonian terrane of southeastern Massachusetts, Rhode Island and Eastern Connecticut, U.S.A. In *Profiles of Orogenic Belts*, ed. N. Rast and F. Delaney, 275–300. Washington, D.C.: American Geophysical Union, Geodynamics Series.

Skehan, J. W. 1997. Assembly and dispersal of supercontinents: The view from Avalon. *Journal of Geodynamics* 23(3/4):237–62.

Skehan, J. W. 2001. *Roadside Geology of Massachusetts.* Missoula, Mont.: Mountain Press Publishing Company.

Skehan, J. W., and N. Rast. 1990. Pre-Mesozoic evolution of Avalon terranes of southern New England. In *Geology of the Composite Avalon Terrane of Southern New England*, ed. A. D. Socci, J. W. Skehan, and G. W. Smith, 13–53. Geological Society of America Special Paper 245.

Skehan, J. W., N. Rast, and D. F. Logue. 1981. The geology of Cambrian rocks of Conanicut Island, Jamestown, Rhode Island. In *Guidebook to Geologic Field Studies in Rhode Island and Adjacent Areas*, ed. J. C. Boothroyd and O. D. Hermes, 237–64. New England Intercollegiate Geological Conference, 73rd annual meeting, University of Rhode Island, Kingston.

Skehan, J. W., N. Rast, and S. Mosher. 1986. Paleoenvironmental and tectonic controls of sedimentation in coal-forming basins of southeastern New England. In *Paleoenvironmental and Tectonic Controls in Coal-Forming Basins of the United States*, ed. P. C. Lyons and C. L. Rice, 9–30. Geological Society of America Special Paper 210.

Skinner, B. J. 1980. The mineral wealth of Connecticut—present, past and future. *Discovery Magazine* 15: 27–31. New Haven: Peabody Museum Associates, Yale University.

Skinner, B. J., and A. R. Philpotts, eds. 2005. *Guidebook to Field Trips in Connecticut.* New England Intercollegiate Geological Conference, 97th annual meeting, Yale University.

Stanley, R. S., and N. M. Ratcliffe. 1985. Tectonic synthesis of the Taconian orogeny in western New England. *Geological Society of America Bulletin* 96:1227–50.

Stone, B. D., and H. W. Borns, Jr. 1986. Pleistocene glacial and interglacial stratigraphy of New England, Long Island and adjacent Georges Bank and Gulf of Maine. *Quaternary Science Reviews* 5:39–52.

Stone, J. R., and D. C. Dickerman. 2002. *Glacial Geology and Aquifer Characteristics of the Big River Area, Central Rhode Island.* U.S. Geological Survey Water Resources Investigations Report 01-4169.

Stone, J. R., J. P. Schafer, E. B. H. London, M. L. DiGiacomo-Cohen, R. S. Lewis, and W. B. Thompson. 1998. *Quaternary Geologic Map of Connecticut and Long Island Sound Basin.* U.S. Geological Survey Open File Report 98-371.

Stone, J. R., J. P. Schafer, E. B. H. London, M. L. DiGiacomo-Cohen, R. S. Lewis, and W. B. Thompson. 2005. *Quaternary Geologic Map of Connecticut and Long Island Sound Basin.* U.S. Geological Survey Geologic Investigations Series Map I-2784, scale 1:125,000.

Sullivan, E. C. 1983. *History and Minerals of Old Mine Park.* Trumball, Conn.: Trumbull Printing.

Thompson, M. D., and O. D. Hermes. 2003. Early rifting in the Narragansett Basin, Massachusetts–Rhode Island: Evidence from Late Devonian bimodal volcanic rocks. *Journal of Geology* 111:597–604.

Thompson, M. D., O. D. Hermes, S. A. Bowering, C. E. Isachsen, J. R. Besancon, and K. L. Kelly. 1996. Tectonostratigraphic implications of Late Proterozoic U-Pb Zircon ages in the Avalon Zone of Southeastern New England. In *Avalonian and Related Peri-Gondwanan Terranes of the Circum-North Atlantic,* ed. R. D. Nance and M. D. Thompson, 179–91. Geological Society of America Special Paper 304.

Tuttle, C. R., W. B. Allen, and G. W. Hahn. 1961. A seismic record of Mesozoic rocks on Block Island, Rhode Island. U.S. Geological Survey Professional Paper 424-C, C254–C256.

Veeger, A. I., H. E. Johnston, B. D. Stone, and L. A. Sirkin. 1996. *Hydrogeology and Water Resources of Block Island, Rhode Island.* U.S. Geological Survey Water-Resources Investigations Report 94-4096.

Walsh, G. J., J. N. Aleinikoff, and R. P. Wintsch. 2007. Origin of the Lyme Dome and implications for the timing of multiple Alleghanian deformational and intrusive events in southern Connecticut. *American Journal of Science* 307:168–215.

Webster, M. J. 1986. *The Structure of the Precambrian Newport Neck, the Lower Cambrian Pirate Cove, and the East Passage Formations, southeastern Rhode Island.* M.S. Thesis. Chestnut Hill, Mass.: Boston College.

Webster, J. R., and R. P. Wintsch. 1987. Petrochemistry and origin of the Killingworth dome rocks, Bronson Hill anticlinorium, south-central Connecticut. *Geological Society of America Bulletin* 98:465–74.

Wintsch, R. P., and J. N. Aleinikoff. 1987. U-Pb isotopic and geologic evidence for late Paleozoic anatexis, deformation and accretion of the Late Proterozoic Avalon terrane, southcentral Connecticut: *American Journal of Science* 287:107–26.

Wintsch, R. P., J. N. Aleinikoff, G. J. Walsh, W. A. Bothner, A. M. Hussey, II, and C. M. Fanning. 2007. Shrimp U-Pb evidence for a late Silurian age of metasedimentary rocks in the Merrimack and Putnam-Nashoba terranes, eastern New England. *American Journal of Science* 307:119–67.

Wintsch, R. P., M. J. Kunk, and J. N. Aleinikoff. 1998. The hinterland of the Alleghanian orogen in southern New England: Late Paleozoic metamorphic and structural overprint on Acadian metamorphic rocks. In *Guidebook to Field Trips in Rhode Island and Adjacent Regions of Connecticut and Massachusetts,* ed. D. P. Murray. New England Intercollegiate Geological Conference, 90th annual meeting, University of Rhode Island, Kingston.

Wintsch, R. P., K. L. Kelsheimer, M. J. Kunk, and J. N. Aleinikoff. 2001. A new look at the Alleghanian overprint of Acadian metamorphic rocks in southern New England: Evidence from structure, petrology and thermochronology. In *Guidebook for Geological Field Trips in New England,* ed. D. P. West and R. H. Bailey, V1–V26. Geological Society of America annual meeting, Boston.

Index

Page numbers in italics refer to photographs

About the Author

James W. Skehan is a professor emeritus in the Department of Geology and Geophysics at Boston College and a director emeritus of Weston Observatory. He holds a doctorate in geology from Harvard University as well as a master's in theology from Weston College. As a Jesuit priest and geologist, he actively promotes dialogue among scientists and theologians. Skehan is the author of *Roadside Geology of Massachusetts* as well as many other books and articles, and he has received national recognition for his contributions to science and education. The National Association of Geology Teachers named him Teacher of the Year in 1976. In 2002 he was honored to have *Skehanos*, a trilobite genus that lived 505 million years ago, named for him. In 2004 Skehan was inducted into the Massachusetts Hall of Fame for Science Educators, and in 2005 the American Institute of Professional Geologists awarded him the Ben H. Parker Memorial Medal. His long, distinguished career has inspired plenty of fans, including mystery writer and geologist Sarah Andrews, who wrote him into her novel *In Cold Pursuit*, published in 2007.